Teacher Edition

Eureka Math
Grade 1
Module 1

Special thanks go to the Gordon A. Cain Center and to the Department of Mathematics at Louisiana State University for their support in the development of *Eureka Math*.

For a free *Eureka Math* Teacher
Resource Pack, Parent Tip
Sheets, and more please
visit www.Eureka.tools

Published by the non-profit Great Minds

Printed in the U.S.A.
This book may be purchased from the publisher at eureka-math.org

10 9 8 7 6 5

ISBN 978-1-63255-345-4

Eureka Math: A Story of Units **Contributors**

Katrina Abdussalaam, Curriculum Writer
Tiah Alphonso, Program Manager—Curriculum Production
Kelly Alsup, Lead Writer / Editor, Grade 4
Catriona Anderson, Program Manager—Implementation Support
Debbie Andorka-Aceves, Curriculum Writer
Eric Angel, Curriculum Writer
Leslie Arceneaux, Lead Writer / Editor, Grade 5
Kate McGill Austin, Lead Writer / Editor, Grades PreK–K
Adam Baker, Lead Writer / Editor, Grade 5
Scott Baldridge, Lead Mathematician and Lead Curriculum Writer
Beth Barnes, Curriculum Writer
Bonnie Bergstresser, Math Auditor
Bill Davidson, Fluency Specialist
Jill Diniz, Program Director
Nancy Diorio, Curriculum Writer
Nancy Doorey, Assessment Advisor
Lacy Endo-Peery, Lead Writer / Editor, Grades PreK–K
Ana Estela, Curriculum Writer
Lessa Faltermann, Math Auditor
Janice Fan, Curriculum Writer
Ellen Fort, Math Auditor
Peggy Golden, Curriculum Writer
Maria Gomes, Pre-Kindergarten Practitioner
Pam Goodner, Curriculum Writer
Greg Gorman, Curriculum Writer
Melanie Gutierrez, Curriculum Writer
Bob Hollister, Math Auditor
Kelley Isinger, Curriculum Writer
Nuhad Jamal, Curriculum Writer
Mary Jones, Lead Writer / Editor, Grade 4
Halle Kananak, Curriculum Writer
Susan Lee, Lead Writer / Editor, Grade 3
Jennifer Loftin, Program Manager—Professional Development
Soo Jin Lu, Curriculum Writer
Nell McAnelly, Project Director

This page intentionally left blank

A STORY OF UNITS

Mathematics Curriculum

Table of Contents

GRADE 1 • MODULE 1

Sums and Differences to 10

Grade 1 • Module 1

Sums and Differences to 10

OVERVIEW

In this first module of Grade 1, students make significant progress towards fluency with addition and subtraction of numbers to 10 (**1.OA.6**) as they are presented with opportunities intended to advance them from counting all to counting on, which leads many students then to decomposing and composing addends and total amounts. In Kindergarten, students achieved fluency with addition and subtraction facts to 5. This means they can decompose 5 into 4 and 1, 3 and 2, and 5 and 0. They can do this without counting all. They perceive the 3 and 2 embedded within the 5.

Topic A continues the work of developing this ability with all the numbers within 10 in *put together* situations (**1.OA.1**), with a special focus on the numbers 6, 7, 8, and 9, since recognizing how much a number needs to make 10 is part of the Kindergarten standards (**K.OA.4**) and easier for most children. Students decompose numbers into two sets, or conceptually subitize, in Lessons 1 and 2, and record their decompositions as number bonds.

> T: How many dots do you see?
>
> S: 8.
>
> T: What two parts do you see?
>
> S: I see 5 and 3.
>
> T: Did you need to count all the dots?
>
> S: No! I could see the top row was a full five, so I just said 6, 7, 8.

In Lesson 3, students see and describe *1 more* as + 1. They use the structure of the first addend rather than its cardinality, just as the student speaking in the above vignette used the five. The number is a unit to which they can add one, or count on by one, without recounting. All three lessons in Topic A prepare students to solve addition problems by counting on rather than counting all (**1.OA.5**).

Topic B continues the process of having the students compose and decompose. They describe *put together* situations (pictured to the right) with number bonds and count on from the first part to totals of 6, 7, 8, 9, and 10 (**1.OA.1, 1.OA.5**). As they represent all the partners of a number, they reflect and see the decompositions, "Look at all these ways to make 8. I can see connections between them."

Through dialogue, they engage in seeing both the composition invited by the *put together* situation and the decomposition invited by the number bonds. Expressions are another way to model both the stories and the bonds, the compositions and the decompositions (**1.OA.1**).

In Topic C, students interpret the meaning of addition from *adding to with result unknown* or *putting together with result unknown* story problems by drawing their own pictures and generating solution equations. Advancing beyond the Kindergarten word problem types, students next solve *add to with change unknown* problems such as, "Ben has 5 pencils. He got some more from his mother. Now, he has 9 pencils. How many pencils did Ben get from his mother?" These problems set the foundation early in the module for relating addition to subtraction in Topic G (**1.OA.4**).[1]

In Topic D, students work outside the context of stories for three days to further their understanding of and skill with counting on using 5-group cards. The first addend is represented with a numeral card, symbolizing the structure to count on from. The number to be added is represented using the dot side of the 5-group card. Students count on from the first addend. They learn to replace counting the dots by tracking the count on their fingers to find the solution (**1.OA.5**). In Lesson 16, they solve problems such as 4 + ___ = 7 by tracking the number of counts as they say, "5, 6, 7" (**1.OA.8**).

In Topic E, in the context of addition to 10, students expand their knowledge of two basic ideas of mathematics: equality and the commutativity of addition (**1.OA.3** and **1.OA.7**). The lesson on the equal sign precedes the lessons on commutativity in order to allow students to later construct true number sentences such as 4 + 3 = 3 + 4 without misunderstanding the equal sign to mean that the numbers are the same. Students apply their new generalization about the position of the addends to count on from the larger number. For example, "I can count on 2 from 7 when I solve 2 + 7."

Like Topic E, Topic F leads students to make more generalizations that support their deepening understanding of addition within 10. They learn to recognize doubles and doubles plus 1. They analyze the addition chart for repeated reasoning and structures (such as 5-groups, plus ones, doubles, sums equal to 10, etc.) that can help them to better understand relationships and connections between different addition facts.

Following the Mid-Module Assessment, Topic G relates addition to subtraction. Since Module 4 in Kindergarten, students have been very familiar with subtraction as "take away." During Fluency Practice in the lessons in Topics A through F, students have had opportunities to remember their Kindergarten work with subtraction. Therefore, Topic G starts immediately with the concept of subtraction as a missing addend, just as Grade 3 students learn division as a missing factor in a multiplication problem.

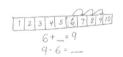

"Ben had 5 crackers. He got some more. Now he has 7. How many crackers did Ben get?"

Having already worked with *add to with change unknown* problems earlier in the module, students revisit this familiar problem type, reinterpreting it as subtraction (**1.OA.1**, **1.OA.4**). The topic then uses the strategies of counting with both 5-group cards and the number path to solve subtraction problems (**1.OA.5**, **1.OA.6**).

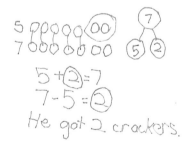

---

[1] For an analysis of addition and subtraction word problem types used in Grades K–2, please refer to the Counting and Cardinality Progression, pages 7 and 9, and the Standards, page 88.

Module 1:   Sums and Differences to 10

3

Topic H is analogous to Topic C. Students interpret the meaning of subtraction as they solve different problem types involving subtraction (**1.OA.1**). Throughout Module 1, rather than using formal drawings or tape diagrams, students are encouraged to make math drawings that flow from their understanding of the stories. They engage in dialogue to relate their drawings to number sentences and explain the meaning of the subtraction symbol.

Topic I follows a week of intensive work with story problems to work on a more abstract level by visiting methods for subtraction involving special cases, subtracting 0 and 1, subtracting the whole number, and subtracting one less than the whole number. These two lessons are followed by three lessons in which students use familiar decompositions (5-groups and partners of 10) to conceptualize subtraction as finding a missing part (**1.OA.6**).

Finally, in Topic J, students analyze the addition chart for repeated reasoning and structures that support their journey towards fluency with subtraction within 10. The module closes with a lesson wherein students create sets of related addition and subtraction facts and use dialogue to explain their found connections (e.g., $7 = 4 + 3$, $7 - 4 = 3$, $4 + 3 = 3 + 4$, $4 = 7 - 3$, etc.). They began the module with very basic counting on and end the module both with the skill to count on and significant movement towards the goal of fluency, achieved as the second addend does not need to be counted or can be counted very quickly.

Please note that the assessments should be read aloud to Grade 1 students.

Notes on Pacing–Grade 1

Module 1

If pacing is a challenge, consider consolidating Lessons 22 and 23 into one lesson and omitting the Problem Sets. Instead, have students create their own flashcards for +0 and +1 facts for Lesson 22 and +2 facts for Lesson 23. Students can mix up their flashcards and order them (e.g., 2 columns for Lesson 22 and 3 columns for Lesson 23), thinking of the answers as they go, or they can quiz each other.

$1 + 0$	$1 + 1$	$1 + 2$
$2 + 0$	$2 + 1$	$2 + 2$
$3 + 0$	$3 + 1$	$3 + 2$
$4 + 0$	$4 + 1$	$4 + 2$
$5 + 0$	$5 + 1$	$5 + 2$
$6 + 0$	$6 + 1$	$6 + 2$
$7 + 0$	$7 + 1$	$7 + 2$
$8 + 0$	$8 + 1$	$8 + 2$
$9 + 0$	$9 + 1$	
$10 + 0$		

Consider consolidating Topics G and H by using the following sequence of lessons.

   Day 1: Lesson 25—*Add to with change unknown* math stories related to subtraction.

   Day 2: Lesson 30—*Add to with change unknown* math stories related to subtraction.

   Day 3: Consolidate Lessons 28 and 29—*Take from* and *take apart* math stories.

   Day 4: Lesson 31—*Take from with change unknown* math stories.

   Day 5: Lesson 32—*Put together/take apart with addend unknown* math stories.

If the above sequence is used, teach Lessons 26 and 27 at the beginning of Topic I (Lessons 33–37) where the number path is used as a strategy for decomposition. These changes will provide time to focus on the concept of subtraction through word problems before the lessons on strategies for decomposition.

Consider omitting the Problem Sets from Lessons 38 and 39. Instead, have students create their own flashcards for related subtraction facts to be used in the same manner as the addition flashcards mentioned above.

Module 2

If pacing is a challenge, embed conversations about efficiency and strategy comparison throughout Module 2. Application Problems and Student Debriefs can provide opportunities to share and compare students' varied strategies. This allows omission of four lessons: 5, 9, 11, and 21. In Lesson 16, consider focusing on the finger work to practice the take from ten strategy rather than focusing on relating counting on to making ten and taking from ten. Consider omitting Lesson 24 if Application Problems are completed daily and if students have completed Lessons 22 and 23, which also focus on solving word problems. Note that it may be useful to extend Lessons 10, 19, 20, or 25 to provide extra practice as students develop their understanding of making ten, taking from ten, and the meaning of the equal sign.

Module 3

Students need Module 3's fluency before advancing to Module 4. In the event that there are critical pacing issues, consider moving Topic D (Lessons 10–13, focusing on graphing and data interpretation) to another time in the day (e.g., science, morning routine).

Note that Lessons 2, 4, 6, and 9 are the most essential lessons of Module 3.

Module 4

The work of this module is foundational to the Number and Operations in Base Ten domain of the Grade 1 standards. Therefore, it is not recommended to omit any lessons from Module 4.

Module 5

The work of this module is foundational to the Geometry domain of the Grade 1 standards. Therefore, it is not recommended to omit any lessons from Module 5.

Module 6

During Module 4, addition and subtraction work is limited to numbers within 40. In Module 6, students extend into numbers within 100. If students are readily able to apply their learning from Module 4 to Module 6, consider consolidating lessons in Topics A, B, and C (e.g., Lessons 3 and 4, Lessons 5 and 6, and Lessons 10 and 11). In Topic C, use each day's Exit Ticket to determine whether the lessons that follow can be omitted or consolidated.

Topic E, Coins and Their Values, might be modified, omitted, or embedded throughout the instructional day depending on the standards in the state implementing the curriculum.

Distribution of Instructional Minutes

This diagram represents a suggested distribution of instructional minutes based on the emphasis of particular lesson components in different lessons throughout the module.

- ■ Fluency Practice
- ▨ Concept Development
- ▨ Application Problems
- ▨ Student Debrief

Lessons

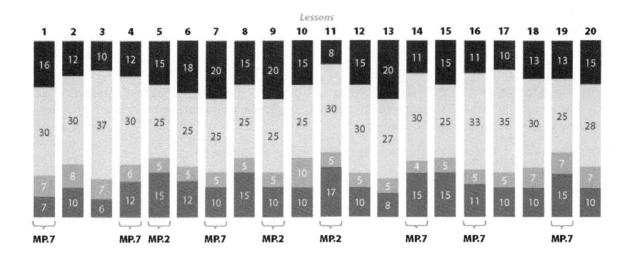

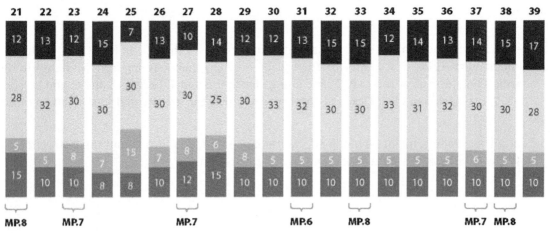

MP = Mathematical Practice

Module 1:   Sums and Differences to 10

EUREKA MATH™

Focus Grade Level Standards[2]

Represent and solve problems involving addition and subtraction.[3]

1.OA.1   Use addition and subtraction within 20 to solve word problems involving situations of adding to, taking from, putting together, taking apart, and comparing, with unknowns in all positions, e.g., by using objects, drawings, and equations with a symbol for the unknown number to represent the problem.

Understand and apply properties of operations and the relationship between addition and subtraction.

1.OA.3   Apply properties of operations as strategies to add and subtract. (Students need not use formal terms for these properties.) *Examples: If 8 + 3 = 11 is known, then 3 + 8 = 11 is also known. (Commutative property of addition.) To add 2 + 6 + 4, the second two numbers can be added to make a ten, so 2 + 6 + 4 = 2 + 10 = 12. (Associative property of addition.)*

1.OA.4   Understand subtraction as an unknown-addend problem. *For example, subtract 10 − 8 by finding the number that makes 10 when added to 8.*

Add and subtract within 20.

1.OA.5   Relate counting to addition and subtraction (e.g., by counting on 2 to add 2).

1.OA.6   Add and subtract within 20, demonstrating fluency for addition and subtraction within 10. Use strategies such as counting on; making ten (e.g., 8 + 6 = 8 + 2 + 4 = 10 + 4 = 14); decomposing a number leading to a ten (e.g., 13 − 4 = 13 − 3 − 1 = 10 − 1 = 9); using the relationship between addition and subtraction (e.g., knowing that 8 + 4 = 12, one knows 12 − 8 = 4); and creating equivalent but easier or known sums (e.g., adding 6 + 7 by creating the known equivalent 6 + 6 + 1 = 12 + 1 = 13).

Work with addition and subtraction equations.

1.OA.7   Understand the meaning of the equal sign, and determine if equations involving addition and subtraction are true or false. *For example, which of the following equations are true and which are false? 6 = 6, 7 = 8 − 1, 5 + 2 = 2 + 5, 4 + 1 = 5 + 2.*

1.OA.8   Determine the unknown whole number in an addition or subtraction equation relating three whole numbers. *For example, determine the unknown number that makes the equation true in each of the equations 8 + ? = 11, 5 = □ − 3, 6 + 6 = □.*

---

[2] In this module, work is limited to within 10.

[3] 1.OA.2 is addressed in Module 2.

Foundational Standards

K.CC.2   Count forward beginning from a given number within the known sequence (instead of having to begin at 1).

K.CC.4b Understand that the last number name said tells the number of objects counted. The number of objects is the same regardless of their arrangement or the order in which they were counted.

K.CC.4c Understand that each successive number name refers to a quantity that is one larger.

K.OA.3   Decompose numbers less than or equal to 10 into pairs in more than one way, e.g., by using objects or drawings, and record each decomposition by a drawing or equation (e.g., $5 = 2 + 3$ and $5 = 4 + 1$).

K.OA.4   For any number from 1 to 9, find the number that makes 10 when added to the given number, e.g., by using objects or drawings, and record the answer with a drawing or equation.

K.OA.5   Fluently add and subtract within 5.

Focus Standards for Mathematical Practice

MP.2   **Reason abstractly and quantitatively.** Students make sense of quantities and their relations as they reason about two new problem types in Grade 1: *change unknown* and *addend unknown.* They write an addition sentence that corresponds to the situation and then reason to see that a subtraction number sentence also can be used to solve for the unknown. Furthermore, in Topic D, students decontextualize addition from stories and work on strategies for computing.

MP.6   **Attend to precision.** Students clarify the meaning of the commutative property as they represent the same stories with repositioned addends. Students also state the meaning of the equal sign when they represent one amount with two different expressions connected by the equal sign.

MP.7   **Look for and make use of structure.** Students use the structure of embedded numbers or a known part from which to count on to find a total. After studying the commutative property, the larger addend becomes a structure from which to count on. Also, they analyze the addition chart for repeated reasoning and structures (such as 5-groups, plus ones, doubles, sums equal to 10, etc.) that can help them to better understand relationships and connections between different addition facts.

MP.8   **Look for and express regularity in repeated reasoning.** Students recognize when they are adding they are counting on by the same amount (e.g., + 2 or + 3 is the same as counting on by 2 or 3). Therefore, they apply the same strategy to solve other problems, recognizing the repetition of the reasoning.

Overview of Module Topics and Lesson Objectives

Standards	Topics and Objectives		Days
1.OA.1 1.OA.5	A	**Embedded Numbers and Decompositions**	3
		Lesson 1: Analyze and describe embedded numbers (to 10) using 5-groups and number bonds.	
		Lesson 2: Reason about embedded numbers in varied configurations using number bonds.	
		Lesson 3: See and describe numbers of objects using *1 more* within 5-group configurations.	
1.OA.1 1.OA.5 1.OA.6	B	**Counting On from Embedded Numbers**	5
		Lessons 4–5: Represent *put together* situations with number bonds. Count on from one embedded number or part to totals of 6 and 7, and generate all addition expressions for each total.	
		Lessons 6–7: Represent *put together* situations with number bonds. Count on from one embedded number or part to totals of 8 and 9, and generate all expressions for each total.	
		Lesson 8: Represent all the number pairs of 10 as number bonds from a given scenario, and generate all expressions equal to 10.	
1.OA.1 1.OA.6 1.OA.5	C	**Addition Word Problems**	5
		Lesson 9: Solve *add to with result unknown* and *put together with result unknown* math stories by drawing, writing equations, and making statements of the solution.	
		Lesson 10: Solve *put together with result unknown* math stories by drawing and using 5-group cards.	
		Lesson 11: Solve *add to with change unknown* math stories as a context for counting on by drawing, writing equations, and making statements of the solution.	
		Lesson 12: Solve *add to with change unknown* math stories using 5-group cards.	
		Lesson 13: Tell *put together with result unknown*, *add to with result unknown*, and *add to with change unknown* stories from equations.	

Standards		Topics and Objectives	Days
1.OA.5 1.OA.8 1.OA.6	D	**Strategies for Counting On** Lessons 14–15: Count on up to 3 more using numeral and 5-group cards and fingers to track the change. Lesson 16: Count on to find the unknown part in missing addend equations such as 6 + __ = 9. Answer, "How many more to make 6, 7, 8, 9, and 10?"	3
1.OA.3 1.OA.7	E	**The Commutative Property of Addition and the Equal Sign** Lessons 17–18: Understand the meaning of the equal sign by pairing equivalent expressions and constructing true number sentences. Lesson 19: Represent the same story scenario with addends repositioned (the commutative property). Lesson 20: Apply the commutative property to count on from a larger addend.	4
1.OA.3 1.OA.6	F	**Development of Addition Fluency Within 10** Lesson 21: Visualize and solve doubles and doubles plus 1 with 5-group cards. Lesson 22: Look for and make use of repeated reasoning on the addition chart by solving and analyzing problems with common addends. Lesson 23: Look for and make use of structure on the addition chart by looking for and coloring problems with the same total. Lesson 24: Practice to build fluency with facts to 10.	4
		Mid-Module Assessment: Topics A–F (assessment 1 day, return 1 day, remediation or further applications 1 day)	3
1.OA.1 1.OA.4 1.OA.5	G	**Subtraction as an Unknown Addend Problem** Lesson 25: Solve *add to with change unknown* math stories with addition, and relate to subtraction. Model with materials, and write corresponding number sentences. Lessons 26–27: Count on using the number path to find an unknown part.	3
1.OA.1 1.OA.4 1.OA.5 1.OA.8	H	**Subtraction Word Problems** Lesson 28: Solve *take from with result unknown* math stories with math drawings, true number sentences, and statements, using horizontal marks to cross off what is taken away. Lesson 29: Solve *take apart with addend unknown* math stories with math drawings, equations, and statements, circling the known part to find the unknown.	5

Standards		Topics and Objectives	Days
		Lesson 30: Solve *add to with change unknown* math stories with drawings, relating addition and subtraction.	
		Lesson 31: Solve *take from with change unknown* math stories with drawings.	
		Lesson 32: Solve *put together/take apart with addend unknown* math stories.	
1.OA.5 **1.OA.6** **1.OA.4**	I	**Decomposition Strategies for Subtraction**	5
		Lesson 33: Model 0 less and 1 less pictorially and as subtraction number sentences.	
		Lesson 34: Model $n - n$ and $n - (n - 1)$ pictorially and as subtraction sentences.	
		Lesson 35: Relate subtraction facts involving fives and doubles to corresponding decompositions.	
		Lesson 36: Relate subtraction from 10 to corresponding decompositions.	
		Lesson 37: Relate subtraction from 9 to corresponding decompositions.	
1.OA.6	J	**Development of Subtraction Fluency Within 10**	2
		Lesson 38: Look for and make use of repeated reasoning and structure, using the addition chart to solve subtraction problems.	
		Lesson 39: Analyze the addition chart to create sets of related addition and subtraction facts.	
		End-of-Module Assessment: Topics A–J (assessment 1 day, return 1 day, remediation or further applications 1 day)	3
Total Number of Instructional Days			45

©2015 Great Minds. eureka-math.org
G1-M1-TE-BK1-1.3.1-01.2016

Terminology

New or Recently Introduced Terms

- Count on (count up from one addend to the total)
- Track (use different objects to track the count on from one addend to the total)
- Expression (e.g., 2 + 1 or 5 – 3)
- Addend (one of the numbers being added)
- Doubles (e.g., 3 + 3 or 4 + 4)
- Doubles plus 1 (e.g., 3 + 4 or 4 + 5)

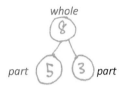

whole

part *part*

Number Bond

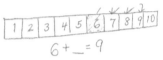

$6 + \underline{\ \ } = 9$

$9 - 6 = \underline{\ \ }$

Number Path

Familiar Terms and Symbols[4]

- Part (e.g., "What is the unknown part? 3 + ___ = 8")
- Total and whole (use interchangeably instead of sum; e.g., "What is the total when we add 3 and 5?")
- Label (using letters or words on a math drawing to indicate the referents from the story's context)
- Addition, equal, and subtraction signs
- Equation and number sentence (used interchangeably throughout the module)
- Number bond (graphic showing part–part–whole)
- Equal sign (=)
- 5-groups (as pictured in the dot cards below), 2 rows of 5

Rekenrek

Hide Zero Cards

Suggested Tools and Representations

- Number bonds
- Addition chart
- Rekenrek
- Counters
- Number path
- 5-Group cards
- Hide Zero cards

Numerals

5-Groups

5-Group Cards

1 + 0	1 + 1	1 + 2	1 + 3	1 + 4	1 + 5	1 + 6	1 + 7	1 + 8	1 + 9
2 + 0	2 + 1	2 + 2	2 + 3	2 + 4	2 + 5	2 + 6	2 + 7	2 + 8	
3 + 0	3 + 1	3 + 2	3 + 3	3 + 4	3 + 5	3 + 6	3 + 7		
4 + 0	4 + 1	4 + 2	4 + 3	4 + 4	4 + 5	4 + 6			
5 + 0	5 + 1	5 + 2	5 + 3	5 + 4	5 + 5				
6 + 0	6 + 1	6 + 2	6 + 3	6 + 4					
7 + 0	7 + 1	7 + 2	7 + 3						
8 + 0	8 + 1	8 + 2							
9 + 0	9 + 1								
10 + 0									

Addition Chart

---

[4] These are terms and symbols students have used or seen previously.

EUREKA MATH™

Suggested Methods of Instructional Delivery

Directions for Administration of Sprints

Sprints are designed to develop fluency. They should be fun, adrenaline-rich activities that intentionally build energy and excitement. A fast pace is essential. During Sprint administration, teachers assume the role of athletic coaches. A rousing routine fuels students' motivation to do their personal best. Student recognition of increasing success is critical, and so every improvement is celebrated.

One Sprint has two parts with closely related problems on each. Students complete the two parts of the Sprint in quick succession with the goal of improving on the second part, even if only by one more.

With practice, the following routine takes about 9 minutes.

Sprint A

Pass Sprint A out quickly, face down on student desks with instructions to not look at the problems until the signal is given. (Some Sprints include words. If necessary, prior to starting the Sprint, quickly review the words so that reading difficulty does not slow students down.)

   T: You will have 60 seconds to do as many problems as you can. I do not expect you to finish all of them. Just do as many as you can, your personal best. (If some students are likely to finish before time is up, assign a number to count by on the back.)

   T: Take your mark! Get set! THINK!

Students immediately turn papers over and work furiously to finish as many problems as they can in 60 seconds. Time precisely.

   T: Stop! Circle the last problem you did. I will read just the answers. If you got it right, call out "Yes!" If you made a mistake, circle it. Ready?

   T: (Energetically, rapid-fire call the first answer.)

   S: Yes!

   T: (Energetically, rapid-fire call the second answer.)

   S: Yes!

Repeat to the end of Sprint A or until no student has a correct answer. If needed, read the count-by answers in the same way you read Sprint answers. Each number counted-by on the back is considered a correct answer.

   T: Fantastic! Now, write the number you got correct at the top of your page. This is your personal goal for Sprint B.

   T: How many of you got one right? (All hands should go up.)

   T: Keep your hand up until I say the number that is one more than the number you got correct. So, if you got 14 correct, when I say 15, your hand goes down. Ready?

   T: (Continue quickly.) How many got two correct? Three? Four? Five? (Continue until all hands are down.)

If the class needs more practice with Sprint A, continue with the optional routine presented below.

Module 1:   Sums and Differences to 10

T: I'll give you one minute to do more problems on this half of the Sprint. If you finish, stand behind your chair.

As students work, the student who scored highest on Sprint A might pass out Sprint B.

T: Stop! I will read just the answers. If you got it right, call out "Yes!" If you made a mistake, circle it. Ready? (Read the answers to the first half again as students stand.)

Movement

To keep the energy and fun going, always do a stretch or a movement game in between Sprints A and B. For example, the class might do jumping jacks while skip-counting by 5 for about 1 minute. Feeling invigorated, students take their seats for Sprint B, ready to make every effort to complete more problems this time.

Sprint B

Pass Sprint B out quickly, face down on student desks with instructions to not look at the problems until the signal is given. (Repeat the procedure for Sprint A up through the show of hands for how many right.)

T: Stand up if you got more correct on the second Sprint than on the first.

S: (Stand.)

T: Keep standing until I say the number that tells how many more you got right on Sprint B. If you got three more right on Sprint B than you did on Sprint A, when I say *three,* you sit down. Ready? (Call out numbers starting with one. Students sit as the number by which they improved is called. Celebrate the students who improved most with a cheer.)

T: Well done! Now, take a moment to go back and correct your mistakes. Think about what patterns you noticed in today's Sprint.

T: How did the patterns help you get better at solving the problems?

T: Rally Robin your thinking with your partner for 1 minute. Go!

Rally Robin is a style of sharing in which partners trade information back and forth, one statement at a time per person, for about 1 minute. This is an especially valuable part of the routine for students who benefit from their friends' support to identify patterns and try new strategies.

Students may take Sprints home.

Personal White Boards

Materials Needed for Personal White Boards

    1 heavy duty clear sheet protector
    1 piece of stiff red tag board 11" × 8 ¼"
    1 piece of stiff white tag board 11" × 8 ¼"
    1 3" × 3" piece of dark synthetic cloth for an eraser (e.g., felt)
    1 low odor blue dry erase marker, fine point

Directions for Creating Personal White Boards

Cut your white and red tag to specifications. Slide into the sheet protector. Store your eraser on the red side. Store markers in a separate container to avoid stretching the sheet protector.

©2015 Great Minds. eureka-math.org
G1-M1-TE-BK1-1.3.1-01.2016

Frequently Asked Questions About Personal White Boards

Why is one side red and one white?

- The white side of the board is the "paper." Students generally write on it, and if working individually, turn the board over to signal to the teacher that they have completed their work. The teacher then says, "Show me your boards," when most of the class is ready.

What are some of the benefits of a personal white board?

- The teacher can respond quickly to a gap in student understandings and skills. "Let's do some of these on our personal white boards until we have more mastery."
- Students can erase quickly so that they do not have to suffer the evidence of their mistake.
- They are motivating. Students love both the drill and thrill capability and the chance to do story problems with an engaging medium.
- Checking work gives the teacher instant feedback about student understanding.

What is the benefit of this personal white board over a commercially purchased dry erase board?

- It is much less expensive.
- Templates such as place value charts, number bond mats, hundreds boards, and number lines can be stored between the two pieces of tag board for easy access and reuse.
- Worksheets, story problems, and other problem sets can be done without marking the paper so that students can work on the problems independently at another time.
- Strips with story problems, number lines, and arrays can be inserted and still have a full piece of paper on which to write.
- The red versus white side distinction clarifies your expectations. When working collaboratively, there is no need to use the red side. When working independently, the students know how to keep their work private.
- The tag board can be removed if necessary to project the work.

Homework

Homework at the K–1 level is not a convention in all schools. In this curriculum, homework is an opportunity for additional practice of the content from the day's lesson. The teacher is encouraged, with the support of parents, administrators, and colleagues, to discern the appropriate use of homework for his or her students. Fluency exercises can also be considered as an alternative homework assignment.

©2015 Great Minds. eureka-math.org
G1-M1-TE-BK1-1.3.1-01.2016

Scaffolds[5]

The scaffolds integrated into *A Story of Units* give alternatives for how students access information as well as express and demonstrate their learning. Strategically placed margin notes are provided within each lesson elaborating on the use of specific scaffolds at applicable times. They address many needs presented by English language learners, students with disabilities, students performing above grade level, and students performing below grade level. Many of the suggestions are organized by Universal Design for Learning (UDL) principles and are applicable to more than one population. To read more about the approach to differentiated instruction in *A Story of Units,* please refer to "How to Implement *A Story of Units*."

Preparing to Teach a Module

Preparation of lessons will be more effective and efficient if there has been an adequate analysis of the module first. Each module in *A Story of Units* can be compared to a chapter in a book. How is the module moving the plot, the mathematics, forward? What new learning is taking place? How are the topics and objectives building on one another? The following is a suggested process for preparing to teach a module.

Step 1: Get a preview of the plot.

A: Read the Table of Contents. At a high level, what is the plot of the module? How does the story develop across the topics?

B: Preview the module's Exit Tickets[6] to see the trajectory of the module's mathematics and the nature of the work students are expected to be able to do.

Note: When studying a PDF file, enter "Exit Ticket" into the search feature to navigate from one Exit Ticket to the next.

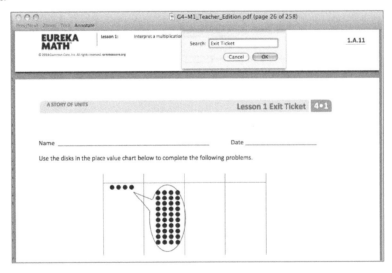

---

[5] Students with disabilities may require Braille, large print, audio, or special digital files. Please visit the website www.p12.nysed.gov/specialed/aim for specific information on how to obtain student materials that satisfy the National Instructional Materials Accessibility Standard (NIMAS) format.

[6] A more in-depth preview can be done by searching the Problem Sets rather than the Exit Tickets. Furthermore, this same process can be used to preview the coherence or flow of any component of the curriculum, such as Fluency Practice or Application Problems.

Step 2: Dig into the details.

A: Dig into a careful reading of the Module Overview. While reading the narrative, *liberally* reference the lessons and Topic Overviews to clarify the meaning of the text—the lessons demonstrate the strategies, show how to use the models, clarify vocabulary, and build understanding of concepts. Consider searching the video gallery on *Eureka Math*'s website to watch demonstrations of the use of models and other teaching techniques.

B: Having thoroughly investigated the Module Overview, read through the chart entitled Overview of Module Topics and Lesson Objectives to further discern the plot of the module. How do the topics flow and tell a coherent story? How do the objectives move from simple to complex?

Step 3: Summarize the story.

Complete the Mid- and End-of-Module Assessments. Use the strategies and models presented in the module to explain the thinking involved. Again, liberally reference the work done in the lessons to see how students who are learning with the curriculum might respond.

Preparing to Teach a Lesson

A three-step process is suggested to prepare a lesson. It is understood that at times teachers may need to make adjustments (customizations) to lessons to fit the time constraints and unique needs of their students. The recommended planning process is outlined below. Note: The ladder of Step 2 is a metaphor for the teaching sequence. The sequence can be seen not only at the macro level in the role that this lesson plays in the overall story, but also at the lesson level, where each rung in the ladder represents the next step in understanding or the next skill needed to reach the objective. To reach the objective, or the top of the ladder, all students must be able to access the first rung and each successive rung.

Step 1: Discern the plot.

A: Briefly review the Table of Contents for the module, recalling the overall story of the module and analyzing the role of this lesson in the module.

B: Read the Topic Overview of the lesson, and then review the Problem Set and Exit Ticket of each lesson of the topic.

C: Review the assessment following the topic, keeping in mind that assessments can be found midway through the module and at the end of the module.

Step 2: Find the ladder.

A: Complete the lesson's Problem Set.

B: Analyze and write notes on the new complexities of each problem as well as the sequences and progressions throughout problems (e.g., pictorial to abstract, smaller to larger numbers, single- to multi-step problems). The new complexities are the rungs of the ladder.

C: Anticipate where students might struggle, and write a note about the potential cause of the struggle.

D: Answer the Student Debrief questions, always anticipating how students will respond.

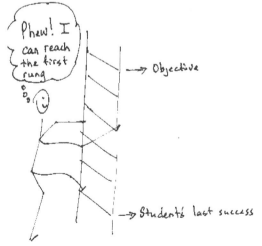

Step 3: Hone the lesson.

At times, the lesson and Problem Set are appropriate for all students and the day's schedule. At others, they may need customizing. If the decision is to customize based on either the needs of students or scheduling constraints, a suggestion is to decide upon and designate "Must Do" and "Could Do" problems.

A: Select "Must Do" problems from the Problem Set that meet the objective and provide a coherent experience for students; reference the ladder. The expectation is that the majority of the class will complete the "Must Do" problems within the allocated time. While choosing the "Must Do" problems, keep in mind the need for a balance of calculations, various word problem types[7], and work at both the pictorial and abstract levels.

B: "Must Do" problems might also include remedial work as necessary for the whole class, a small group, or individual students. Depending on anticipated difficulties, those problems might take different forms as shown in the chart below.

Anticipated Difficulty	"Must Do" Remedial Problem Suggestion
The first problem of the Problem Set is too challenging.	Write a short sequence of problems on the board that provides a ladder to Problem 1. Direct the class or small group to complete those first problems to empower them to begin the Problem Set. Consider labeling these problems "Zero Problems" since they are done prior to Problem 1.
There is too big of a jump in complexity between two problems.	Provide a problem or set of problems that creates a bridge between the two problems. Label them with the number of the problem they follow. For example, if the challenging jump is between Problems 2 and 3, consider labeling these problems "Extra 2s."
Students lack fluency or foundational skills necessary for the lesson.	Before beginning the Problem Set, do a quick, engaging fluency exercise, such as a Rapid White Board Exchange, "Thrilling Drill," or Sprint. Before beginning any fluency activity for the first time, assess that students are poised for success with the easiest problem in the set.
More work is needed at the concrete or pictorial level.	Provide manipulatives or the opportunity to draw solution strategies. Especially in Kindergarten, at times the Problem Set or pencil and paper aspect might be completely excluded, allowing students to simply work with materials.
More work is needed at the abstract level.	Hone the Problem Set to reduce the amount of drawing as appropriate for certain students or the whole class.

---

[7] See the Progression Documents "K, Counting and Cardinality" and "K–5, Operations and Algebraic Thinking" pp. 9 and 23, respectively.

C: "Could Do" problems are for students who work with greater fluency and understanding and can, therefore, complete more work within a given time frame. Adjust the Exit Ticket and Homework to reflect the "Must Do" problems or to address scheduling constraints.

D: At times, a particularly tricky problem might be designated as a "Challenge!" problem. This can be motivating, especially for advanced students. Consider creating the opportunity for students to share their "Challenge!" solutions with the class at a weekly session or on video.

E: Consider how to best use the vignettes of the Concept Development section of the lesson. Read through the vignettes, and highlight selected parts to be included in the delivery of instruction so that students can be independently successful on the assigned task.

F: Pay close attention to the questions chosen for the Student Debrief. Regularly ask students, "What was the lesson's learning goal today?" Hone the goal with them.

Assessment Summary

Type	Administered	Format	Standards Addressed
Mid-Module Assessment Task	After Topic F	Constructed response with rubric	1.OA.1 1.OA.3 1.OA.5 1.OA.6 1.OA.7 1.OA.8
End-of-Module Assessment Task	After Topic J	Constructed response with rubric	1.OA.1 1.OA.3 1.OA.4 1.OA.5 1.OA.6 1.OA.7 1.OA.8

Mathematics Curriculum

1
GRADE

Topic A

Embedded Numbers and Decompositions

1.OA.1, 1.OA.5

Focus Standard:	1.OA.1	Use addition and subtraction within 20 to solve word problems involving situations of adding to, taking from, putting together, taking apart, and comparing, with unknowns in all positions, e.g., by using objects, drawings, and equations with a symbol for the unknown number to represent the problem.
	1.OA.5	Relate counting to addition and subtraction (e.g., by counting on 2 to add 2).
Instructional Days:	3	
Coherence -Links from:	GK–M4	Number Pairs, Addition and Subtraction to 10
-Links to:	G2–M4	Addition and Subtraction Within 200 with Word Problems to 100

In this first module of Grade 1, students make significant progress towards fluency with addition and subtraction of numbers to 10 (**1.OA.6**). They are presented with opportunities intended to advance them from counting all to counting on, which leads to decomposing and composing addends and total amounts. In Kindergarten, students achieved fluency with addition and subtraction facts to 5. This means they can decompose 5 into 4 and 1, 3 and 2, and 5 and 0. They can do this without counting all. They perceive the 3 and 2 embedded within the 5.

Topic A continues the work of developing this ability with all the numbers within 10 in *put together* situations, with a special focus on the numbers 6, 7, 8, and 9 in 5-group configurations, since recognizing how much a number needs to make 10 is part of the Kindergarten standards (**K.OA.4**) and is easier for most children. Students decompose numbers into two visual sets, or conceptually subitize, and record their decompositions as number bonds. In Lesson 1, students use the 5-group configuration, as this organization allows students to quickly see, or perceptually subitize, the subset of 5. Once they have identified that first subset of 5, they can perceptually subitize the other part:

T: How many dots do you see?

S: 8.

T: What two parts do you see?

S: I see 5 and 3.

T: Did you need to count all the dots?

S: No! I could see the top row was a full five, so I just saw the other part, which was 3.

EUREKA
MATH™

The teacher then guides students to *count on* from the five to determine the total. This process of conceptual subitizing, or breaking apart the total into two easily identifiable subsets, continues into Lesson 2, as students are presented with dots in varied configurations. As students discuss the different parts they each see within the total and the different ways they are able to break the total apart, they begin to understand that a given quantity can be decomposed in a variety of ways. In Lesson 3, students see and describe *1 more* as + 1. They use the structure of the first addend rather than its cardinality: The number is a unit to which they can add one, or *count on* by one, without recounting. Students now stand on this first embedded number, which lays the foundation for the Level 2 strategy of counting on. Students engage in math discussions throughout the lessons as they share their ways of seeing the embedded numbers and thinking of *1 more* (**1.OA.5**).

A Teaching Sequence Toward Mastery of Embedded Numbers and Decompositions
Objective 1: Analyze and describe embedded numbers (to 10) using 5-groups and number bonds. (Lesson 1)
Objective 2: Reason about embedded numbers in varied configurations using number bonds. (Lesson 2)
Objective 3: See and describe numbers of objects using *1 more* within 5-groups configurations. (Lesson 3)

©2015 Great Minds. eureka-math.org
G1-M1-TE-BK1-1.3.1-01.2016

Lesson 1

Objective: Analyze and describe embedded numbers (to 10) using 5-groups and number bonds.

Suggested Lesson Structure

■ Fluency Practice	(16 minutes)
▨ Application Problem	(7 minutes)
▫ Concept Development	(30 minutes)
▨ Student Debrief	(7 minutes)
Total Time	**(60 minutes)**

NOTES ON FLUENCY PRACTICE:

Think of Fluency Practice as having three goals:

1. Maintenance (staying sharp on previously learned skills).

2. Preparation (targeted practice for the current lesson).

3. Anticipation (skills that ensure that students are ready for the in-depth work of upcoming lessons).
    Example of anticipatory fluency: Students must be secure in counting to 10 long before they can be expected to decompose 10.

Fluency Practice (16 minutes)

- Math Fingers Flash **K.CC2, K.CC.4**   (3 minutes)
- Sprint: Count Dots **K.CC.2, K.CC.5**   (13 minutes)

Math Fingers Flash (3 minutes)

Note: Visually recognizing (perceptually subitizing) sets of objects, particularly fingers, allows students to move toward seeing two sets of objects together (conceptually subitizing), thus preparing them for the fluency objective of Grade 1.

 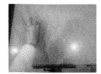  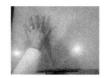 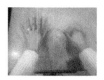

Teacher flashes fingers the Math Way for numbers 0–10. When using a document camera, teacher begins by raising the left pinky and ends with the right pinky as shown above. When facing the students, teacher's raised fingers should begin with the right pinky and end with the left pinky as seen below. At all times, students see fingers move from left to right.

T: I'm going to hold up some fingers the Math Way and then hide them. Look carefully and say the number you saw when I snap.

T: (Flash 3 fingers for 2–3 seconds and then hide them.) Ready (snap).

S: 3.

Repeat process for numbers within 5.

T: (Flash 7 fingers.) Ready (snap).

©2015 Great Minds. eureka-math.org
G1-M1-TE-BK1-1.3.1-01.2016

T: (Hold up 5 fingers on the right hand.) How many fingers are on this hand?

S: 5.

T: 5 (hold up the five hand and then hold up the other fingers, one at a time) 6, 7.

Repeat the process for numbers 6–10, inviting students to count on from 5.

Sprint: Count Dots (13 minutes)

Materials: (S) 5-group dots Sprint

Note: Visually recognizing two sets of objects together (conceptually subitizing) provides students with a foundation for counting on as they solve addition problems. See the Suggested Methods of Instructional Delivery section of the Module Overview for directions on giving Sprints.

Application Problem (7 minutes)

Dora found 5 leaves that blew in through the window. Then, she found 2 more leaves that blew in. Draw a picture and use numbers to show how many leaves Dora found in all.

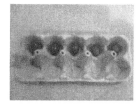

Note: Rather than specifying to write a number sentence or number bond, since it is the first day of school, this Application Problem is more open-ended so that students can demonstrate their thinking and representational skills. This problem serves as a lead-up to the Concept Development of seeing the quantity of 5 and another number.

Concept Development (30 minutes)

Materials: (T) 1 egg carton cut to 10 slots (S) 1 egg carton cut to 10 slots, bag with 9 beads (or other fun classroom objects), number bond (Template), personal white board

Before the lesson, insert the number bond template into each student's personal white board.

T: Take out your egg carton. Count to find out how many slots there are. Wait for the signal to tell me. (Pause. When all are ready, give the signal.)

S: 10.

T: Someone already cut 2 off.

T: How many slots are in the top row?

S: 5.

Lesson 1:   Analyze and describe embedded numbers (to 10) using 5-groups and   23
number bonds.

©2015 Great Minds. eureka-math.org
G1-M1-TE-BK1-1.3.1-01.2016

T: How many slots are in the bottom row?

S: 5.

T: Take out the objects in your bag. First, count 5 into the top row from left to right. (Pause.) How many beads do you have in your top row?

S: 5.

T: Now, we are going to be number detectives. Let's see what numbers are *hiding* inside of 5.

T: I see 2 hiding inside. Look. (Show the two objects.) What other numbers do you see hiding inside 5? Talk to your partner.

T: (Circulate and listen. Encourage those who are touching and counting, rather than seeing the embedded numbers, to recognize quantities of at least 2 or 3.)

T: (Write the 5 in the total box of a number bond.) That's our total, or whole. Do you remember these *number bonds* from kindergarten?

S: Yes!

T: You said there was a 2 hiding inside of 5. That's a part. (Write the 2 in the number bond.)

T: Let's cover those 2 beads. What is the other part?

S: 3.

T: Let's write that in the other part of the number bond. (Write 3.)

T: What two parts did we find make 5, detectives?

S: 2 and 3.

T: Let's see if we can find different numbers inside of 5. (Write 5 in the total box inside a new number bond.)

T: (Continue to find the other numbers inside of 5 and generate the corresponding number bonds using the same process.)

T: Let's take out 2 more beads, and put them in the bottom row of the egg carton.

T: How many beads are there now?

S: 7.

T: Turn and talk to your partner about what numbers you see inside 7.

S: (Circulate and share their observations.)

NOTES ON
MULTIPLE MEANS
OF ACTION
AND EXPRESSION:

Discourage the touch and count behavior which many students mistake for being good at school. Grade 1 students can subitize twos and threes without counting. They should be encouraged to recognize this since seeing embedded numbers (or subitizing) is the beginning of counting on.

Number Bond

total

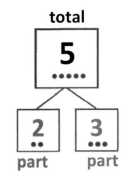

NOTES ON
MULTIPLE MEANS
OF REPRESENTATION:

Have students write the two parts on their number bond template. For further support for counting on, have them draw the beads at first, and then later in the lesson, represent the 5-groups numerically.

©2015 Great Minds. eureka-math.org
G1-M1-TE-BK1-1.3.1-01.2016

T: I heard a student say that she saw 5 beads. Are there 5 beads?

S: Yes!

T: Let's draw 5 dots as a part in our number bond instead of the number 5.

T: Where did you see the 5?

S: In the top row.

T: Let's cover the 5. What is the other part to make 7?

S: 2.

T: Let's draw in 2 dots as the other part in the number bond.

T: Let's count on from 5 to find our total. Count with me. Let's start with 5.

MP.7   (Point to the fifth dot.)

T/S: Fiiiiiive, 6, 7. (Point to each of the dots as you count them. Draw 7 dots in the total box the 5-group way.)

T: Let's now represent this number bond with numbers instead of dots. (Lead students to make the number bond numerically on their personal white boards.)

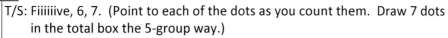

Number bond with parts drawn the 5-groups way

Continue to find five and its partner within 6, 7, 8, and 9. Other combinations will be explored in Lesson 2. Release students to work independently.

Problem Set (10 minutes)

Students should do their personal best to complete the Problem Set within the allotted 10 minutes. Some problems do not specify a method for solving. This is an intentional reduction of scaffolding that invokes MP.5, Use Appropriate Tools Strategically. Students should solve these problems using the RDW approach used for Application Problems.

For some classes, it may be appropriate to modify the assignment by specifying which problems students should work on first. With this option, let the purposeful sequencing of the Problem Set guide each selection so that problems continue to be scaffolded. Balance word problems with other problem types to ensure a range of practice. Consider assigning incomplete problems for homework or at another time during the day.

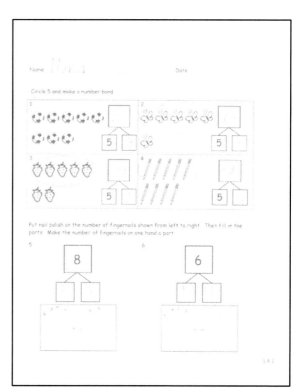

Lesson 1:   Analyze and describe embedded numbers (to 10) using 5-groups and number bonds.

25

©2015 Great Minds. eureka-math.org
G1-M1-TE-BK1-1.3.1-01.2016

Student Debrief (7 minutes)

Lesson Objective: Analyze and describe embedded numbers (to 10) using 5-groups and number bonds.

The Student Debrief is intended to invite reflection and active processing of the total lesson experience.

Invite students to review their solutions for the Problem Set. Have them work in pairs to check over their work and discuss how they saw the 5 and the other part to make their number bonds and find the totals. Then go over answers as a class. Look for misconceptions or misunderstandings that can be addressed in the Student Debrief. Guide students in a conversation to debrief the Problem Set and process the lesson.

Any combination of the questions below may be used to lead the discussion.

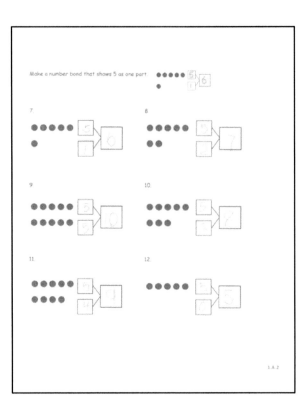

- Are there 5 butterflies? Strawberries? (We want students to see that there are 5 butterflies, etc., embedded within the larger numbers. Have them identify the other part once they have seen the five within the number.)

- Look at the soccer balls and the pencils. What is the same about them? What is different about them? (Guide students to see that both 8 and 9 have 5 embedded in them. If they notice the other embedded numbers of 1 to 8, that is great!)

- Can you show me 5 fingers? Show me 5 with two hands (i.e., 4 and 1, or 3 and 2). Now, show me 5 with one hand.

- Can you show me 6 the Math Way with your fingers? (Five fingers on the left hand and the thumb on the right hand.) Can you show me the 5 inside 6? Continue with 7, 8, 9, and 10.

- (Show examples of student work from the Application Problem.) What were the two parts in our story problem? What does that have in common with today's lesson?

Exit Ticket (3 minutes)

After the Student Debrief, instruct students to complete the Exit Ticket. A review of their work will help with assessing students' understanding of the concepts that were presented in today's lesson and planning more effectively for future lessons. The questions may be read aloud to the students.

Homework

Homework at the K–1 level is not a convention in all schools. In this curriculum, homework is an opportunity for additional practice of the content from the day's lesson. The teacher is encouraged, with the support of parents, administrators, and colleagues, to discern the appropriate use of homework for his or her students. Fluency exercises can also be considered as an alternative homework assignment.

©2015 Great Minds. eureka-math.org
G1-M1-TE-BK1-1.3.1-01.2016

A

Number Correct: _____

Name _____ Date _____

*Write the number of dots. Find 1 or 2 groups that make finding the total number of dots easier!

1.	••		16.	••••• ••••	
2.	•••		17.	••••• •••	
3.	••••		18.	••••• •••••	
4.	•••		19.	••••• ••	
5.	•		20.	••••• •	
6.	••••		21.	••••• ••••	
7.	•••••		22.	••••• ••••	
8.	••••		23.	•••• •••••	
9.	••••• •		24.	••••• •••	
10.	••••• ••		25.	••• •• •••••	
11.	•••••		26.	••••• ••	
12.	••••		27.	••• ••• •• •••	
13.	••••• •		28.	••• •• •• ••	
14.	••••• •••		29.	•• ••• • ••	
15.	••••• ••		30.	•• • •• ••• ••	

EUREKA MATH

Lesson 1:   Analyze and describe embedded numbers (to 10) using 5-groups and number bonds.

27

B

Number Correct:

Name _____ Date _____

*Write the number of dots. Find 1 or 2 groups that make finding the total number of dots easier!

1.	●		16.	●●●●● ●●●	
2.	●●		17.	●●●●● ●●●●	
3.	●		18.	●●●●● ●●	
4.	●●●●		19.	●●●●● ●●●	
5.	●●●		20.	●●●●● ●●●●●	
6.	●●●●●		21.	●●●●● ●●●●	
7.	●●●●		22.	●●●●● ●●●●●	
8.	●●●●●		23.	● ●●●● ●●●●●	
9.	●●●●● ●●		24.	●●●●● ●●●●●	
10.	●●●●● ●		25.	●● ●●●●●	
11.	●●●●● ●●●		26.	●●● ● ●● ●●	
12.	●●●●● ●		27.	●● ●●● ●●● ●●	
13.	●●●●●		28.	●● ●● ●● ●	
14.	●●●●● ●●		29.	●●● ●● ●● ●●	
15.	●●●●● ●		30.	●● ●●●● ●●	

Lesson 1: Analyze and describe embedded numbers (to 10) using 5-groups and number bonds.

EUREKA MATH™

Name _____   Date _____

Circle 5, and then make a number bond.

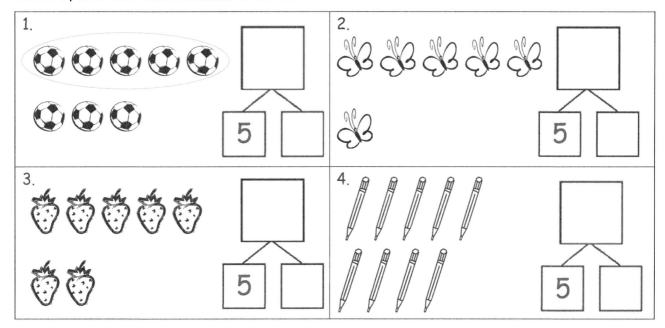

Put nail polish on the number of fingernails shown from left to right. Then, fill in the parts. Make the number of fingernails on one hand a part.

5.

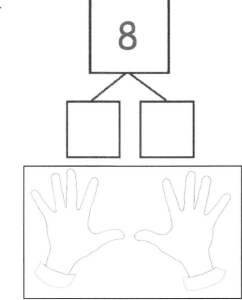

6.

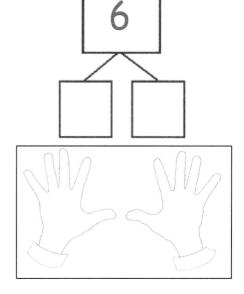

Lesson 1:   Analyze and describe embedded numbers (to 10) using 5-groups and number bonds.

29

Make a number bond that shows 5 as one part.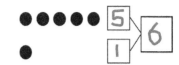

7.

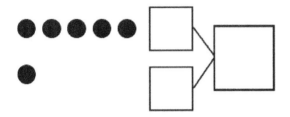

8.

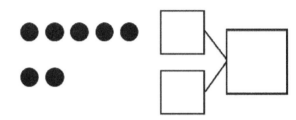

9.

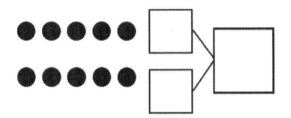

10.

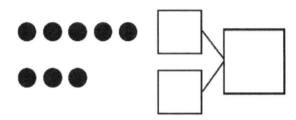

11.

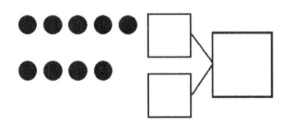

12.

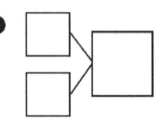

Lesson 1:   Analyze and describe embedded numbers (to 10) using 5-groups and number bonds.

EUREKA MATH

Name _____ Date _____

Make a number bond for the pictures that shows 5 as one part.

1.

2.

EUREKA MATH

Lesson 1:   Analyze and describe embedded numbers (to 10) using 5-groups and
number bonds.

©2015 Great Minds. eureka-math.org
G1-M1-TE-BK1-1.3.1-01.2016

31

Name _____   Date _____

Circle 5, and then make a number bond.

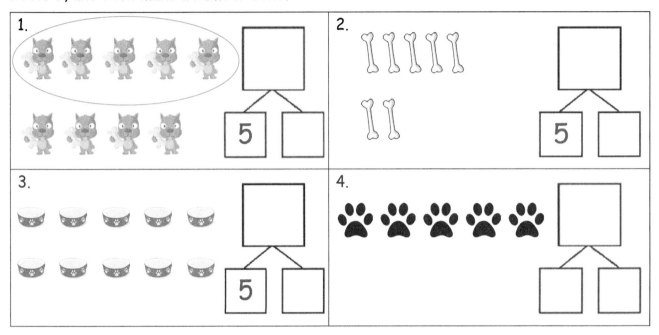

Make a number bond that shows 5 as one part.

5.

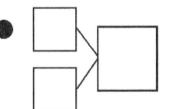

6.

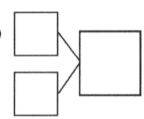

7.

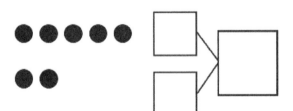

8.

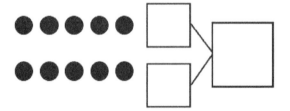

Lesson 1:   Analyze and describe embedded numbers (to 10) using 5-groups and number bonds.

EUREKA MATH

Make a number bond for the dominoes.

9.

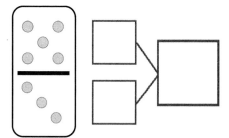

10.

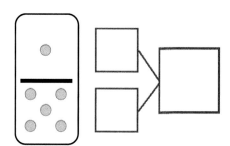

11.

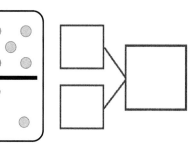

12.

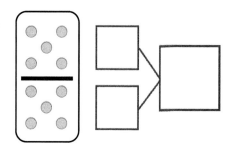

Circle 5 and count. Then, make a number bond.

13.	14.
15.	16.

EUREKA
MATH™

Lesson 1:   Analyze and describe embedded numbers (to 10) using 5-groups and
            number bonds.

33

©2015 Great Minds. eureka-math.org
G1-M1-TE-BK1-1.3.1-01.2016

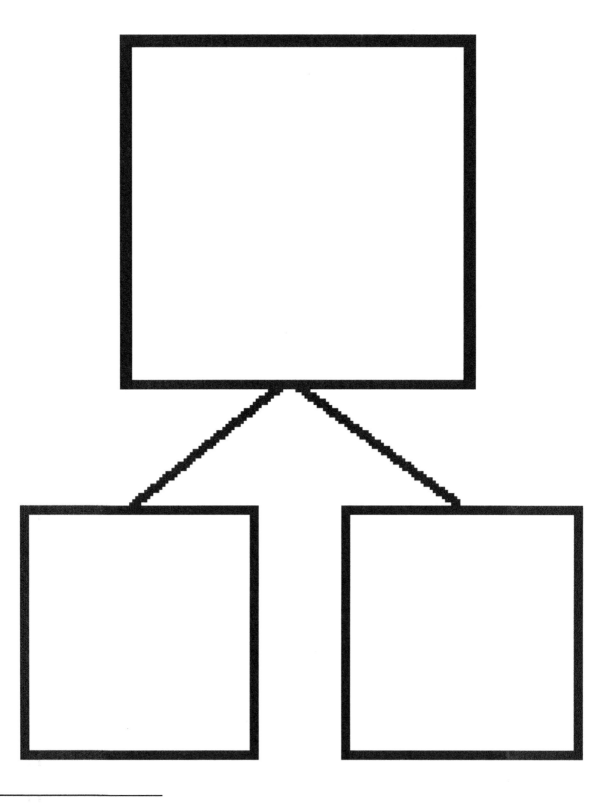

number bond

Lesson 1: Analyze and describe embedded numbers (to 10) using 5-groups and number bonds.

©2015 Great Minds. eureka-math.org
G1-M1-TE-BK1-1.3.1-01.2016

Lesson 2

Objective: Reason about embedded numbers in varied configurations using number bonds.

Suggested Lesson Structure

■ Fluency Practice   (12 minutes)
■ Application Problem   (8 minutes)
■ Concept Development   (30 minutes)
■ Student Debrief   (10 minutes)

   Total Time   **(60 minutes)**

Fluency Practice (12 minutes)

- Finger Counting from Left to Right **K.CC.2, K.OA.5**   (2 minutes)
- Show Me Your Math Fingers: Partners to 5 and 5 More **K.CC.2, K.OA.3**   (5 minutes)
- Number Bond Dash: 5 **K.OA.3, K.OA.5**   (5 minutes)

Finger Counting from Left to Right (2 minutes)

Note: Counting from left to right with their fingers allows students an organized way to use their most readily available tool—their fingers! This type of counting also mimics the number path used in later lessons.

Instruct students to count with their "piano fingers." Count by ones within 10 on the fingers from left to right, from pinky on the left hand as 1, to pinky on the right hand as 10.

Hover the fingers as if playing the piano. Drop the finger as it is counted and leave it down. Start and end at different numbers. (For example, in counting from 5 to 7, the 5 fingers of the left hand have played, and students say, "6, 7," while playing the thumb and pointer finger of the right hand.)

Show Me Your Math Fingers: Partners to 5 and 5 More (5 minutes)

Note: This activity addresses the core fluency objective for Grade 1 of adding and subtracting within 10.

The teacher calls out numbers within 5, and students hold up their fingers the Math Way. Each time students hold up their fingers, ask how many more fingers are needed to make 5. As students say the partner to 5, affirm their answers aloud, "Yes. 3 and 2 make 5."

Move on to numbers 6–10. For each number, use the example below to reinforce the embedded five within each number.

EUREKA
MATH™

Lesson 2:   Reason about embedded numbers in varied configurations using
              number bonds.

35

©2015 Great Minds. eureka-math.org
G1-M1-TE-BK1-1.3.1-01.2016

T: Show me 6 the Math Way.

S: (Hold up all fingers on their left hand and their right thumb).

T: Now, hold your 5 up high. How many fingers are on your other hand?

S.   1.

T.   Yes. 5 and 1 make 6.

Number Bond Dash: 5 (5 minutes)

Materials: (T) Stopwatch or timer (S) Number bond dash 5 (Fluency Template), marker to correct work

Note: The Number Bond Dash is a new routine that will be used throughout Module 1. By using the same system, students focus on the mathematics, rather than figuring out the routine.

Distribute Dash, face down, to students. Instruct students to flip their papers when they hear, "Go!" and complete as many number bonds as they can in 90 seconds. Assure them that it is okay if they run out of time before they finish. Tell them if they finish before time, they can practice counting to 20 on the back of their papers, starting with the number 5. Change the counting sequence to meet the needs of each student in later lessons.

T: (Set the timer for 90 seconds.) On your mark, get set, GO! (Press start.)

T: (When the timer goes off, tell students to put down their pencils and grab a marker to correct their work.)

T: When you get an answer correct, put a check mark on the problem number. If you make a mix-up, fix it with your marker.

T: (Read the number bonds aloud, starting with Problem 1. When the answers to all problems have been provided, tell students to write the number they got correct in the star-like shape on top. Encourage them to remember their scores because they are going to try to do even better tomorrow.)

Tell students to remember how many problems they get correct so they can try to improve their scores tomorrow.

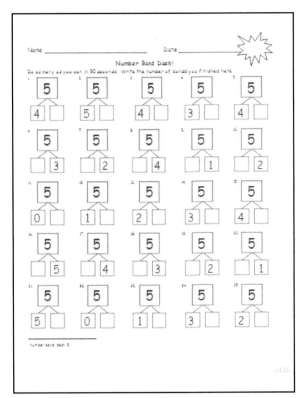

Lesson 2:   Reason about embedded numbers in varied configurations using number bonds.

EUREKA MATH

©2015 Great Minds. eureka-math.org
G1-M1-TE-BK1-1.3.1-01.2016

Application Problem (8 minutes)

T: (Read the story aloud to students.)

Bella spilled some pencils on the carpet. Geno came over to help her pick them up. Geno found 5 pencils under the desk and Bella found 4 by the door. How many pencils did they find together? Draw a math picture and write a number bond and a number sentence that tells about the story.

(Bonus: Have early finishers draw the 9 pencils in a different arrangement to show two parts.)

Note: This Application Problem is designed as a bridge from the previous lesson, which focused on seeing and counting on from 5. Students again work with 5 and another number to encourage this counting on.

Concept Development (30 minutes)

Materials: (T) Dot cards of 6–9 (Template) (S) Dot cards of 6–9 (Template), personal white board

T: (Draw 7 apples on the board, as shown to the right.) How many apples are there? (Pause. When all are ready, give the signal.)

S: 7.

T: Talk to your partner about the different groups of apples you see hiding inside of 7. (Circulate and listen to student discussion.) What two different groups or number partners do you see?

S: (Answers may vary.) I saw 4 and 3.

T: (Group 4 and 3 apples by drawing a circle around them.)

T: **Count on** to find the total. Start with 4. (Point to each apple in the 3 group.)

T/S: Foooouuuur, 5, 6, 7. What is the total?

S: 7.

T: What are the parts?

S: 4 and 3.

T: Let's make a number bond to match this picture. (Draw the bond. Ask students to name the parts and the whole.)

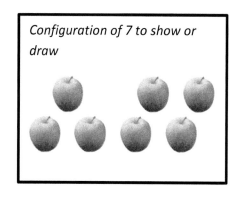

Configuration of 7 to show or draw

NOTES ON
MULTIPLE MEANS
OF ENGAGEMENT:

Provide challenging extensions for some students. While holding a dot card, cover some of the dots. Tell them the whole, and see if they can figure out the two parts without seeing what is being hidden.

Lesson 2:   Reason about embedded numbers in varied configurations using number bonds.

37

©2015 Great Minds. eureka-math.org
G1-M1-TE-BK1-1.3.1-01.2016

T: What other number partners do you see? (Elicit other ways that students see two embedded numbers within 7 and make corresponding number bonds.)

T: (Continue modeling, decomposing 6, 8, or 9 and filling in the two-part number bond by counting on to find the total.)

T: Let's play Parts and Bonds.

T: Show a dot card inside your personal board to your partner. He circles two parts. You write a number bond to match his parts. Switch roles using the same dot card (change cards after two turns).

As students work, circulate and encourage active counting on.

Problem Set (10 minutes)

Students should do their personal best to complete the Problem Set within the allotted 10 minutes. For some classes, it may be appropriate to modify the assignment by specifying which problems they work on first. Some problems do not specify a method for solving. Students solve these problems using the RDW approach used for Application Problems.

Note: Once students have circled the parts, encourage them to count on from one quantity to determine the total (at this point it does not matter if it is the larger or the smaller quantity). If a student is reluctant, hide one part with a paper or hand, and ask, "How many are under my hand?" Let students recount if necessary and hide the part again. Then, have them count on from the hidden part once they are confident.

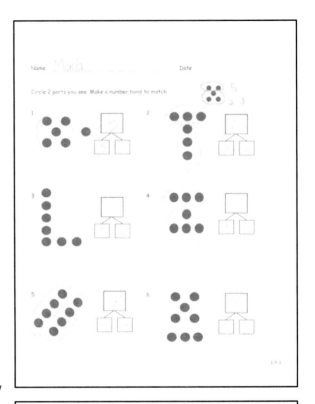

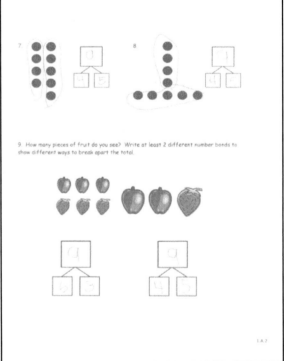

Lesson 2: Reason about embedded numbers in varied configurations using number bonds.

©2015 Great Minds. eureka-math.org
G1-M1-TE-BK1-1.3.1-01.2016

EUREKA
MATH

Student Debrief (10 minutes)

Lesson Objective: Reason about embedded numbers in varied configurations using number bonds.

The Student Debrief is intended to invite reflection and active processing of the total lesson experience.

Invite students to review their solutions for the Problem Set. They should check work by comparing answers with a partner, discussing how they found embedded numbers and counted on to determine the total, before going over answers as a class. Look for misconceptions or misunderstandings that can be addressed in the Student Debrief. Guide students in a conversation to debrief the Problem Set and process the lesson.

Any combination of the questions below may be used to lead the discussion.

- Talk to your partner about how you found the total in Problem 6. Did you count all of the dots, or did you **count on** from a part you saw?
- Pick one problem where you and your partner came up with a different way to make the total. How is the total the same when you came up with different parts?
- Is there always more than one way to make the total?
- Look at Problem 9. How were your solutions different from or similar to your partner's solutions?
- (Show examples of student work from the Application Problem.) What were the two parts in our story problem? What does that have in common with today's lesson? Can you see another way to arrange these pencils?
- Turn to your partner and share what you learned in today's lesson. What did you get better at doing today?

Exit Ticket (3 minutes)

After the Student Debrief, instruct students to complete the Exit Ticket. A review of their work will help with assessing students' understanding of the concepts that were presented in today's lesson and planning more effectively for future lessons. The questions may be read aloud to the students.

Lesson 2:   Reason about embedded numbers in varied configurations using
              number bonds.

©2015 Great Minds. eureka-math.org
G1-M1-TE-BK1-1.3.1-01.2016

39

Name _____ Date _____

Circle 2 parts you see. Make a number bond to match.

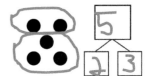

1.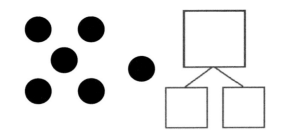

2.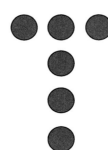

3.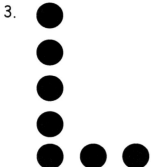

4.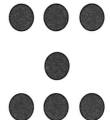

5.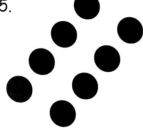

6.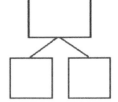

Lesson 2:   Reason about embedded numbers in varied configurations using number bonds.

EUREKA
MATH™

7.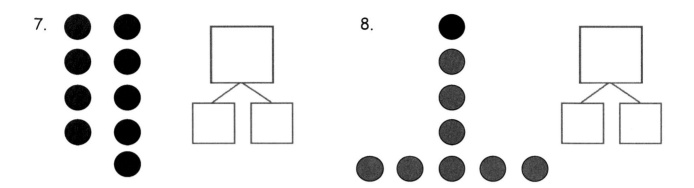

8.

9. How many pieces of fruit do you see? Write at least 2 different number bonds to show different ways to break apart the total.

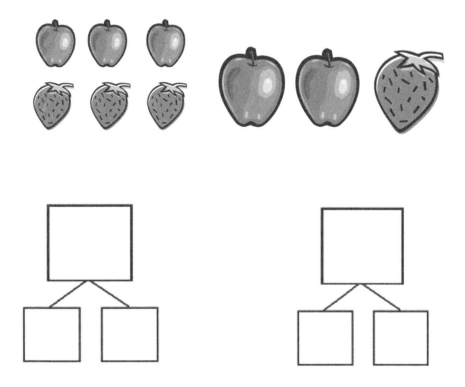

EUREKA
MATH™

Lesson 2: Reason about embedded numbers in varied configurations using number bonds.

41

©2015 Great Minds. eureka-math.org
G1-M1-TE-BK1-1.3.1-01.2016

Name _____ Date _____

Circle 2 parts you see. Make a number bond to match.

1.

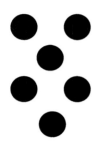 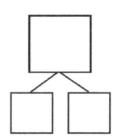

2.

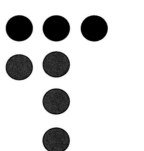 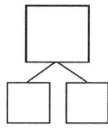

3.

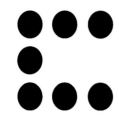 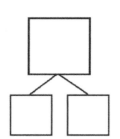

4.

 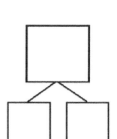

Lesson 2: Reason about embedded numbers in varied configurations using number bonds.

EUREKA MATH™

Name _____   Date _____

Circle 2 parts you see. Make a number bond to match.

1.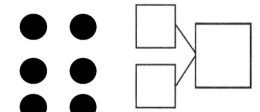

2.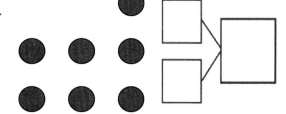

3.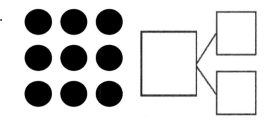

4.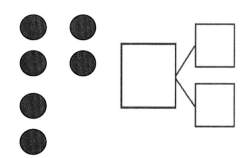

5.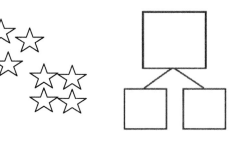

6.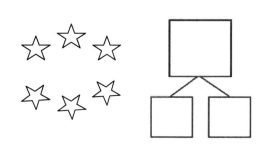

7.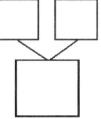

8.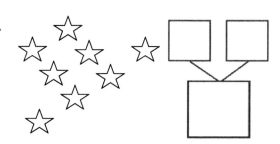

EUREKA MATH™

Lesson 2:   Reason about embedded numbers in varied configurations using
             number bonds.

43

©2015 Great Minds. eureka-math.org
G1-M1-TE-BK1-1.3.1-01.2016

How many animals do you see? Write at least 2 different number bonds to show different ways to break apart the total.

9.

10.

Lesson 2:   Reason about embedded numbers in varied configurations using
number bonds.

EUREKA
MATH™

Name _____ Date _____

Number Bond Dash!

Do as many as you can in 90 seconds. Write the number of bonds you finished here: _____

1.
2.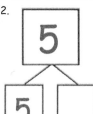
3.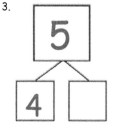
4.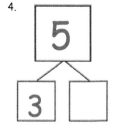
5.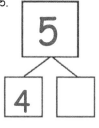
6.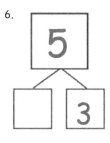
7.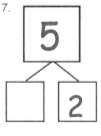
8.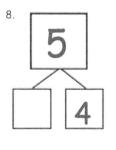
9.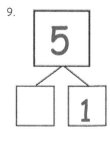
10.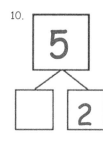
11.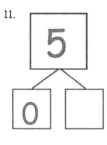
12.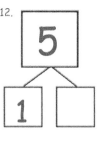
13.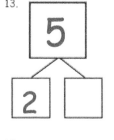
14.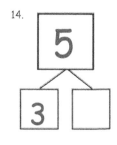
15.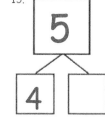
16.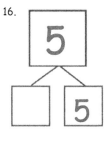
17.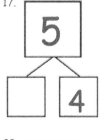
18.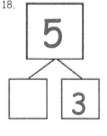
19.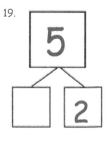
20.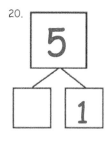
21.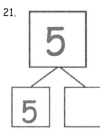
22.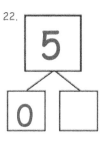
23.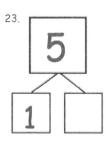
24.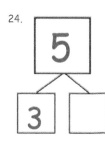
25.

number bond dash 5

EUREKA MATH™

Lesson 2: Reason about embedded numbers in varied configurations using number bonds.

45

©2015 Great Minds. eureka-math.org
G1-M1-TE-BK1-1.3.1-01.2016

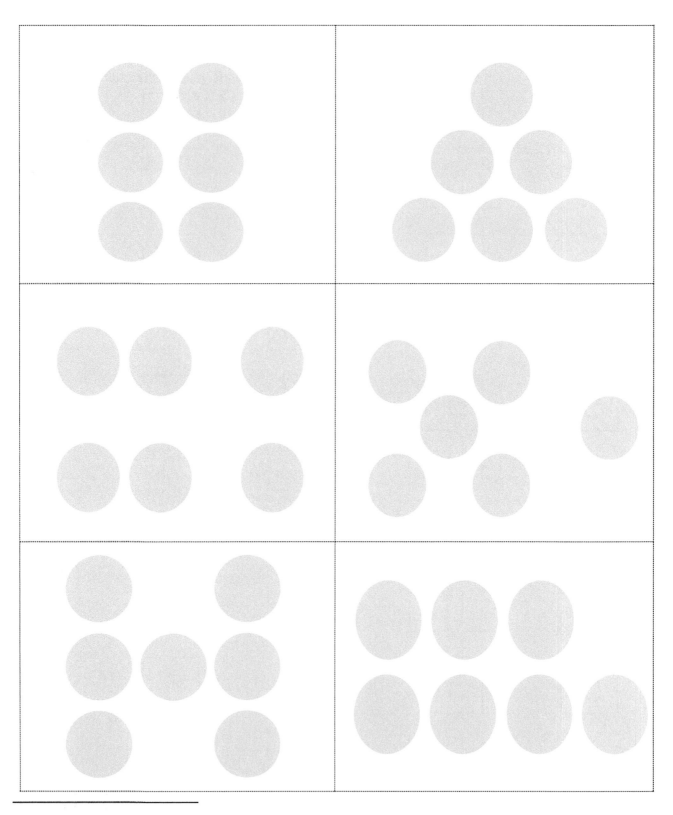

dot cards of 6–9

Lesson 2:   Reason about embedded numbers in varied configurations using number bonds.

EUREKA MATH™

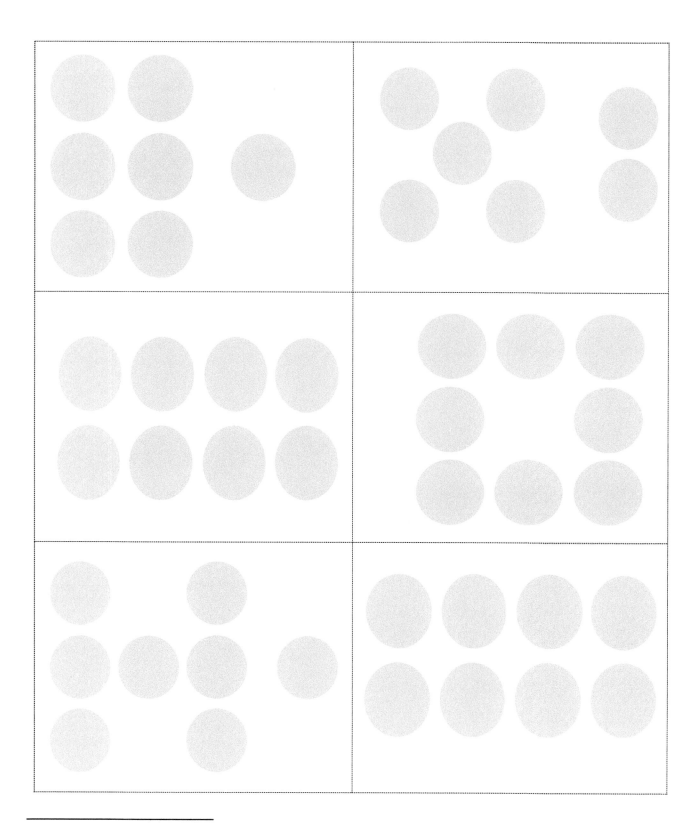

dot cards of 6–9

Lesson 2: Reason about embedded numbers in varied configurations using number bonds.

47

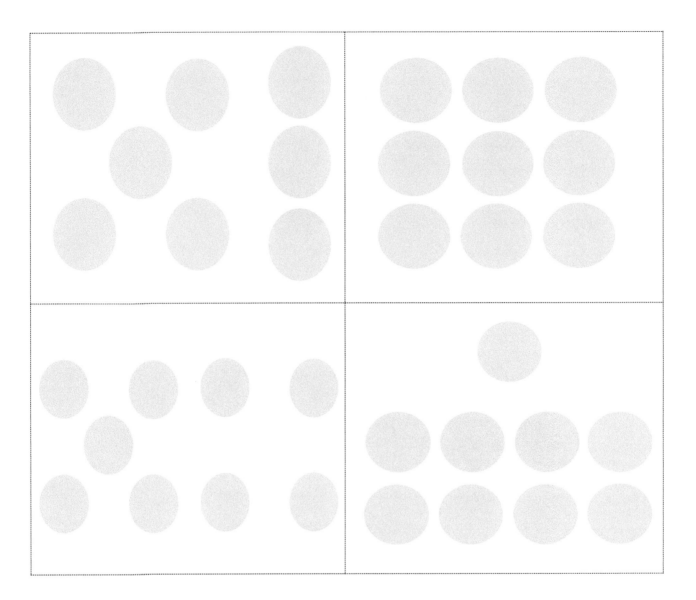

dot cards of 6–9

Lesson 2: Reason about embedded numbers in varied configurations using number bonds.

©2015 Great Minds. eureka-math.org
G1-M1-TE-BK1-1.3.1-01.2016

EUREKA
MATH™

Lesson 3

Objective: See and describe numbers of objects using *1 more* within 5-group configurations.

Suggested Lesson Structure

■ Fluency Practice	(12 minutes)
▦ Application Problem	(7 minutes)
▢ Concept Development	(35 minutes)
▦ Student Debrief	(6 minutes)
Total Time	**(60 minutes)**

Fluency Practice (12 minutes)

- Happy Counting by Ones Within 10 **K.CC.1, K.CC.2**   (4 minutes)
- 5-Group Flash **K.OA.4, 1.OA.5**   (3 minutes)
- Number Bond Dash: 5 **K.OA.3, K.OA.5**   (5 minutes)

Happy Counting by Ones Within 10 (4 minutes)

Materials: (T) Rekenrek

Note: Counting forward and backward by ones affords students a review of this strategy as it relates to addition and subtraction. It also directly relates to the current lesson objective. This game may be challenging for students at first. A Rekenrek helps students visualize numbers and makes it easier for them to change direction as they count. Rekenreks can be made simply and inexpensively with cardboard, elastic, and beads. If this is not available, there are also interactive Rekenreks online.

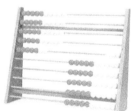

Rekenrek

Move the beads on the Rekenrek to model counting forward and backward by ones within ten. Students count along with the beads (e.g., 1, 2, 3, 2, 3, 4, 5, 6, 5, etc.). When students are ready, put the Rekenrek away.

> T: Let's play Happy Counting! We're going to count by ones. When I hold my hand like this (point thumb and motion up), I want you to count up. If I put my hand like this (point thumb and motion down), I want you to count down. If I do this (thumb to the side) that means stop, but try hard to remember the last number you said. (See illustration on the next page.)

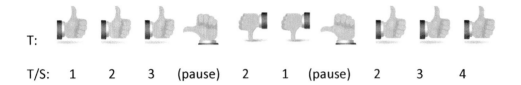

T/S: 1   2   3   (pause)   2   1   (pause)   2   3   4

5-Group Flash (3 minutes)

Materials: (T) 5-group cards (the dot cards from the 1 More game in this lesson may be used, as long as they have been enlarged on the copier)

Note: This activity relates to the core fluency objective of Grade 1 of adding and subtracting within 10.

Teacher flashes 5-group cards for 2–3 seconds, and instructs students to say the number when teacher snaps. After flashing all the numbers from 0 to 10 (in a random order), flash the cards again and count on from the number flashed, up to 10.

Number Bond Dash: 5   (5 minutes)

Materials: (T) Stopwatch or timer (S) Number bond dash 5 (Lesson 2 Fluency Template), marker to correct work

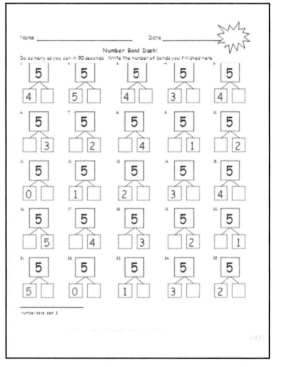

Note: Reviewing number bonds allows students to build and maintain fluency with addition and subtraction facts within 10 and gets them ready for the upcoming lesson.

Distribute Dash face down to students. Instruct students to flip their papers when they hear, "Go!" and complete as many number bonds as they can in 90 seconds. Assure them that it is okay if they run out of time before they finish. Tell them that if they finish before time, they can practice counting backwards from 20 on the back of their papers.

T: Take a second to remember the score you got on yesterday's Number Bond Dash so you can try to do even better today.

T: (Set the timer for 90 seconds.) On your mark, get set, GO! (Press start.)

T: (When the timer goes off, tell students to put down their pencils and grab a marker to correct their work.)

T: When you get an answer correct, put a check mark on the problem number. If you make a mix-up, fix it with your marker.

Read the number bonds aloud, starting with Problem 1. When you are finished checking all the problems, tell students to write the number they got correct in the star-like shape on the top and show you a big smile if they improved their score from yesterday.

EUREKA MATH™

Application Problem (7 minutes)

Alex had 9 marbles in his hand. He hid his hands behind his back and put some in one hand and some in the other. How many marbles might be in each hand? Use pictures or numbers to draw a number bond to show your idea.

Note: This problem is designed as a bridge from the previous lesson, which focused on reasoning about embedded numbers and finding various decompositions.

Concept Development (35 minutes)

Materials: (T) Sentence frame 1 more (Template 1) (S) 5-group mat (Template 2), bag with 9 linking cubes of the same color, 1 linking cube of another color, personal white board, 1 more game cards (Template 3)

T: Show me 5 fingers on one hand the Math Way.

S: (Hold up their left hand, showing 5 fingers.)

T: Show me 4 fingers inside your 5.

T: Show me your 5.

T: Show me your 4.

T: How much does 4 need to make 5?

S: 1.

T: Show me 7 fingers the Math Way.

T: Show me 6.

T: Show me 7.

T: Show me 6.

T: How much does 6 need to make 7?

S: 1.

T: Put 5 cubes that are the same color onto your 5-group mat. How many cubes do you have?

S: 5.

T: Use a different color cube and put 1 more on your mat. Now, how many do you have?

S: 6.

T: How did you know that so quickly?

S: I counted on from 5. → It was just 1 more. → I saw 5 and 1. → I just knew it. → I counted on from 5. It was just 1 more.

T: What is 1 more than 5?

S: 6.

T: Let's say that in a full sentence. (Point to the sentence frame as students speak. 1 more than ____ is ____.)

T/S: 1 more than 5 is 6.

EUREKA
MATH™

Lesson 3:   See and describe numbers of objects using *1 more* within 5-group configurations.

©2015 Great Minds. eureka-math.org
G1-M1-TE-BK1-1.3.1-01.2016

51

T: Let's try saying this in a different way. What was the first part we saw?

S: 5.

T: How many more did 5 need to make 6?

S: 1.

T: So, we can say 6 is 1 more than.... (Invite student responses.)

S: 5.

T: Say it as a whole sentence. (Point to the sentence frame as students speak. _____ is 1 more than _____.)

S: 6 is 1 more than 5.

T: Help me write our parts and total in a number sentence, or equation. (Write the components of the number sentence as each question is asked.) What did we start with?

S: 5.

T: How many cubes did we add?

S: 1.

T: How many cubes do we have altogether?

S: 6.

T: Let's read our number sentence together.

T/S: 5 + 1 = 6.

**NOTES ON
MULTIPLE MEANS
OF EXPRESSION:**

For students who may need additional support with the language of *1 more than ___ is ____* and *____ is 1 more than ___*, insert a sentence frame into their personal white boards, and allow them to write the numbers into the blanks. Pointing to each word and reading the number can provide a bridge between the concrete and the abstract.

Have students clear their mats, and continue this process with 7, 8, and 9. Have students say both "8 is 1 more than 7," and "1 more than 7 is 8." When writing the number sentence, be sure to have the equal sign on either side of the equation (i.e., 7 + 1 = 8 and 8 = 7 + 1).

T: Now, you'll get to work with a partner to play the 1 More game! The goal is to match a dot card with the card that has 1 more. Here are the directions:

1. Put all of your cards face down, with dot cards on one side and sentence cards on the other.
2. Flip over a dot card.
3. Flip over a sentence card.
4. Keep the pair if the sentence card is one more than the dot card.
5. Turn both cards back over if they do not match.
6. When you and your partner have made all the pairs, write a number sentence for each pair.

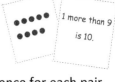

Model how to play this with students. Practice the language *1 more than _____ is _____* and *_____ is 1 more than _____*.

52   Lesson 3:   See and describe numbers of objects using *1 more* within 5-group configurations.

©2015 Great Minds. eureka-math.org
G1-M1-TE-BK1-1.3.1-01.2016

EUREKA
MATH™

Problem Set (10 minutes)

Students should do their personal best to complete the Problem Set within the allotted 10 minutes. For some classes, it may be appropriate to modify the assignment by specifying which problems they work on first. Some problems do not specify a method for solving. Students solve these problems using the RDW approach used for Application Problems.

Student Debrief (6 minutes)

Lesson Objective: See and describe numbers of objects using *1 more* within 5-group configurations.

The Student Debrief is intended to invite reflection and active processing of the total lesson experience.

Invite students to review their solutions for the Problem Set. They should check work by comparing answers with a partner before going over answers as a class. Look for misconceptions or misunderstandings that can be addressed in the Student Debrief. Guide students in a conversation to debrief the Problem Set and process the lesson.

Any combination of the questions below may be used to lead the discussion.

- What is the same and different about Problem 4 and Problem 8?
- Look at Problems 8, 7, 6, and 5. What do you notice about how these are changing?
- If we had to find 2 more, how would today's lesson help us?
- What did you notice about the number sentences in Problems 5 and 6?
- Using what you learned today, what is 1 more than 13? How do you know?
- Turn and talk to your partner about what we did today. What were we learning about, understanding, and getting good at?

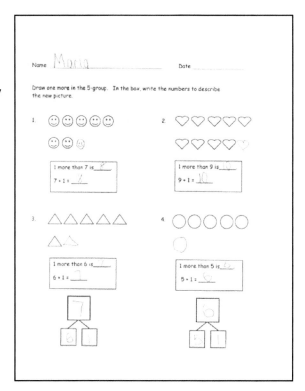

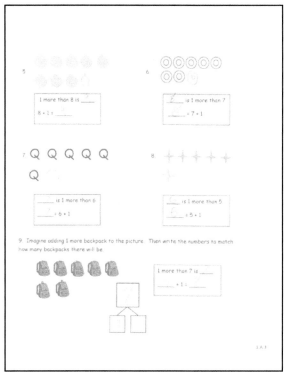

Lesson 3:   See and describe numbers of objects using *1 more* within 5-group configurations.

53

©2015 Great Minds. eureka-math.org
G1-M1-TE-BK1-1.3.1-01.2016

Exit Ticket (3 minutes)

After the Student Debrief, instruct students to complete the Exit Ticket. A review of their work will help with assessing students' understanding of the concepts that were presented in today's lesson and planning more effectively for future lessons. The questions may be read aloud to the students.

Lesson 3:   See and describe numbers of objects using *1 more* within 5-group configurations.

©2015 Great Minds. eureka-math.org
G1-M1-TE-BK1-1.3.1-01.2016

Name _____   Date _____

Draw one more in the 5-group. In the box, write the numbers to describe the new picture.

1.

2.

1 more than 7 is _____.

7 + 1 = _____

1 more than 9 is _____.

9 + 1 = _____

3.

4.

1 more than 6 is _____.

6 + 1 = _____

1 more than 5 is _____.

5 + 1 = _____

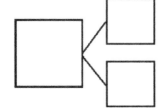

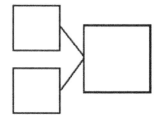

EUREKA MATH

Lesson 3:   See and describe numbers of objects using *1 more* within 5-group configurations.

55

5.

1 more than 8 is _____.

8 + 1 = _____

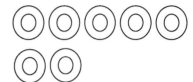

6.

_____ is 1 more than 7.

_____ = 7 + 1

7.

_____ is 1 more than 6.

_____ = 6 + 1

8.

_____ is 1 more than 5.

_____ = 5 + 1

9. Imagine adding 1 more backpack to the picture. Then, write the numbers to match how many backpacks there will be.

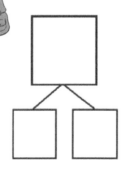

1 more than 7 is _____.

_____ + 1 = _____

Lesson 3: See and describe numbers of objects using *1 more* within 5-group configurations.

EUREKA MATH

Name _____   Date _____

How many objects do you see? Draw one more. How many objects are there now?

1.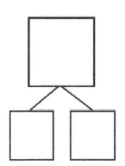

_____ is 1 more than 9.
9 + 1 = _____

2.

1 more than 6 is _____.
_____ + 1 = _____

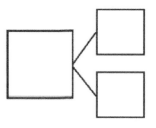

EUREKA MATH™

Lesson 3: See and describe numbers of objects using *1 more* within 5-group configurations.

©2015 Great Minds. eureka-math.org
G1-M1-TE-BK1-1.3.1-01.2016

57

Name _____   Date _____

How many objects do you see? Draw one more. How many objects are there now?

1.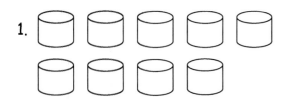

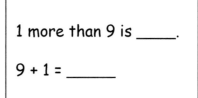

1 more than 9 is _____.

9 + 1 = _____

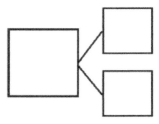

2.

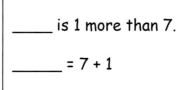

_____ is 1 more than 7.

_____ = 7 + 1

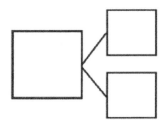

3.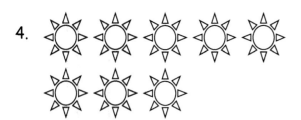

_____ is 1 more than 5.

_____ = 5 + 1

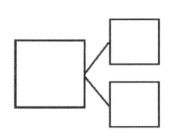

4.

1 more than 8 is _____.

_____ + 1 = _____

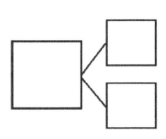

Lesson 3:   See and describe numbers of objects using *1 more* within 5-group configurations.

©2015 Great Minds. eureka-math.org
G1-M1-TE-BK1-1.3.1-01.2016

EUREKA
MATH™

5. Imagine adding 1 more pencil to the picture.
    Then, write the numbers to match how many pencils there will be.

    1 more than 5 is _____.

    5 + 1 = _____

6. Imagine adding 1 more flower to the picture.
    Then, write the numbers to match how many flowers there will be.

    _____ is 1 more than 8.

    _____ + 1 = _____

EUREKA MATH

Lesson 3:   See and describe numbers of objects using *1 more* within 5-group
              configurations.

©2015 Great Minds. eureka-math.org
G1-M1-TE-BK1-1.3.1-01.2016

59

_____ is 1 more than _____ .

_____ is _____ 1 more than .

sentence frame 1 more

Lesson 3:   See and describe numbers of objects using *1 more* within 5-group configurations.

©2015 Great Minds. eureka-math.org
G1-M1-TE-BK1-1.3.1-01.2016

EUREKA
MATH™

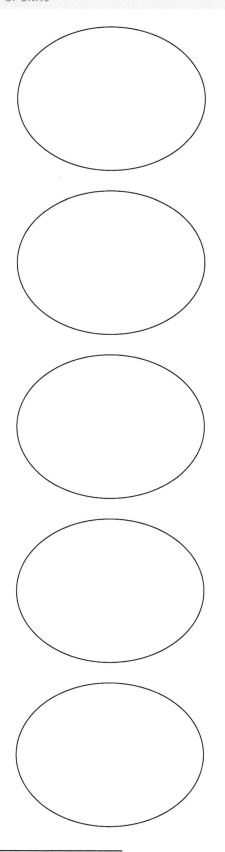
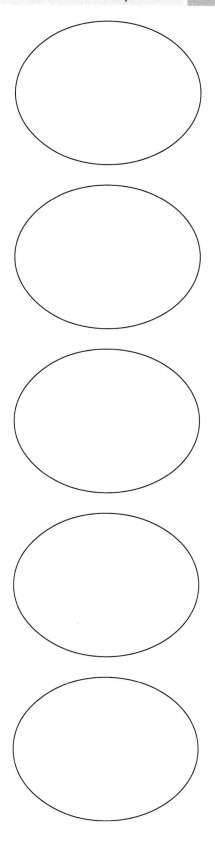

5-group mat

EUREKA
MATH™

Lesson 3:   See and describe numbers of objects using *1 more* within 5-group configurations.

61

©2015 Great Minds. eureka-math.org
G1-M1-TE-BK1-1.3.1-01.2016

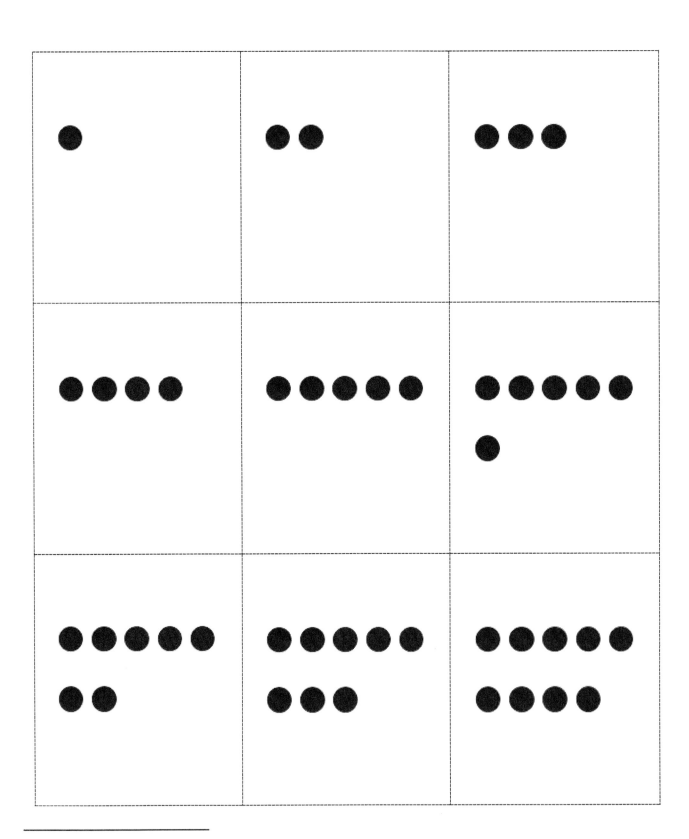

1 more game cards

Lesson 3:   See and describe numbers of objects using *1 more* within 5-group configurations.

©2015 Great Minds. eureka-math.org
G1-M1-TE-BK1-1.3.1-01.2016

EUREKA
MATH™

2 is 1 more than 1.	3 is 1 more than 2.	4 is 1 more than 3.
1 more than 4 is 5.	1 more than 5 is 6.	1 more than 6 is 7.
8 is 1 more than 7.	1 more than 8 is 9.	1 more than 9 is 10.

1 more game cards

Lesson 3:   See and describe numbers of objects using *1 more* within 5-group configurations.

©2015 Great Minds. eureka-math.org
G1-M1-TE-BK1-1.3.1-01.2016

Mathematics Curriculum

GRADE 1 • MODULE 1

Topic B

Counting On from Embedded Numbers

1.OA.1, 1.OA.5, 1.OA.6

Focus Standard:	1.OA.1	Use addition and subtraction within 20 to solve word problems involving situations of adding to, taking from, putting together, taking apart, and comparing, with unknowns in all positions, e.g., by using objects, drawings, and equations with a symbol for the unknown number to represent the problem.
	1.OA.5	Relate counting to addition and subtraction (e.g., by counting on 2 to add 2).
	1.OA.6	Add and subtract within 20, demonstrating fluency for addition and subtraction within 10. Use strategies such as counting on; making ten (e.g., $8 + 6 = 8 + 2 + 4 = 10 + 4 = 14$); decomposing a number leading to a ten (e.g., $13 - 4 = 13 - 3 - 1 = 10 - 1 = 9$); using the relationship between addition and subtraction (e.g., knowing that $8 + 4 = 12$, one knows $12 - 8 = 4$); and creating equivalent but easier or known sums (e.g., adding $6 + 7$ by creating the known equivalent $6 + 6 + 1 = 12 + 1 = 13$).
Instructional Days:	5	
Coherence -Links from:	GK–M4	Number Pairs, Addition and Subtraction to 10
-Links to:	G2–M4	Addition and Subtraction Within 200 with Word Problems to 100

As students move into Topic B, they gain momentum with putting together, composing and decomposing, and counting on to determine the total. Students use both concrete and pictorial situations to describe all of the decompositions of 6, 7, 8, 9, and 10 (**1.OA.5**). Lesson 4 begins with six children posed at the front of the class. They will be put together in different ways to show the various combinations of 6, such as 2 boys and 4 girls and 3 wearing long sleeves and 3 wearing short sleeves. During this process, the *put together* situation will be highlighted, engaging students in counting on from one addend, or part, to find the total (**1.OA.1, 1.OA.5**). As students progress through the lesson, they come to see that 6 is constructed of several different decompositions, by using two-color counters and recording the decomposition in number bonds and as expressions (**1.OA.1**). They record each decomposition of 6 and reflect upon all of these number partners, "Look at all these ways to make 6! I can see connections between them!"

EUREKA MATH™

Lessons 5, 6, 7, and 8 continue this same process of putting together, composing, and decomposing. In Lesson 5, students use an engaging drawing (pictured on the previous page) to find and show ways to make 7 with 2 groups. "I see 5 kids sitting and 2 kids standing. There are 7 kids altogether." They use their 5-group cards to represent the partners of 7, and they record the decompositions in number bonds and expressions.

Lesson 6 has students exploring and discussing the decompositions of 8 using their 5-group cards, beginning with the numeral side first as a way to encourage counting on. In Lesson 7, students explore the partners of 9 using cubes to help them count on from the first addend. Finally, the topic ends with Lesson 8, where students make Rekenrek bracelets with 10 beads. These bracelets become tools for students to show all ways to make 10 (pictured below).

Rekenrek bracelet with
5 white beads and
5 red beads.

Each lesson in Topic B ends with students creating a shared chart representing all of the decompositions of each number: 6, 7, 8, 9, and 10. These charts provide a foundation for supporting understanding of addition and subtraction facts. Teachers keep the charts hanging in their classrooms and have students start portfolios. Both of these serve as references throughout the school year as students master these numerical combinations (**1.OA.6**).

A Teaching Sequence Toward Mastery of Counting On from Embedded Numbers
Objective 1: Represent *put together* situations with number bonds. Count on from one embedded number or part to totals of 6 and 7, and generate all addition expressions for each total. (Lessons 4–5)
Objective 2: Represent *put together* situations with number bonds. Count on from one embedded number or part to totals of 8 and 9, and generate all expressions for each total. (Lessons 6–7)
Objective 3: Represent all the number pairs of 10 as number bonds from a given scenario, and generate all expressions equal to 10. (Lesson 8)

©2015 Great Minds. eureka-math.org
G1-M1-TE-BK1-1.3.1-01.2016

Lesson 4

Objective: Represent *put together* situations with number bonds. Count on from one embedded number or part to totals of 6 and 7, and generate all addition expressions for each total.

Suggested Lesson Structure

■ Fluency Practice   (12 minutes)
▨ Application Problem   (6 minutes)
▨ Concept Development   (30 minutes)
■ Student Debrief   (12 minutes)

   Total Time   **(60 minutes)**

Fluency Practice (12 minutes)

- Sprint: 1 More with Dots and Numerals **1.OA.6**   (10 minutes)
- Happy Counting by Ones, 10–20 **1.NBT.1** (K.CC.1, K.CC.2)   (2 minutes)

Sprint: 1 More with Dots and Numerals (10 minutes)

Materials: (S) Sprint: 1 More with Dots and Numerals

Note: This activity addresses the core fluency objective for Grade 1 of adding and subtracting within 10.

Happy Counting by Ones, 10–20 (2 minutes)

Materials: (S) Rekenrek

Note: Counting forward and backward by ones affords students review with the counting sequence.

Play Happy Counting (see Lesson 3) from 10 through 20 and back, first the regular way, then the Say Ten Way, as shown below.

Regular way: 8, 9, 10, 11, 12, 13, 14…

Say Ten way: 8, 9, ten 1, ten 2, ten 3, ten 4…

Lesson 4:   Represent *put together* situations with number bonds. Count on from
                 one embedded number or part to totals of 6 and 7, and generate all
                 addition expressions for each total.

©2015 Great Minds. eureka-math.org
G1-M1-TE-BK1-1.3.1-01.2016

EUREKA MATH™

Application Problem (6 minutes)

Our class had 4 pumpkins. On Monday, Marta brought 1 more pumpkin. How many pumpkins did our class have on Monday?

On Tuesday, Beto brought 1 more pumpkin. How many pumpkins did our class have on Tuesday?

Then, on Wednesday, Shea brought 1 more pumpkin. How many pumpkins did our class have on Wednesday? Draw a picture and write a number sentence to show your thinking. What do you notice about what happened each day?

Extension: If this pattern continues, how many pumpkins will our class have on Friday?

Note: This problem is designed as a bridge from the previous lesson, which focused on *1 more*. As students represent decompositions with drawings, they are preparing for today's Concept Development.

Concept Development (30 minutes)

Materials: (T) Chart to record decompositions of 6 (S) Bag of 10 two-color beans (painted white on one side and red on the other), 6 apples picture card (Template)

Choose a group of students who have different attributes to represent decompositions of 6 (e.g., 4 boys, 2 girls; 5 with shoelaces, 1 without; 3 with short sleeves, 3 with long sleeves). Be sure to encourage the actors themselves to participate in the mathematics of the lesson.

    T: How many students do you see?

    S: 6.

    T: How many boys are there?

    S: 4.

    T: How many girls are there?

    S: 2.

    T: Talk to your partner about what would be a good strategy to see how many students there are altogether. (Circulate and listen to student discussion.)

    S: We can count on from 4.

    T: Point with me to keep **track** as we count on from 4. (Gesture around the group of 4, and then touch the 2 students on the head as you count on with the class.)

    S: Fouuuur, 5, 6.

MP.7 T: What parts did we put together to make 6?

    S: 4 and 2.

    T: Let's write those parts in a number sentence. (Call on students to help you write the equation $6 = 4 + 2$ on the board.)

    T: (Ask the 2 girls to move to the left and the 4 boys to move to the right.) What would our number sentence look like if we started with the girls first? Talk to your partner about what the number sentence would be.

Lesson 4:   Represent *put together* situations with number bonds. Count on from one embedded number or part to totals of 6 and 7, and generate all addition expressions for each total.

©2015 Great Minds. eureka-math.org
G1-M1-TE-BK1-1.3.1-01.2016

67

T: (Circulate and listen to student discussion. Call on students to help you write the equation 6 = 2 + 4 on the board.)

T: Now, look at the shoes on these students. I notice shoes that have….

S: (Answers may vary.) Shoelaces!

Repeat the earlier process with decomposing according to having shoelaces and not, and again with short sleeves and not, in order to complete decomposing 6.

Bring up the topic of zero and the total as a possible decomposition:

T: How many students do you see up here?

S: 6.

T: How many tigers do you see up here?

S: 0.

T: How many living things do you see up here?

S: 6.

T: How can we write that story in a number sentence?

S: 6 + 0 = 6.

T: Think of a different story that shows 6 + 0 = 6. (If necessary ask, "Think of what we can make the zero represent.") Call on students to share.

T: When we add zero, we add nothing to the other part. And, this is another way we can make 6! Six and zero makes 6.

NOTES ON MULTIPLE MEANS OF ENGAGEMENT:

For students who still need to count all of the objects, scaffold their learning and allow them to count all. After they have mastered counting all, be sure to model counting on so that they have an example of how they should be thinking when counting.

Problem Set (10 minutes)

Distribute the picture card for 6, the Problem Set, and a bag of 10 two-color beans to each student.

T: Let's look at the picture of 6 apples and use our beans to find different ways to make 6.

T: How many apples do you see?

S: 6.

T: Let's see how many apples with stems are there. Put a red bean on each apple as we count.

S: 1, 2, 3, 4.

T: How many apples do not have stems? Let's put a white bean on each stem-less apple and count.

S: 1, 2.

T: Let's see how many apples there are by counting on from the red beans. As you count, touch each bean.

S: Foooour, 5, 6.

T: (Have students write the expressions to match these parts.) When we just write 4 + 2, without writing the full number sentence, we call it an **expression**. (Point to 4 + 2.) See, it doesn't have an equal sign!

NOTES ON MULTIPLE MEANS OF REPRESENTATION:

Look for ways to connect real life experiences in math. Use apples during this lesson as a connection to science curriculum. Cut the apples to explore the parts of the apple connecting to *total* and *part* vocabulary.

Lesson 4: Represent *put together* situations with number bonds. Count on from one embedded number or part to totals of 6 and 7, and generate all addition expressions for each total.

©2015 Great Minds. eureka-math.org
G1-M1-TE-BK1-1.3.1-01.2016

Repeat this process to explore the rest of the apple combinations in the picture and to complete the remainder of the Problem Set. Help students set up a portfolio to save their work with decompositions of 6.

In the upcoming lessons, they will save decompositions of 7, 8, 9, and 10. You do not need to focus on the commutative property in this lesson.

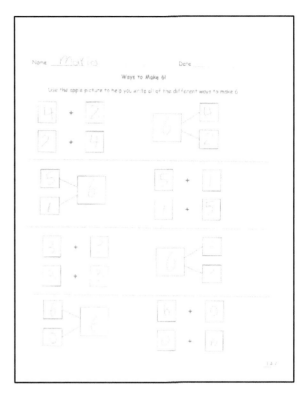

Student Debrief (12 minutes)

Lesson Objective: Represent *put together* situations with number bonds. Count on from one embedded number or part to totals of 6 and 7, and generate all addition expressions for each total.

The Student Debrief is intended to invite reflection and active processing of the total lesson experience.

Invite students to review their solutions for the Problem Set. They should check work by comparing answers with a partner before going over answers as a class. Look for misconceptions or misunderstandings that can be addressed in the Student Debrief. Guide students in a conversation to debrief the Problem Set and process the lesson.

Any combination of the questions below may be used to lead the discussion.

NOTES ON MULTIPLE MEANS OF ACTION AND EXPRESSION:

Display charts with the number bonds for 6 so students can refer to it if needed. Creating a place in the classroom for students to access this information will help those students who are visual learners or students who have trouble committing things to memory.

- T: Why did we keep **track** of the apples as we counted?
- S: So we wouldn't count any twice or miss any!
- T: Talk with your partner about all of the different ways you made 6.
- S: (Work together to check their work and the numbers' referents in the picture.)
- T: We will write number bonds to show all the different ways you made 6. What was the biggest part you found in your number bond, and what was its partner?
- S: 6. And 0.
- T: (Record this number bond on a chart, and call on students to help you write the expressions.)

Repeat this process in order to record all of the decompositions of 6 (5 + 1, 4 + 2, 3 + 3). Ask the following questions to close the lesson:

- What do you notice about the two parts in the **expressions** that make 6 as we look at them in order from left to right?

- What is different about this (point to 4 + 2), the expression, and this (point to 4 + 2 = 6), the number sentence?
- Turn to your partner and talk about what we learned about in today's lesson. What did you get really good at today?

Exit Ticket (3 minutes)

After the Student Debrief, instruct students to complete the Exit Ticket. A review of their work will help with assessing students' understanding of the concepts that were presented in today's lesson and planning more effectively for future lessons. The questions may be read aloud to the students.

Lesson 4:   Represent *put together* situations with number bonds. Count on from one embedded number or part to totals of 6 and 7, and generate all addition expressions for each total.

©2015 Great Minds. eureka-math.org
G1-M1-TE-BK1-1.3.1-01.2016

EUREKA
MATH™

A

Number Correct: _____

Name _____   Date _____

*Write the number that is 1 more.

1.	●●●			16.	●●●●● ●●●●	
2.	●●			17.	9	
3.	●●●			18.	7	
4.	●●●●			19.	●●●●● ●●	
5.	●●●●●			20.	8	
6.	●●●●● ●			21.	7	
7.	●●●●●			22.	●●●●● ●●●	
8.	5			23.	●●●●● ●●●●	
9.	●●●●● ●●			24.	10	
10.	6			25.	●●●●● ●●●●●	
11.	●●●●● ●			26.	●●●●● ●●●	
12.	7			27.	●● ●● ●● ●●	
13.	●●●●● ●●			28.	9	
14.	●●●●● ●●●			29.	●●● ●●● ●●●	
15.	8			30.	●●● ●●● ●●● ●●●	

EUREKA MATH™

Lesson 4: Represent *put together* situations with number bonds. Count on from one embedded number or part to totals of 6 and 7, and generate all addition expressions for each total.

©2015 Great Minds. eureka-math.org
G1-M1-TE-BK1-1.3.1-01.2016

71

B

Name _____

Number Correct: ⛤

Date _____

*Write the number that is 1 more.

1.	●●		16.	●●●●● ●●●	
2.	●		17.	8	
3.	●●		18.	9	
4.	●●●		19.	●●●●● ●●●●	
5.	●●●●		20.	●●●●● ●●●●●	
6.	●●●●●		21.	10	
7.	●●●●		22.	●●●●● ●●●	
8.	4		23.	●●●●● ●●●●	
9.	●●●●●		24.	10	
10.	5		25.	●●●●● ●●●●	
11.	●●●●●		26.	●● ●● ●● ●●	
12.	7		27.	●● ●● ●● ●●	
13.	●●●●● ●●		28.	8	
14.	●●●●● ●		29.	●● ●● ●● ●●●	
15.	6		30.	●●● ●●●● ●● ●●●●	

Lesson 4: Represent *put together* situations with number bonds. Count on from one embedded number or part to totals of 6 and 7, and generate all addition expressions for each total.

©2015 Great Minds. eureka-math.org
G1-M1-TE-BK1-1.3.1-01.2016

EUREKA MATH

Name _____   Date _____

Ways to Make 6.

Use the apple picture to help you write all of the different ways to make 6.

□ + □

□ + □

□ ⟨ □ / □ ⟩

□ ⟩ □ / □ ⟨

□ + □

□ + □

□ + □

□ + □

□ ⟨ □ / □ ⟩

□ ⟩ □ / □ ⟨

□ + □

□ + □

EUREKA MATH™

Lesson 4:   Represent *put together* situations with number bonds. Count on from one embedded number or part to totals of 6 and 7, and generate all addition expressions for each total.

73

©2015 Great Minds. eureka-math.org
G1-M1-TE-BK1-1.3.1-01.2016

Name _____   Date _____

Show different ways to make 6. In each set, shade some circles and leave the others blank.

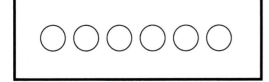 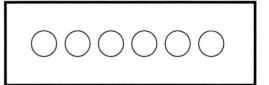

Write a number bond to match this picture.

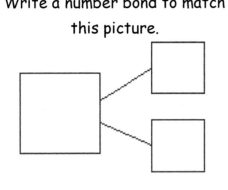

Write a number sentence to match this picture.

☐ + ☐ = ☐

Lesson 4:   Represent *put together* situations with number bonds. Count on from one embedded number or part to totals of 6 and 7, and generate all addition expressions for each total.

EUREKA MATH™

Name _____   Date _____

Today, we learned the different combinations that make 6. For homework, cut out the flashcards below, and write the number sentences that you learned today on the back. Keep these flashcards in the place where you do your homework to practice ways to make 6 until you know them really well! As we continue to learn different ways to make 7, 8, 9, and 10 in the upcoming days, continue to make new flashcards.

*Note to families: Be sure students make each of the combinations that make 6. The flashcards can look something like this:

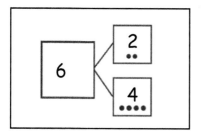

2 + 4 = 6

Front of Card   Back of Card

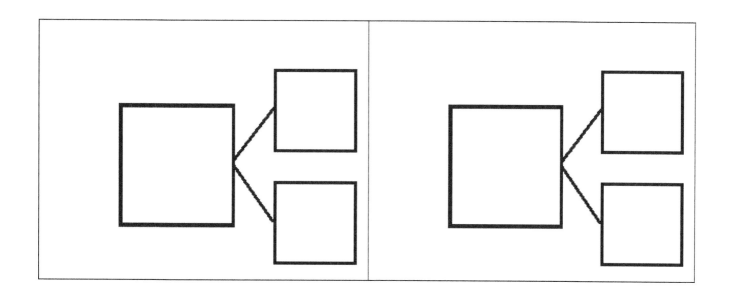

EUREKA
MATH™

Lesson 4:   Represent *put together* situations with number bonds. Count on from one embedded number or part to totals of 6 and 7, and generate all addition expressions for each total.

75

©2015 Great Minds. eureka-math.org
G1-M1-TE-BK1-1.3.1-01.2016

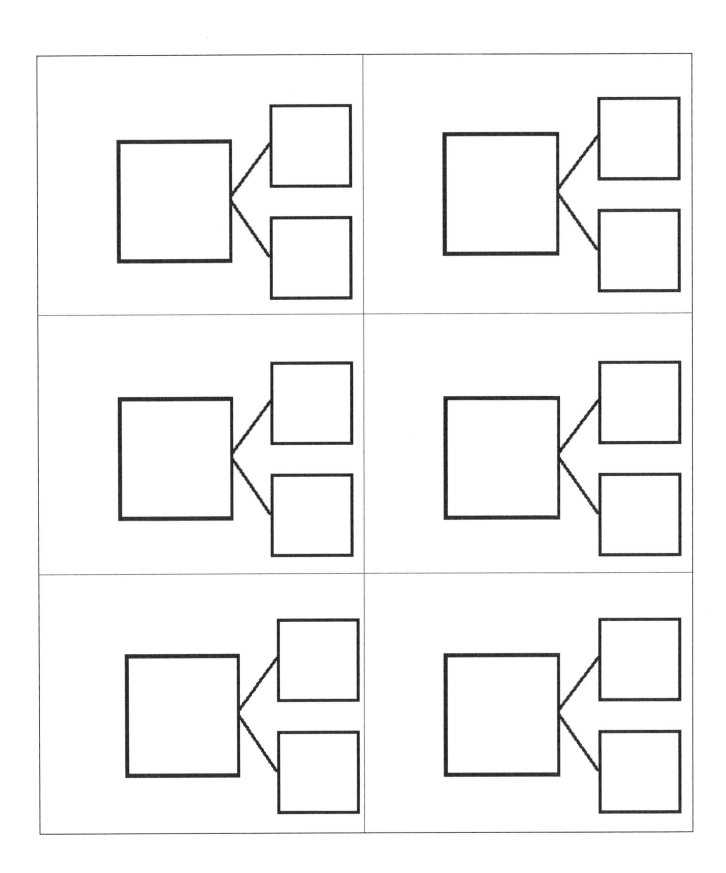

Lesson 4:   Represent *put together* situations with number bonds. Count on from
one embedded number or part to totals of 6 and 7, and generate all
addition expressions for each total.

©2015 Great Minds. eureka-math.org
G1-M1-TE-BK1-1.3.1-01.2016

6 apples picture card

Lesson 4:   Represent *put together* situations with number bonds. Count on from
one embedded number or part to totals of 6 and 7, and generate all
addition expressions for each total.

©2015 Great Minds. eureka-math.org
G1-M1-TE-BK1-1.3.1-01.2016

77

Lesson 5

Objective: Represent *put together* situations with number bonds. Count on from one embedded number or part to totals of 6 and 7, and generate all addition expressions for each total.

Suggested Lesson Structure

■ Fluency Practice	(15 minutes)
■ Application Problem	(5 minutes)
■ Concept Development	(25 minutes)
■ Student Debrief	(15 minutes)
Total Time	**(60 minutes)**

Fluency Practice (15 minutes)

- Math Finger Flash (with Number Sentences) **1.OA.6**   (3 minutes)
- Shake Those Disks: 6 **1.OA.6**   (7 minutes)
- Number Bond Dash: 6 **1.OA.6**   (5 minutes)

Math Finger Flash (with Number Sentences) (3 minutes)

Note: This activity addresses the core fluency objective for Grade 1 of adding and subtracting within 10.

Flash fingers within 5 the Math Way for 2–3 seconds. Hide your fingers, and then ask students to identify the number of fingers flashed at the snap. Then, ask students to say an addition sentence that shows how to make 5. An example is given below.

    T: (Flash 4 fingers, hide them, and then snap.)

    S: 4.

    T: Now, use 4 in an adding sentence to make 5.

    S: 4 + 1 = 5.

Continue flashing numbers between 5 and 10. For this portion, ask for a 5 + ___ addition sentence for each number.

    T: (Flash 8 fingers, hide them, and then snap.)

    S: 8.

    T: Now, say a 5+ adding sentence for 8.

Lesson 5:   Represent *put together* situations with number bonds. Count on from
one embedded number or part to totals of 6 and 7, and generate all
addition expressions for each total.

S: 5 + 3 = 8.

T: (Hold up 5 and 3 as students say the equation.)

Shake Those Disks: 6 (7 minutes)

Materials: (S) Per set of partners: 6 disks (e.g., counters, two-color beans, or pennies), 1 shake those disks 6 board (Fluency Template 1)

Note: This activity addresses the core fluency objective for Grade 1 of adding and subtracting within 10.

Break students into partners. Give each set of partners 6 disks. Instruct them to take turns as the Shaker and the Recorder. The Shaker shakes the disks and tosses them on the table. The Recorder then records the roll on the Shake Those Disks board. (For example, if the Shaker rolls 4 red and 2 white, the Recorder puts an X on the graph above the 4 and 2 number bond.)

Number Bond Dash: 6 (5 minutes)

Materials: (T) Stopwatch or timer (S) Number bond dash 6 (Fluency Template 2), marker to correct work

Note: By using the same system, the Number Bond Dash, students focus on the mathematics, rather than figuring out the routine. Unlike most Number Bond Dashes, students will not have a chance to improve their scores on Day 2 during this round, as Topic B progresses through exploration of decompositions of 6, 7, 8, 9, and 10, giving students practice with a new number each day.

Distribute the Dash to students, face down. Instruct students to flip their papers when you say, "Go!" and complete as many number bonds as they can in 90 seconds. Assure them it is okay if they run out of time before they finish. Tell them if they finish, they can practice counting to 20 on the back of their papers, starting with the number 5. Change the counting sequence to meet the needs of students, in later lessons. As you choose a counting sequence, consider counting forward or back by different numbers. When counting forward, it is beneficial to change the starting number.

T: (Set the timer for 90 seconds.) On your mark, get set, GO! (Press start.)

T: (When the timer goes off, tell students to put down their pencils and grab a marker to correct their work.)

T: When you get an answer correct, put a check mark on the problem number. If you need to change your answer, just change it with your marker.

T: (Read the number bonds aloud, starting with Problem 1.) When you are finished checking all the problems, write the number you got correct in the star-like shape on top.

Lesson 5:   Represent *put together* situations with number bonds. Count on from one embedded number or part to totals of 6 and 7, and generate all addition expressions for each total.

79

©2015 Great Minds. eureka-math.org
G1-M1-TE-BK1-1.3.1-01.2016

Application Problem (5 minutes)

Marcus had 6 pieces of candy. He decided to give some to his mother and keep some for himself. Use pictures and numbers to show two ways that Marcus could have split up 6 pieces of his candy.

$3 + 3 = 6$

$5 + 1 = 6$

Note: This problem is designed as a bridge from the previous lesson's focus on decompositions of 6, reminding students that they can break apart numbers in more than one way.

Concept Development (25 minutes)

Materials: (T) Number bond on the white board, markers, chart to record decompositions of 7
(S) 5-group cards (Template 1), 7 children picture card (Template 2), scissors, glue stick, a sheet of blank paper for Student Debrief

Have students sit in a big semi-circle facing the number bond on the board. Distribute 5-group cards to each pair of students. Tell them they will be using the cards to show different ways to make 7. Instruct students to put their cards in order from smallest to largest.

Using students as actors, choose a group of students who have different attributes that represent decompositions of 7, and have them line up at the board (e.g., 6 with short hair, 1 with long hair).

Note: Be sure to encourage the actors themselves to participate in the mathematics of the lesson.

T: How many students are here?

S: 7.

T: (Write 7 in the total box of the number bond.)

T: What does this 7 represent? (Point to the 7.)

S: (Responses may vary.) The kids.

T   The 7 in our *whole* represents the number of students. (Label the whole with the word *students*.)

T: There's 1 student up here who has something different from the rest! What is it?

S: 1 has long hair!

T: (Write 1 in the number bond.)

T: What does this 1 represent? (Point to the 1.)

S: Long hair.

T: The 1 represents the *part* of our students with long hair, so I am going to label this part *long hair*.

MP.2   (Write *long hair* next to the part with the number 1.)

T: Show 1 with your 5-group card using the dot side, and put it in front of you.

T: If [Student 1 with long hair] has long hair, what about the rest of these students?

S: They have short hair.

Represent *put together* situations with number bonds. Count on from one embedded number or part to totals of 6 and 7, and generate all addition expressions for each total.

EUREKA MATH

T: How many students have short hair?

S: 6.

T: (Write 6 in the number bond.)

T: How should I label this part?

S: Short hair.

T: Yes. Six represents the number of students with short hair. (Write *short hair* next to the part with the number 6.)

T: Now, show 6 with your 5-group card using the dot side, right next to your first card.

T: What's the best strategy to find out how many students there are altogether?

S: (Responses may vary.) Count on from 1.

T: Point with me to keep track as we count on from 1. (Gesture around the group of 1, and then count on with the class by touching the 6 students on the head; have them sit down as they are counted.)

T: Now, it's your turn to count on. Flip your 1 dot card to show the number 1. Then, count on from 1. Be sure to touch and count!

S: (Count on from 1 to 7, pointing to each dot.)

T: What are the two parts that make 7?

S: 1 and 6.

T: Say the number sentence that makes 7. (Point to each box in the number bond as students respond.)

S: 1 + 6 = 7.

T: (Record this on the chart.)

T: Say the number sentence starting with the students with short hair.

S: 6 + 1 = 7.

T: Say the number sentence starting with the total.

S: 7 = 1 + 6.

T: Say the number sentence starting with the total, but flip the parts this time.

S: 7 = 6 + 1.

Continue this process with the other decompositions of 7. Keep the same actors, but rearrange them to show different decompositions of 7 (e.g., 2 sit, 5 stand; 3 smiling, 4 frowning). Review zero if necessary.

NOTES ON MULTIPLE MEANS FOR ACTION AND EXPRESSION:

Once students have shown how to make 7 with their 5-group cards, call on a volunteer to come fill in the number bond on the board. See if other volunteers can write the number sentence(s) that go along with the 5-group cards and number bond on the board. Maybe have another volunteer illustrate the number bond. Providing a variety of ways for students to respond allows them to make choices and engage when they know they will be successful at the task.

Lesson 5:   Represent *put together* situations with number bonds. Count on from one embedded number or part to totals of 6 and 7, and generate all addition expressions for each total.

81

©2015 Great Minds. eureka-math.org
G1-M1-TE-BK1-1.3.1-01.2016

Problem Set (10 minutes)

Distribute the picture card with seven students in a classroom, the Problem Set, and 5-group cards for each student. Similar to Lesson 4, students record all of the decompositions of 7 (in number bonds and as expressions) on their Problem Set as they use the 5-group cards to count on, just as they did during the Concept Development. Judge to determine whether students should complete this as whole group, in small groups, or independently.

Students should do their personal best to complete the Problem Set within the allotted 10 minutes. For some classes, it may be appropriate to modify the assignment by specifying which problems they work on first. Some problems do not specify a method for solving. Students solve these problems using the RDW approach used for Application Problems.

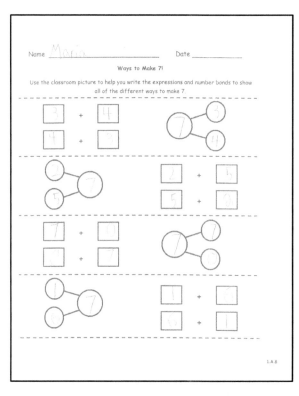

Student Debrief (15 minutes)

Lesson Objective: Represent *put together* situations with number bonds. Count on from one embedded number or part to totals of 6 and 7, and generate all addition expressions for each total.

The Student Debrief is intended to invite reflection and active processing of the total lesson experience.

Have students bring their Problem Set to the meeting area. Ask them to cut out their number bonds from the sheet, and place them in an order that is numerical (students may begin with 7 + 0, then 6 + 1, 5 + 2, etc., or 0 + 7, 1 + 6, 2 + 5, etc.).

> T: Talk with your partner about how you put your number bonds of 7 in an order based on the numbers. Does your way of ordering look the same as or different from your partner's?
>
> S: (Responses may vary.)
>
> T: Let's write all of the number bonds of 7. (Record all of the number bonds of 7 on a chart beginning with 7 and 0, and call on students to help write the expressions.)

Have the students glue their number bonds in order, starting with 7 and 0, on a blank sheet of paper. Students will refer to this sheet as they work towards mastering all decompositions of 7.

NOTES ON
MULTIPLE MEANS
FOR ACTION AND
EXPRESSION:

Involving students to make the 7 chart is a great way to get them excited about creating displays for the classroom. When students are involved in making these pieces, they are more likely to remember them in the room and use them when needed.

82   **Lesson 5:**   Represent *put together* situations with number bonds. Count on from
                          one embedded number or part to totals of 6 and 7, and generate all
                          addition expressions for each total.

©2015 Great Minds. eureka-math.org
G1-M1-TE-BK1-1.3.1-01.2016

Ask the following questions to close the lesson:

NOTES ON
MATHEMATICAL
PRACTICE:

All through this module, students must pay attention to the units they are counting and use precise language to convey their knowledge (MP.6).

- Look at all the ways we made 7 in this poster. What patterns do you see?
- Let's revisit our poster for 6. What do you see is the same and different about our poster showing ways to make 6 and our poster showing ways to make 7? Talk to you partner.
- What did you get really good at today?

Exit Ticket (3 minutes)

After the Student Debrief, instruct students to complete the Exit Ticket. A review of their work will help with assessing students' understanding of the concepts that were presented in today's lesson and planning more effectively for future lessons. The questions may be read aloud to the students.

Lesson 5:   Represent *put together* situations with number bonds. Count on from one embedded number or part to totals of 6 and 7, and generate all addition expressions for each total.

83

©2015 Great Minds. eureka-math.org
G1-M1-TE-BK1-1.3.1-01.2016

Name _____   Date _____

Ways to Make 7.   Use the classroom picture to help you write the expressions and number bonds to show all of the different ways to make 7.

Lesson 5:   Represent *put together* situations with number bonds. Count on from one embedded number or part to totals of 6 and 7, and generate all addition expressions for each total.

EUREKA MATH

Name _____   Date _____

Color in two dice that make 7 together. Then, fill in the number bond and number sentences to match the dice you colored.

   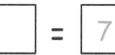

Lesson 5:   Represent *put together* situations with number bonds. Count on from one embedded number or part to totals of 6 and 7, and generate all addition expressions for each total.

©2015 Great Minds. eureka-math.org
G1-M1-TE-BK1-1.3.1-01.2016

85

Name _____   Date _____

1. Match the dice to show different ways to make 7. Then, draw a number bond for each pair of dice.

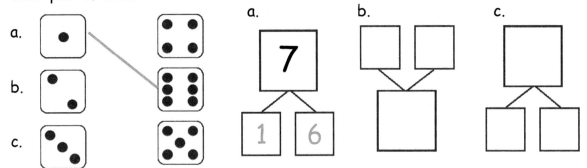

2. Make 2 number sentences. Use the number bonds above for help.

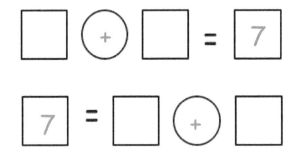

3. Fill in the missing number in the number bond. Then, write addition number sentences for the number bond you made.

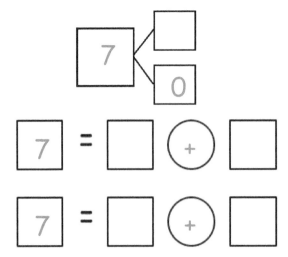

Lesson 5:   Represent *put together* situations with number bonds. Count on from one embedded number or part to totals of 6 and 7, and generate all addition expressions for each total.

©2015 Great Minds. eureka-math.org
G1-M1-TE-BK1-1.3.1-01.2016

EUREKA MATH™

4. Color the dominoes that make 7.

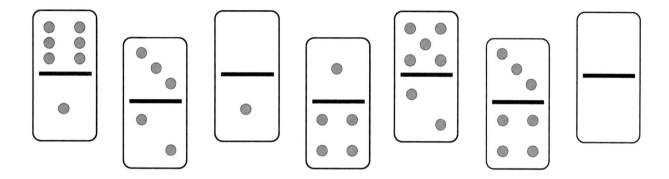

5. Complete the number bonds for the dominoes you colored.

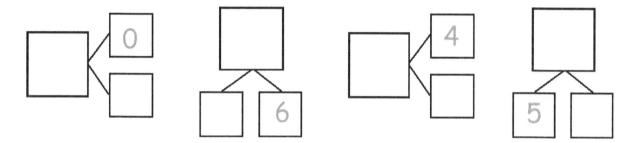

Lesson 5: Represent *put together* situations with number bonds. Count on from one embedded number or part to totals of 6 and 7, and generate all addition expressions for each total.

©2015 Great Minds. eureka-math.org
G1-M1-TE-BK1-1.3.1-01.2016

87

Shake Those Disks!—6

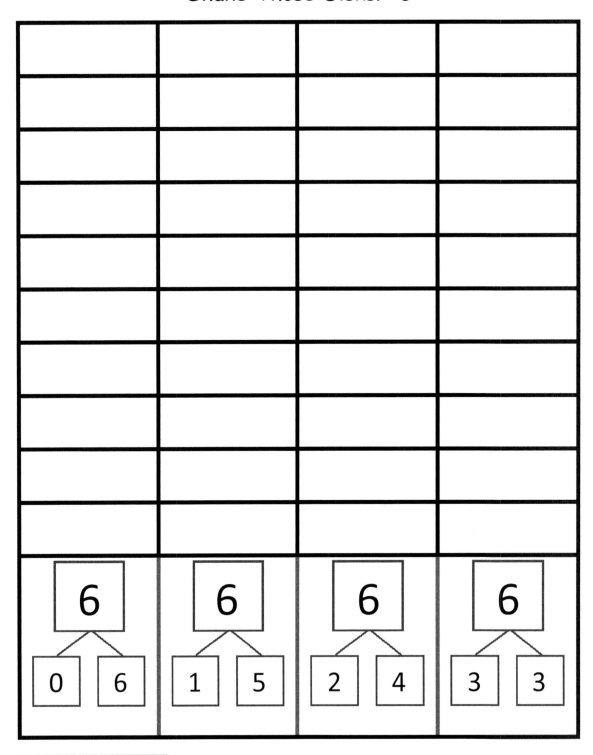

shake those disks 6 board

Lesson 5:   Represent *put together* situations with number bonds. Count on from one embedded number or part to totals of 6 and 7, and generate all addition expressions for each total.

EUREKA
MATH™

Name _____   Date _____

Do as many as you can in 90 seconds. Write the number of bonds you finished here:

1.
6
6 □

2.
6
5 □

3.
6
4 □

4.
6
5 □

5.
6
6 □

6.
6
□ 5

7.
6
□ 4

8.
6
□ 5

9.
6
□ 4

10.
6
□ 3

11.
6
3 □

12.
6
4 □

13.
6
2 □

14.
6
3 □

15.
6
2 □

16.
6
□ 5

17.
6
□ 1

18.
6
□ 0

19.
6
□ 1

20.
6
□ 0

21.
6
1 □

22.
6
5 □

23.
6
4 □

24.
6
2 □

25.
6
3 □

_____

number bond dash 6

Lesson 5:   Represent *put together* situations with number bonds. Count on from
one embedded number or part to totals of 6 and 7, and generate all
addition expressions for each total.

0	1	2	3
4	5	6	7
8	9	10	10
	10	5	5

5-group cards

Lesson 5: Represent *put together* situations with number bonds. Count on from one embedded number or part to totals of 6 and 7, and generate all addition expressions for each total.

EUREKA MATH

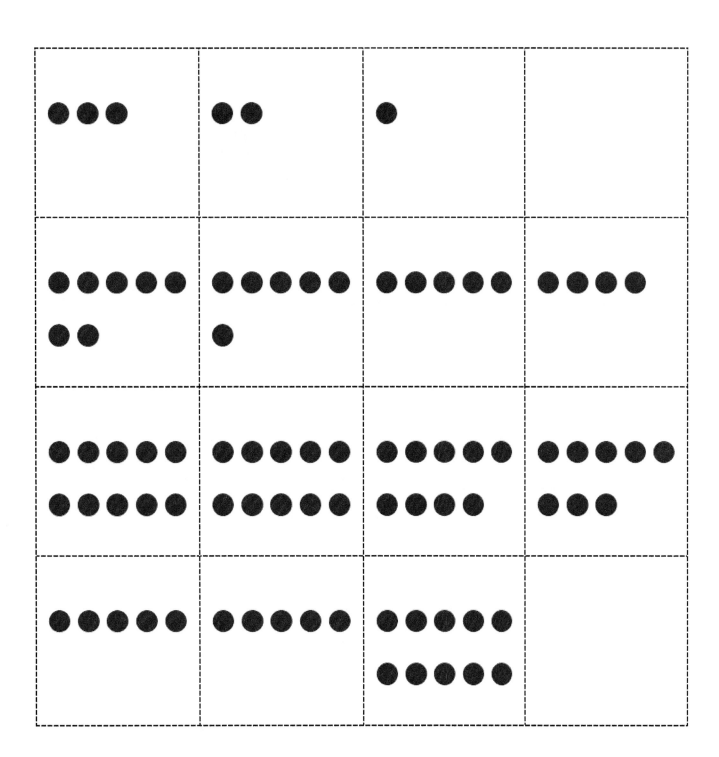

5-group cards, dot side

EUREKA
MATH™

Lesson 5:   Represent *put together* situations with number bonds. Count on from
one embedded number or part to totals of 6 and 7, and generate all
addition expressions for each total.

91

©2015 Great Minds. eureka-math.org
G1-M1-TE-BK1-1.3.1-01.2016

7 children picture card

Lesson 5:   Represent *put together* situations with number bonds. Count on from
              one embedded number or part to totals of 6 and 7, and generate all
              addition expressions for each total.

EUREKA
MATH™

Lesson 6

Objective: Represent *put together* situations with number bonds. Count on from one embedded number or part to totals of 8 and 9, and generate all expressions for each total.

Suggested Lesson Structure

■ Fluency Practice   (18 minutes)
▦ Application Problem   (5 minutes)
▢ Concept Development   (25 minutes)
■ Student Debrief   (12 minutes)

   Total Time   **(60 minutes)**

Fluency Practice (18 minutes)

▪ Red Light/Green Light: Counting by Ones **1.NBT.1**   (5 minutes)
▪ Target Practice: 6 and 7 **1.OA.6**   (8 minutes)
▪ Number Bond Dash: 7 **1.OA.6**   (5 minutes)

Red Light/Green Light: Counting by Ones (5 minutes)

Note: By providing students with ongoing practice with counting throughout the year, they build and maintain their counting skills. This counting work is also foundational for later Grade 1 work with adding and subtracting within 100.

Say a number between 1 and 100. When they hear "green light," students begin running in place and counting aloud together, beginning with the number given. When students hear "red light," they stop counting and freeze. Any students who are still moving or counting after they hear "red light" should sit down until the next game. Continue playing with a new starting number every time "green light" is said. Play until only a few students are standing. Then, instruct the whole class to stand and start the game again.

A suggested sequence of start numbers would be 15, 28, 35, 48, 55, 68…

NOTES ON
MULTIPLE MEANS
OF REPRESENTATION:

For those students who are still developing basic counting skills, until this skill becomes automatic, provide a visual tool such as the hundreds chart in a place where they can easily see it during the game.

Lesson 6:   Represent *put together* situations with number bonds. Count on from one embedded number or part to totals of 8 and 9, and generate all expressions for each total.

©2015 Great Minds. eureka-math.org
G1-M1-TE-BK1-1.3.1-01.2016

93

Target Practice: 6 and 7 (8 minutes)

Materials: (S) 7 counters and a die per partner

Note: This activity addresses the core fluency objective for Grade 1 of adding and subtracting within 10.

Break students into partners. Give each set of partners 6 counters. Instruct them to take turns as the Roller and the Target Finder. The Roller rolls the dice. The Target Finder determines the partner to 6. Students may use counters as needed. First, play with 6 as the target number, and then distribute another counter to each set of partners and practice determining the partner to 7.

Number Bond Dash: 7 (5 minutes)

Materials: (T) Stopwatch or timer (S) Number bond dash 7 (Fluency Template), marker to correct work

Note: By using the same system repeatedly, students can focus on the mathematics alone. This activity addresses the core fluency objective for Grade 1 of adding and subtracting within 10.

Follow procedure for Number Bond Dash (Lesson 5).

Application Problem (5 minutes)

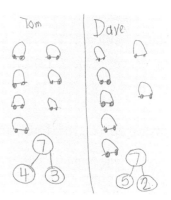

Tom has 4 red cars and 3 green cars. Dave has 5 red cars and 2 green cars. Dave thinks he has more cars than Tom has. Is Dave right? Draw a picture to show how you know. Write a number bond to show each of the boys' sets of cars.

Note: This problem is designed as a bridge from the previous lesson's focus on decompositions of 7 and provides a lead-up to today's Concept Development as students prove that 8 can be decomposed in many ways.

Concept Development (25 minutes)

Materials: (T) 8 animals picture card (Template 1), ways to make 8 (Template 3) (S) 5-group cards 0–8 (Lesson 5 Template 1), 8 animals picture card (Template 1), blank number sentence and number bond (Template 2), personal white board, ways to make 8 (Template 3)

Insert blank number sentence and number bond template (Template 2) into personal white boards prior to the lesson. Assign students partners (A and B), and have them sit on the carpet with their 5-group cards.

**NOTES ON
MULTIPLE MEANS
OF REPRESENTATION:**

Remember to highlight critical vocabulary for students who may need another representation to make the connection. Displaying pictures of the animals talked about in the lesson will help these students. Or, have students share what these animals are called in their native language to make it more personally meaningful.

Lesson 6:   Represent *put together* situations with number bonds. Count on from
one embedded number or part to totals of 8 and 9, and generate all
expressions for each total.

T: (Project 8 animals picture card.) Look at the picture. Talk with your partner about the different parts you see. (Circulate as students discuss.)

S: (Discuss as the teacher circulates.)

T: What two different animals do you see?

S: Frogs and ducks!

T: Partner A, show how many frogs there are with your 5-group cards, using the number side.

S: (Show the numeral 4.)

T: Partner B, show how many ducks there are with your 5-group cards, using the dot side.

S: (Show 4 dots.)

T: Yesterday, what strategy did we use to find how many students were in the classroom?

S: We counted on.

T: Let's count on to see how many animals there are altogether, starting with…

S: 4.

T/S: Foouuur, 5, 6, 7, 8. (Count, while pointing to  .)

T: Work with your partner to write a number sentence that matches our frogs and ducks on your personal white board.

S: (Write 4 + 4 = 8 or 8 = 4 + 4.)

T: How else are these animals different from one another?

> NOTES ON
> MULTIPLE MEANS
> FOR ENGAGEMENT:
>
> Adjust lesson structure to suit specific learning needs, remembering that some students will need to keep counting all (by flipping the cards to expose all of the dots) before they are secure enough in their skills to count on.

Repeat this process as student record the decompositions of 8, using their 5-group cards to count on from one part (the numeral) to find the total and recording the decomposition in an equation on their personal white boards.

T: Now, we're going to play a game called Ways to Make 8. The goal is to find all of the different ways to make 8 with your partner and record it on your recording sheet.

1. Put your 5-group cards together in the center. Partner A's cards should all show the dot side. Partner B's cards should all show the number side.

2. Partner A picks a number card and a dot card that she thinks make 8. Both partners check together by counting on from the number card.

3. Partner A writes the number bond and expressions on her sheet, and Partner B checks it, saying, "That's correct!" or "Try again, friend."

4. Then, you take turns until each of you has all of the different ways to make 8.

(Discuss ways to work with 4 + 4, as this combination requires duplicates. Ask students how they might solve this dilemma!)

As students work, circulate and encourage active counting on. As students finish, have them save their recording sheet to add to their portfolio of number bonds for reference.

Lesson 6: Represent *put together* situations with number bonds. Count on from one embedded number or part to totals of 8 and 9, and generate all expressions for each total.

95

©2015 Great Minds. eureka-math.org
G1-M1-TE-BK1-1.3.1-01.2016

Problem Set (10 minutes)

Students should do their personal best to complete the Problem Set within the allotted 10 minutes. For some classes, it may be appropriate to modify the assignment by specifying which problems they work on first. Some problems do not specify a method for solving. Students solve these problems using the RDW approach used for Application Problems.

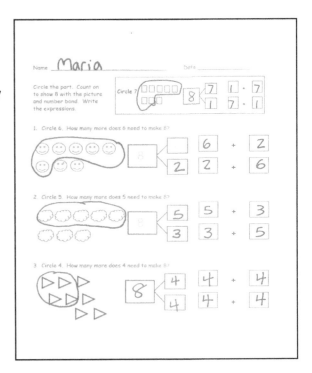

Student Debrief (12 minutes)

Lesson Objective: Represent *put together* situations with number bonds. Count on from one embedded number or part to totals of 8 and 9, and generate all expressions for each total.

The Student Debrief is intended to invite reflection and active processing of the total lesson experience.

Ask students to come to the meeting area.

- T: We're going to write all of the number bonds of 8 in an order based on the numbers. Talk with your partner about how we can do this.
- S: (Responses may vary. Circulate and listen to discussion.)
- T: I heard someone say to start with 8 + 0. How will that be the same as our other number posters? (Refer to the posters of 6 and 7.)
- S: We started with the biggest part.
- T: Let's write all of the number bonds of 8, starting with 8 and 0. (Record all of the number bonds of 8 on a chart, with the first part decreasing by 1 each time, and call on students to help write the expressions.)

Invite students to review their solutions for the Problem Set. They should check work by comparing answers with a partner before going over answers as a class. Look for misconceptions or misunderstandings that can be addressed in the Student Debrief. Guide students in a conversation to debrief the Problem Set and process the lesson.

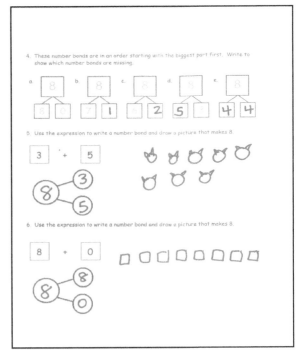

Represent *put together* situations with number bonds. Count on from one embedded number or part to totals of 8 and 9, and generate all expressions for each total.

©2015 Great Minds. eureka-math.org
G1-M1-TE-BK1-1.3.1-01.2016

EUREKA MATH™

Any combination of the questions below may be used to lead the discussion.

- (Show a blank Problem Set, or re-draw the pictures from the Problem Set on the board.) Look at the smiley faces in Problem 1. What other parts can you see hiding in 8? (Repeat with Problems 2 and 3.)
- Look at our poster for all of the different ways to make 8. What patterns to do you see?
- Think about our game, Ways to Make 8. Why did we only use our cards 0 through 8 today?
- Talk with your partner about what you learned today.

Exit Ticket (3 minutes)

After the Student Debrief, instruct students to complete the Exit Ticket. A review of their work will help with assessing students' understanding of the concepts that were presented in today's lesson and planning more effectively for future lessons. The questions may be read aloud to the students.

Lesson 6:   Represent *put together* situations with number bonds. Count on from one embedded number or part to totals of 8 and 9, and generate all expressions for each total.

97

©2015 Great Minds. eureka-math.org
G1-M1-TE-BK1-1.3.1-01.2016

Name _____ Date _____

Circle the part. Count on to show 8 with the picture and number bond. Write the expressions.

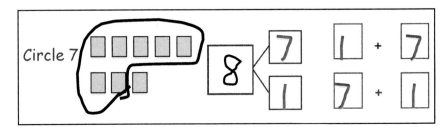

1. Circle 6. How many more does 6 need to make 8?

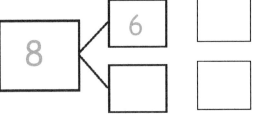
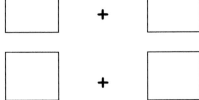

2. Circle 5. How many more does 5 need to make 8?

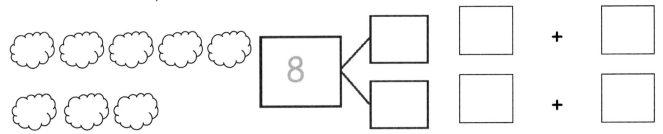

3. Circle 4. How many more does 4 need to make 8?

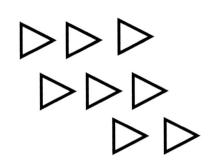
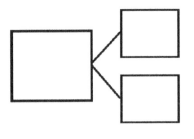
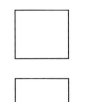

Lesson 6: Represent *put together* situations with number bonds. Count on from one embedded number or part to totals of 8 and 9, and generate all expressions for each total.

EUREKA MATH™

4. These number bonds are in an order starting with the biggest part first. Write to show which number bonds are missing.

a.   b.   c.   d.   e.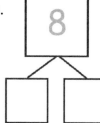

5. Use the expression to write a number bond and draw a picture that makes 8.

 3 + 5

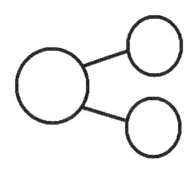

6. Use the expression to write a number bond and draw a picture that makes 8.

 8 + 0

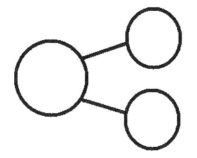

EUREKA MATH™

Lesson 6:   Represent *put together* situations with number bonds. Count on from one embedded number or part to totals of 8 and 9, and generate all expressions for each total.

©2015 Great Minds. eureka-math.org
G1-M1-TE-BK1-1.3.1-01.2016

99

Name _____   Date _____

Fill in the missing part of the number bond, and count on to find the total. Then, write 2 addition sentences for each number bond.

1.

2.

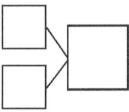

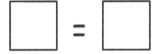

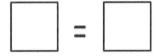

Lesson 6: Represent *put together* situations with number bonds. Count on from one embedded number or part to totals of 8 and 9, and generate all expressions for each total.

©2015 Great Minds. eureka-math.org
G1-M1-TE-BK1-1.3.1-01.2016

EUREKA MATH

Name _____   Date _____

1. Match the dots to show different ways to make 8. Then, draw a number bond for each pair.

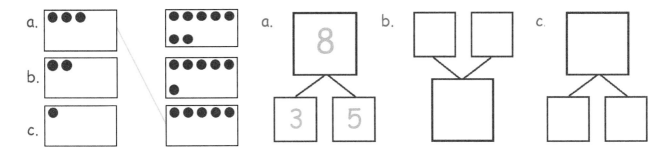

2. Show 2 ways to make 8. Use the number bonds above for help.

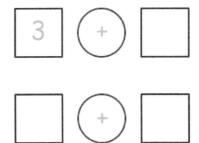

3. Fill in the missing number in the number bond. Write 2 addition sentences for the number bond you made. Notice where the equal sign is to make your sentence true.

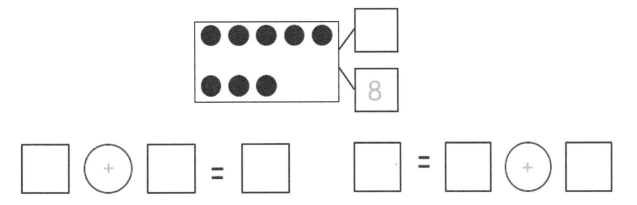

EUREKA MATH™

Lesson 6:   Represent *put together* situations with number bonds. Count on from one embedded number or part to totals of 8 and 9, and generate all expressions for each total.

©2015 Great Minds. eureka-math.org
G1-M1-TE-BK1-1.3.1-01.2016

101

4. These number bonds are in an order starting with the smallest part first. Write to show which number bonds are missing.

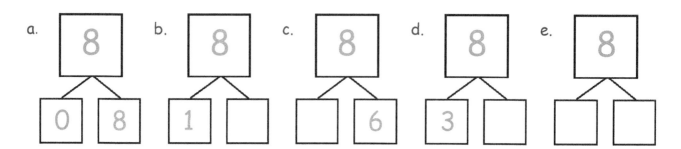

5. Use the expression to write a number bond and draw a picture that makes 8.

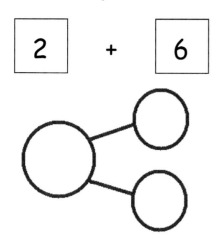

| 2 | + | 6 |

6. Use the expression to write a number bond and draw a picture that makes 8.

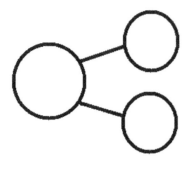

| 0 | + | 8 |

Lesson 6: Represent *put together* situations with number bonds. Count on from one embedded number or part to totals of 8 and 9, and generate all expressions for each total.

EUREKA MATH

Name _____ Date _____

Do as many as you can in 90 seconds. Write the number of bonds you finished here:

1. 7 / 6 ☐
2. 7 / 7 ☐
3. 7 / 6 ☐
4. 7 / 5 ☐
5. 7 / 6 ☐

6. 7 / ☐ 7
7. 7 / ☐ 6
8. 7 / ☐ 5
9. 7 / ☐ 4
10. 7 / ☐ 3

11. 7 / 4 ☐
12. 7 / 3 ☐
13. 7 / 2 ☐
14. 7 / 5 ☐
15. 7 / 2 ☐

16. 7 / ☐ 6
17. 7 / ☐ 1
18. 7 / ☐ 0
19. 7 / ☐ 2
20. 7 / ☐ 5

21. 7 / 1 ☐
22. 7 / 5 ☐
23. 7 / 3 ☐
24. 7 / 0 ☐
25. 7 / 6 ☐

_____
number bond dash 7

Lesson 6: Represent *put together* situations with number bonds. Count on from one embedded number or part to totals of 8 and 9, and generate all expressions for each total.

©2015 Great Minds. eureka-math.org
G1-M1-TE-BK1-1.3.1-01.2016

8 animals picture card

Lesson 6:   Represent *put together* situations with number bonds. Count on from one embedded number or part to totals of 8 and 9, and generate all expressions for each total.

©2015 Great Minds. eureka-math.org
G1-M1-TE-BK1-1.3.1-01.2016

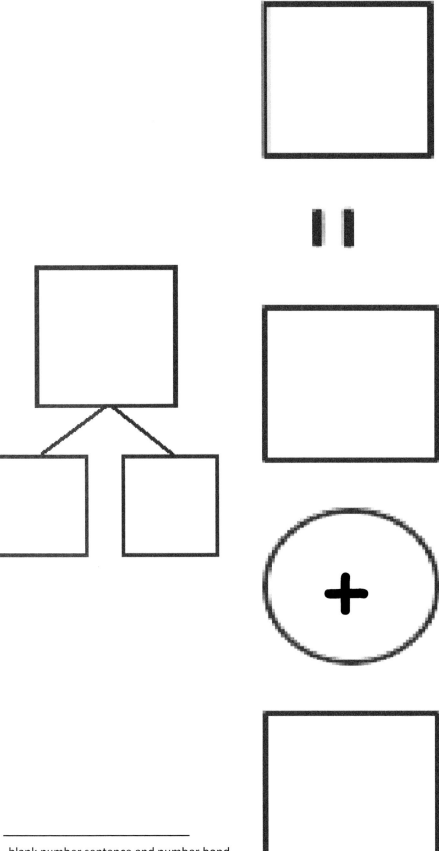

blank number sentence and number bond

Lesson 6: Represent *put together* situations with number bonds. Count on from one embedded number or part to totals of 8 and 9, and generate all expressions for each total.

105

EUREKA MATH™

©2015 Great Minds. eureka-math.org
G1-M1-TE-BK1-1.3.1-01.2016

Name _____   Date _____

Use your 5-group cards to help you write the expressions and number bonds to show all of the different ways to make 8.

[ ] + [ ]

[+] + [ ]

[   ] — [ ]
         — [ ]

[ ] — [   ]
[ ] —

[ ] + [ ]

[ ] + [ ]

[ ] + [ ]

[ ] + [ ]

[   ] — [ ]
         — [ ]

[ ] — [   ]
[ ] —

[ ] + [ ]

[ ] + [ ]

[ ] + [ ]

[ ] + [ ]

[   ] — [ ]
         — [ ]

_____
ways to make 8

Lesson 6:   Represent *put together* situations with number bonds. Count on from one embedded number or part to totals of 8 and 9, and generate all expressions for each total.

Lesson 7

Objective: Represent *put together* situations with number bonds. Count on from one embedded number or part to totals of 8 and 9, and generate all expressions for each total.

Suggested Lesson Structure

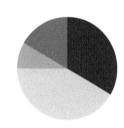

- Fluency Practice   (20 minutes)
- Application Problem   (5 minutes)
- Concept Development   (25 minutes)
- Student Debrief   (10 minutes)

   Total Time   **(60 minutes)**

Fluency Practice (20 minutes)

- Sparkle: The Say Ten Way **1.NBT.2**   (7 minutes)
- Shake Those Disks: 8 **1.OA.6**   (8 minutes)
- Number Bond Dash: 8 **1.OA.6**   (5 minutes)

Sparkle: The Say Ten Way (7 minutes)

Note: Providing students with ongoing practice with counting throughout the year builds and maintains their counting skills. This activity also prepares students for work in later modules as they explore place value and the importance of 10.

Ask students to stand in a circle. Introduce the counting pattern, start number, and end number.

   T: Today, we will count the Say Ten Way from 8 to 13. (Adjust the number range to fit the size of the class, if needed.)

Before the game, practice the counting sequence as a group and say, "Sparkle!" after the ending number is said aloud.

   T: Let's practice. 8, 9, 10, ten 1, ten 2, ten 3, Sparkle!

Begin the game. Students count around the circle, each student saying one number in the counting sequence. After the ending number is said (ten 3), the next student says, "Sparkle!" and the following player sits. Begin again with the start number, and continue counting in the same direction around the circle until only one player is standing. (See image on the next page.)

Lesson 7:   Represent *put together* situations with number bonds. Count on from one embedded number or part to totals of 8 and 9, and generate all expressions for each total.

107

©2015 Great Minds. eureka-math.org
G1-M1-TE-BK1-1.3.1-01.2016

Shake Those Disks: 8 (8 minutes)

Materials: (S) Per set of partners: 8 disks (e.g., counters, two-color beans, or pennies), personal white board with shake those disks 8 board (Fluency Template 1)

Note: This activity addresses the core fluency objective for Grade 1 of adding and subtracting within 10.

Assign students partners. Give each set of partners 6 disks. Instruct them to take turns as the Shaker and the Recorder. The Shaker shakes the disks and tosses them on the table. The Recorder then records the roll on the Shake Those Disks graph. (For example, if the Shaker rolls 6 red and 2 white, the Recorder puts an X on the graph above the 4 and 2 number bond.)

Number Bond Dash: 8 (5 minutes)

Materials: (T) Stopwatch or timer (S) Number bond dash 8 (Fluency Template 2), marker to correct work

Note: By using the same system repeatedly, students can focus on the mathematics alone. This activity also addresses the core fluency objective for Grade 1 of adding and subtracting within 10.

Follow procedure for Number Bond Dash in the Lesson 5 Fluency Practice.

Lesson 7:   Represent *put together* situations with number bonds. Count on from one embedded number or part to totals of 8 and 9, and generate all expressions for each total.

©2015 Great Minds. eureka-math.org
G1-M1-TE-BK1-1.3.1-01.2016

Application Problem (5 minutes)

Jenny has 8 flowers in a vase. The flowers come in two different colors. Draw a picture to show what the vase of flowers might look like. Write a number sentence and a number bond to match your picture.

Note: This problem is designed as a bridge from the previous lesson's focus on decompositions of 8, and provides a logical lead-up to the current lesson's Concept Development as students decompose 9 in various ways.

NOTES ON
MULTIPLE MEANS
OF ENGAGEMENT:

Connect learning to areas of interest. Students who enjoy writing can be given the challenge to write their own Application Problem for 9. Practicing their writing skills during math is a great cross-curricular activity. The problem could be used for learning with the whole class during the week.

Concept Development (25 minutes)

Materials: (T) 9 books picture card (Template 1), 5-group cards (Lesson 5 Template 1), chart to record decompositions of 9 (S) Bag of 10 linking cubes: 5 of each of 2 colors, personal white board, number bond and expression (Template 2)

T: (Distribute 5-group cards and a bag of linking cubes to each student. Show the picture card with 9 books.) How many books do you see here?

S: 9.

T: Turn to your partner and share the different ways you see 9 books. (Circulate as students share.)

S: (Share ideas.)

T: I heard so many students say they saw some books on the top shelf and some on the…

S: Bottom shelf!

T: Using linking cubes that are the same color, show how many books there are on the top shelf, and put them together like a stick. Then, place it into the part box of your number bond.

S: (Place a stick of 5 in the part box.)

T: How many books are on the top shelf?

S: 5.

T: Use the other color to show how many books are on the bottom shelf in the other part box of your number bond. But this time, just put them in a pile, not a stick.

S: (Place 4 individual cubes in the other part box.)

T: How many books are on the bottom shelf?

S: 4.

T: What is a counting strategy to figure out how many books there are in all?

MP.7 S: Count on.

T: Start with the stick of 5, and let's count on. Watch me first. (Model.) Your turn!

S: Fiiiiiive, 6, 7, 8, 9.

Lesson 7:   Represent *put together* situations with number bonds. Count on from one embedded number or part to totals of 8 and 9, and generate all expressions for each total.

109

©2015 Great Minds. eureka-math.org
G1-M1-TE-BK1-1.3.1-01.2016

MP.7

T: How many books are there in all?

S: 9.

T: What 2 parts made 9?

S: 5 and 4.

T: Put 9 other cubes into the space for the total to make our number bond true.

S: (Place 9 cubes in total.)

T: Do the two parts together show the same number as the total?

S: Yes.

T: That means our number bond is true! Write in the parts in your expression boxes.

S: (Write 5 + 4.)

T: Now, change the order.

S: (Write 4 + 5.)

Repeat this process with one more way to make 9 using the picture.

Although the picture card can stay up, the next part of the Concept Development focuses on finding the remaining decompositions of 9 using numerals rather than pictures. As the class comes up with all the decompositions of 9 throughout the rest of the Concept Development, continue recording them on the chart using the number bonds and expressions.

NOTES ON MULTIPLE MEANS OF ENGAGEMENT:

Allow students to move forward in small steps and use the 5-group cards to show the partners of 9 if they need more support to transfer the decompositions from above into the number bonds. For those students who are ready for a challenge, give them ways to expand today's lesson to other decompositions they have practiced.

T: Let's see if we can find the rest of the ways to make 9. When I show you a number, you make a stick of that number using the same color, and then place it on the number bond. Thumbs up if you know what to do.

S: (Show thumbs up.)

T: (Show the numeral 6 using the 5-group card.)

S: (Make sticks of 6 and place them into the part box.)

T: Let's find the other part that goes with 6 to make 9. Use another color to count on until you make 9.

S: Siiiiiiix, 7, 8, 9. (Place 3 individual cubes into the other part box.)

T: How many more does 6 need to get to 9?

S: 3.

T: Great! Fill in your expression boxes.

Repeat this process to make all other decompositions of 9. Continue to give students the first number each time. When appropriate, have students work independently or with a partner to count on and find the other part.

Lesson 7:   Represent *put together* situations with number bonds. Count on from one embedded number or part to totals of 8 and 9, and generate all expressions for each total.

©2015 Great Minds. eureka-math.org
G1-M1-TE-BK1-1.3.1-01.2016

Problem Set (10 minutes)

Students should do their personal best to complete the Problem Set within the allotted 10 minutes. For some classes, it may be appropriate to modify the assignment by specifying which problems they work on first. Some problems do not specify a method for solving. Students solve these problems using the RDW approach used for Application Problems.

Student Debrief (10 minutes)

Lesson Objective: Represent *put together* situations with number bonds. Count on from one embedded number or part to totals of 8 and 9, and generate all expressions for each total.

The Student Debrief is intended to invite reflection and active processing of the total lesson experience.

Invite students to review their solutions for the Problem Set. They should check work by comparing answers with a partner before going over answers as a class. Look for misconceptions or misunderstandings that can be addressed in the Debrief. Guide students in a conversation to debrief the Problem Set and process the lesson.

Any combination of the questions may be used below to lead the discussion.

- Look at the first page of the Problem Set. Are there two problems that are related? How are they related?

- Talk with a partner about the number bond you made for Problem 5(b). How are your number bonds different? How are they the same?

- Let's compare the charts we made for 7, 8, and 9. (Point to the number bond for 5 and 2, 5 and 3, and 5 and 4.) How are these different? Explain why they are different.

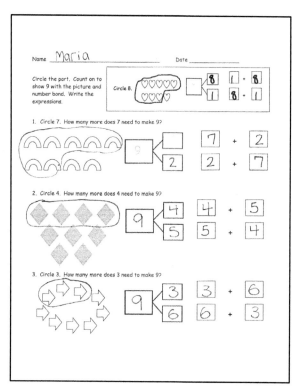

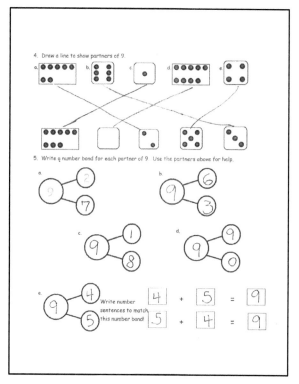

Lesson 7: Represent *put together* situations with number bonds. Count on from one embedded number or part to totals of 8 and 9, and generate all expressions for each total.

111

©2015 Great Minds. eureka-math.org
G1-M1-TE-BK1-1.3.1-01.2016

- Look at the charts we made for 6, 7, 8, and 9. In what ways is the chart for 9 different? (This chart is not organized in any particular order.) Why might we want to rewrite this chart in an order, beginning with the biggest part first? (If students present compelling reasons and wish to have an organized chart, rewrite the chart to represent a predetermined order.)

- Turn to your partner and discuss what we did and what we learned during today's lesson. What did you get better at doing today?

Exit Ticket (3 minutes)

After the Student Debrief, instruct students to complete the Exit Ticket. A review of their work will help with assessing students' understanding of the concepts that were presented in today's lesson and planning more effectively for future lessons. The questions may be read aloud to the students.

Lesson 7: Represent *put together* situations with number bonds. Count on from one embedded number or part to totals of 8 and 9, and generate all expressions for each total.

©2015 Great Minds. eureka-math.org
G1-M1-TE-BK1-1.3.1-01.2016

Name _____   Date _____

Circle the part. Count on to show 9 with the picture and number bond. Write the expressions.

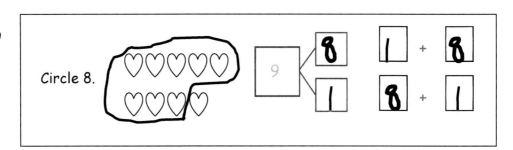

Circle 8.

1. Circle 7. How many more does 7 need to make 9?

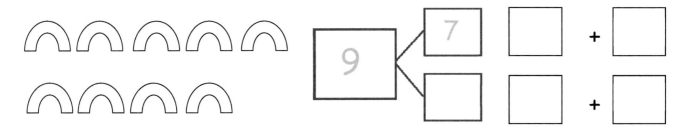

2. Circle 4. How many more does 4 need to make 9?

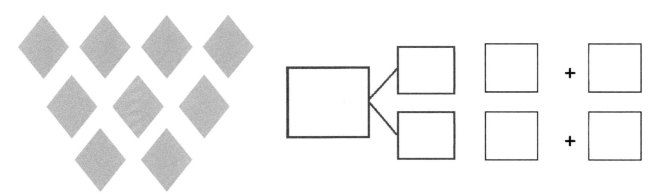

3. Circle 3. How many more does 3 need to make 9?

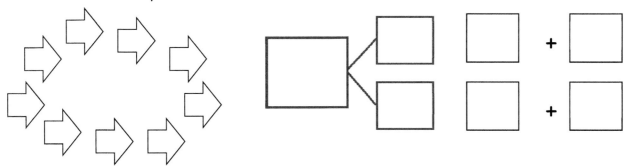

Lesson 7:   Represent *put together* situations with number bonds. Count on from one embedded number or part to totals of 8 and 9, and generate all expressions for each total.

113

EUREKA
MATH™

4. Draw a line to show partners of 9.

a. 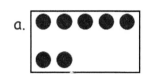 b. c. d. 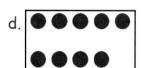 e.

5. Write a number bond for each partner of 9. Use the partners above for help.

a. 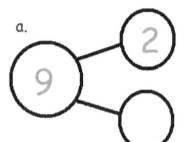 b.

c. 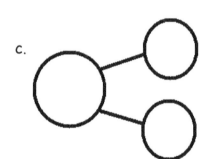 d.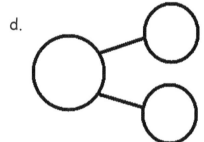

e. 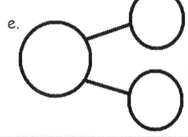 Write number sentences to match this number bond!

 + =

 + =

Lesson 7: Represent *put together* situations with number bonds. Count on from one embedded number or part to totals of 8 and 9, and generate all expressions for each total.

EUREKA MATH

©2015 Great Minds. eureka-math.org
G1-M1-TE-BK1-1.3.1-01.2016

Name _____   Date _____

1. Circle the pairs of numbers that make 9.

2. Complete the number bonds to show 2 different ways to make 9.

a.

b.

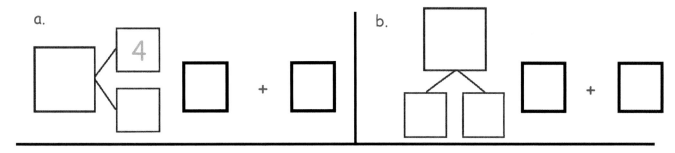

Lesson 7:   Represent *put together* situations with number bonds. Count on from
one embedded number or part to totals of 8 and 9, and generate all
expressions for each total.

©2015 Great Minds. eureka-math.org
G1-M1-TE-BK1-1.3.1-01.2016

115

EUREKA
MATH™

Name _____   Date _____

Ways to Make 9

Use the bookshelf picture to help you write the expressions and number bonds to show all of the different ways to make 9.

☐ + ☐

☐ + ☐

☐ ⟨ ☐ ☐

☐ ☐ ⟩ ☐

☐ + ☐

☐ + ☐

☐ + ☐

☐ + ☐

☐ ☐ ⟩ ☐

☐ ⟨ ☐ ☐

☐ + ☐

☐ + ☐

☐ ☐ ⟩ ☐

☐ + ☐

☐ + ☐

☐ ⟨ ☐ ☐

Lesson 7: Represent *put together* situations with number bonds. Count on from one embedded number or part to totals of 8 and 9, and generate all expressions for each total.

©2015 Great Minds. eureka-math.org
G1-M1-TE-BK1-1.3.1-01.2016

Shake Those Disks!—8

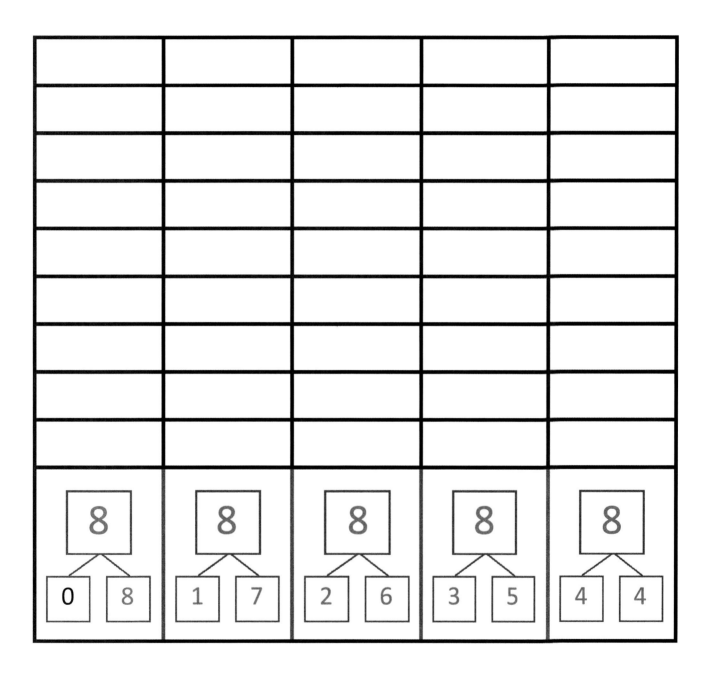

shake those disks 8

Lesson 7:   Represent *put together* situations with number bonds. Count on from
one embedded number or part to totals of 8 and 9, and generate all
expressions for each total.

©2015 Great Minds. eureka-math.org
G1-M1-TE-BK1-1.3.1-01.2016

117

Name _____   Date _____

Do as many as you can in 90 seconds. Write the number of bonds you finished here:

1.
8
8 |

2.
8
7 |

3.
8
6 |

4.
8
7 |

5.
8
6 |

6.
8
 | 5

7.
8
 | 6

8.
8
 | 5

9.
8
 | 4

10.
8
 | 3

11.
8
4 |

12.
8
5 |

13.
8
3 |

14.
8
4 |

15.
8
3 |

16.
8
 | 6

17.
8
 | 2

18.
8
 | 6

19.
8
 | 5

20.
8
 | 3

21.
8
4 |

22.
8
1 |

23.
8
2 |

24.
8
0 |

25.
8
1 |

number bond dash 8

Lesson 7: Represent *put together* situations with number bonds. Count on from one embedded number or part to totals of 8 and 9, and generate all expressions for each total.

EUREKA
MATH™

9 books picture card

Lesson 7:   Represent *put together* situations with number bonds. Count on from
one embedded number or part to totals of 8 and 9, and generate all
expressions for each total.

©2015 Great Minds. eureka-math.org
G1-M1-TE-BK1-1.3.1-01.2016

119

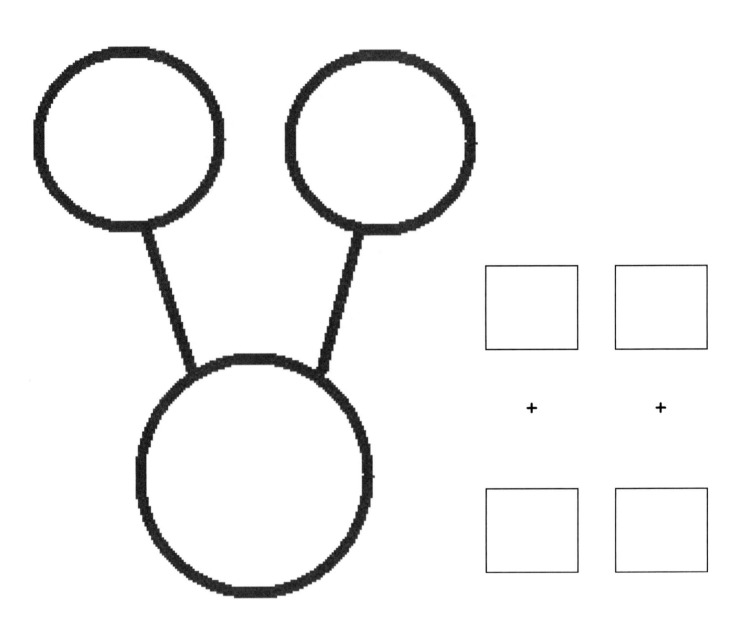

number bond and expression

Lesson 7:   Represent *put together* situations with number bonds. Count on from
one embedded number or part to totals of 8 and 9, and generate all
expressions for each total.

©2015 Great Minds. eureka-math.org
G1-M1-TE-BK1-1.3.1-01.2016

EUREKA
MATH

Lesson 8

Objective: Represent all the number pairs of 10 as number bonds from a given scenario, and generate all expressions equal to 10.

Suggested Lesson Structure

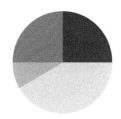

- ■ Fluency Practice   (15 minutes)
- ▨ Application Problem   (5 minutes)
- ▢ Concept Development   (25 minutes)
- ▨ Student Debrief   (15 minutes)

   Total Time   **(60 minutes)**

Fluency Practice (15 minutes)

- Skip-Counting Squats **1.OA.5**   (2 minutes)
- Target Practice: 8 and 9 **1.OA.6**   (8 minutes)
- Number Bond Dash: 9 **1.OA.6**   (5 minutes)

Skip-Counting Squats (2 minutes)

Note: This activity supports the connection of counting on by 2 to adding 2 and counting back by 2 to subtracting 2.

Have students count up from 0 to 20 and back two times, squatting down and touching the floor on odd numbers and standing up for even numbers.

- For the first count, instruct students to whisper when they squat and talk normally when they stand.

- On the second count, encourage students to try thinking of the numbers in their heads when they squat and whisper when they stand.

NOTES ON
MULTIPLE MEANS
OF REPRESENTATION:

Since not all students will be able to participate in this game, adjust the cues for certain students. Deaf and hard-of-hearing students can participate easily in games with visual signals. Blind and visually impaired students can participate by using audible signals, such as snaps.

Lesson 8:   Represent all the number pairs of 10 as number bonds from a given scenario, and generate all expressions equal to 10.

121

©2015 Great Minds. eureka-math.org
G1-M1-TE-BK1-1.3.1-01.2016

Target Practice: 8 and 9 (8 minutes)

Materials: (S) Per pair: 9 counters, 1 die

Note: This activity addresses the core fluency objective for Grade 1 of adding and subtracting within 10.

Assign students partners. Give each set of partners 8 counters. Instruct them to take turns as the Roller and the Target Finder. The Roller rolls the dice. The Target Finder determines the partner to 8. Students may use counters as needed. First, play with 8 as the target number, and then distribute another counter to each set of partners and practice finding numerical partners to 9.

Number Bond Dash: 9 (5 minutes)

Materials: (T) Stopwatch or timer (S) Number bond dash 9 (Fluency Template), marker to correct work

Note: By using the same system, the Number Bond Dash, students focus on the mathematics, rather than figuring out the worksheet.

Follow procedure for the Number Bond Dash (see Lesson 5 Fluency Practice.)

Application Problem (5 minutes)

Rayden received 9 stickers at school. He received 5 stickers in the morning. How many stickers did he receive in the afternoon? Draw a picture, a number bond, and a number sentence to show how you know.

Note: This problem is designed as a bridge from the previous lesson's focus on decompositions of 9 and provides a lead-up to today's Concept Development as students prove that 10 can be decomposed in many ways.

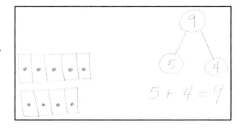

Concept Development (25 minutes)

Materials: (T) Chart to record decompositions of 10, 10 children on the playground picture card (Template), linking cubes in two colors (for Debrief) (S) Pipe cleaners, 10 beads (5 of one color, 5 of another color)

Rekenrek bracelet with 5 white beads and 5 red beads

T: Talk with your partner. What comes in groups of 10?
S: (Discuss. Possible responses include 10 fingers, 10 toes, 10 dimes in a dollar, 10 digits in a phone number, and 10 hot dogs.)
T: We remember from Kindergarten that 10 is an important number. We're going to start by making bracelets with 10 beads to help us show all of the different ways to make 10. We will call these *Rekenrek bracelets* because they have beads organized in rows of 5 and 5, just like a Rekenrek.

Walk students through the process of making a bracelet with 10 beads (5 of 1 color, 5 of another).

Lesson 8:   Represent all the number pairs of 10 as number bonds from a given scenario, and generate all expressions equal to 10.

T: Let's use our Rekenrek bracelets to find out all of the different ways to make 10.

T: (Display template showing children on a playground.) Look at the picture. Talk with your partner about the different parts you see. (Circulate.)

S: (Discuss.)

T: I heard someone say they saw 4 kids on the swing set. Show that on your bracelet.

S: (Show 4 beads to the side.)

T: If 4 kids are on the swings, how many kids are not?

S: 6.

T: What are the parts?

S: 6 and 4.

T: What strategy should we use to find the total?

S: Count on!

T: Touch and count, starting from 4.

S: Fouuuur, 5, 6, 7, 8, 9, 10.

T: What's our total?

S: 10.

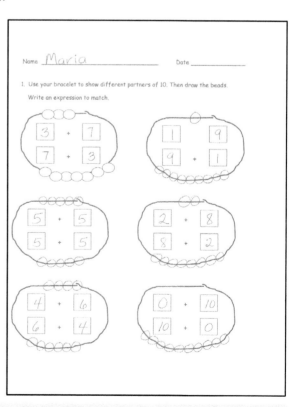

Write the expressions 4 + 6 and 6 + 4 on chart paper. Repeat the above process several times, to familiarize students with showing the decompositions on their Rekenrek bracelets. Record each set of expressions on the chart paper. Have students keep these for use in Topic I.

Problem Set (10 minutes)

Distribute the Problem Set, and then have students use their Rekenrek bracelets to move the beads and record all of the decompositions of 10 on their own. Students should save these as part of their number bond portfolios. They should also save the Rekenrek bracelets.

Students should do their personal best to complete the problem set within the allotted 10 minutes. For some classes, it may be appropriate to modify the assignment by specifying which problems they work on first. Some problems do not specify a method for solving. Students solve these problems using the RDW approach used for Application Problems.

Name Maria _____ Date _____

1. Use your bracelet to show different partners of 10. Then draw the beads. Write an expression to match.

3 + 7
7 + 3

1 + 9
9 + 1

5 + 5
5 + 5

2 + 8
8 + 2

4 + 6
6 + 4

0 + 10
10 + 0

Lesson 8:   Represent all the number pairs of 10 as number bonds from a given scenario, and generate all expressions equal to 10.

123

©2015 Great Minds. eureka-math.org
G1-M1-TE-BK1-1.3.1-01.2016

Student Debrief (15 minutes)

Lesson Objective: Represent all the number pairs of 10 as number bonds from a given scenario, and generate all expressions equal to 10.

The Student Debrief is intended to invite reflection and active processing of the total lesson experience.

Invite students to review their solutions for the Problem Set. They should check work by comparing answers with a partner before going over answers as a class. Look for misconceptions or misunderstandings that can be addressed in the Debrief. Guide students in a conversation to debrief the Problem Set and process the lesson.

Any combination of the questions below may be used to lead the discussion.

Have students come to the meeting area and look at the 10 linking cubes showing the decompositions of 10.

- Talk with your partner. What patterns do you see?
- Look from left to right. What is happening each time?
- Are there any sticks that have the same parts?
- How are these sticks different?

Exit Ticket (3 minutes)

After the Student Debrief, instruct students to complete the Exit Ticket. A review of their work will help with assessing students' understanding of the concepts that were presented in today's lesson and planning more effectively for future lessons. The questions may be read aloud to the students.

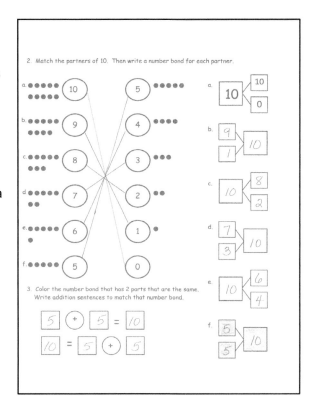

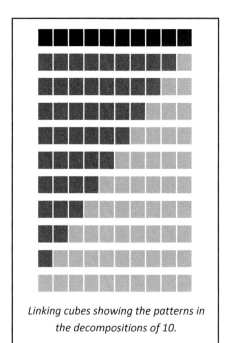

Linking cubes showing the patterns in the decompositions of 10.

Lesson 8:   Represent all the number pairs of 10 as number bonds from a given scenario, and generate all expressions equal to 10.

©2015 Great Minds. eureka-math.org
G1-M1-TE-BK1-1.3.1-01.2016

Name _____ Date _____

1. Use your bracelet to show different partners of 10. Then, draw the beads.
   Write an expression to match.

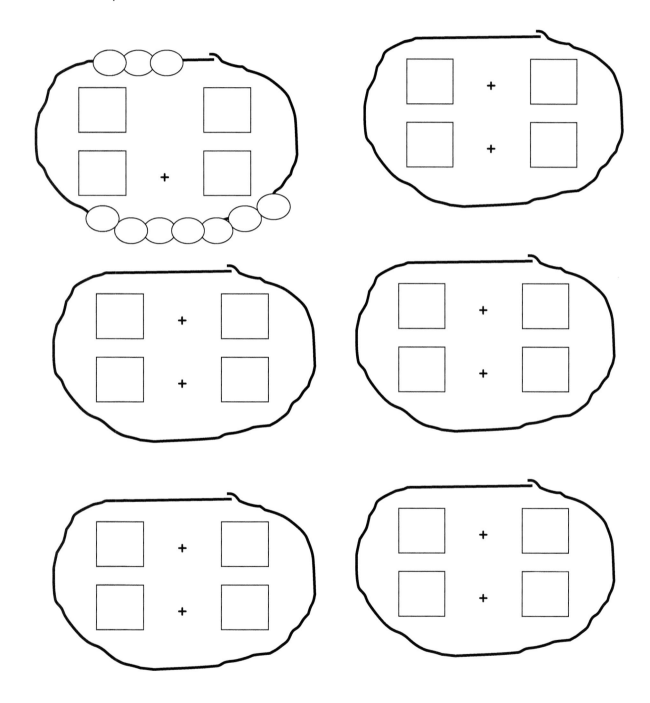

Lesson 8: Represent all the number pairs of 10 as number bonds from a given
scenario, and generate all expressions equal to 10.

©2015 Great Minds. eureka-math.org
G1-M1-TE-BK1-1.3.1-01.2016

2. Match the partners of 10. Then, write a number bond for each partner.

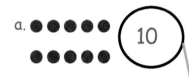

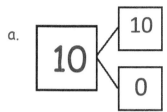

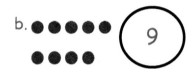

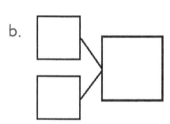

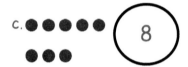

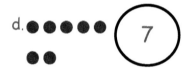

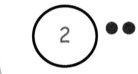

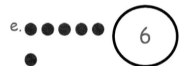
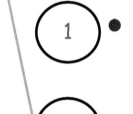
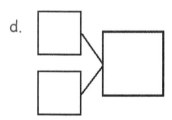

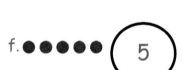
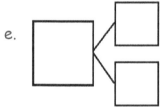

3. Color the number bond that has 2 parts that are the same.
   Write addition sentences to match that number bond.

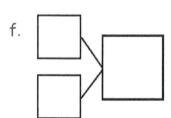

Lesson 8:   Represent all the number pairs of 10 as number bonds from a given
              scenario, and generate all expressions equal to 10.

Name _____   Date _____

Color the partners that make 10.

7 •••

•••• 6

8 ••

6 •••

1 9

5 4

Lesson 8:   Represent all the number pairs of 10 as number bonds from a given
scenario, and generate all expressions equal to 10.

127

©2015 Great Minds. eureka-math.org
G1-M1-TE-BK1-1.3.1-01.2016

Name _____   Date _____

1. Rex found 10 bones on his walk. He can't decide which part he wants to bring to his doghouse and which part he should bury. Help show Rex his choices by filling in the missing parts of the number bonds.

a.
10
5

b.
10
6

c.
10
7

d.
10
8

e.
10
9

2. He decided to bury 3 and bring 7 back home. Write all the adding sentences that match this number bond.

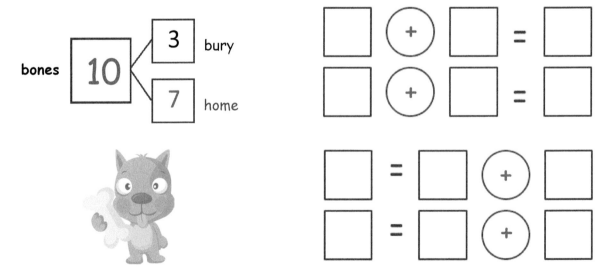

bones 10
3 bury
7 home

☐ ⊕ ☐ = ☐

☐ ⊕ ☐ = ☐

☐ = ☐ ⊕ ☐

☐ = ☐ ⊕ ☐

      Lesson 8:   Represent all the number pairs of 10 as number bonds from a given scenario, and generate all expressions equal to 10.

©2015 Great Minds. eureka-math.org
G1-M1-TE-BK1-1.3.1-01.2016

EUREKA MATH

Name _____   Date _____

Do as many as you can in 90 seconds.   Write the number of bonds you finished here:

1. 9 — 8, __

2. 9 — 7, __

3. 9 — 8, __

4. 9 — 7, __

5. 9 — 9, __

6. 9 — __, 6

7. 9 — __, 7

8. 9 — __, 6

9. 9 — __, 5

10. 9 — __, 4

11. 9 — 8, __

12. 9 — 1, __

13. 9 — 7, __

14. 9 — 2, __

15. 9 — 6, __

16. 9 — __, 5

17. 9 — __, 6

18. 9 — __, 7

19. 9 — __, 2

20. 9 — __, 3

21. 9 — 5, __

22. 9 — 1, __

23. 9 — 2, __

24. 9 — 0, __

25. 9 — 2, __

_____

number bond dash 9

Lesson 8:   Represent all the number pairs of 10 as number bonds from a given scenario, and generate all expressions equal to 10.

10 children on the playground picture card

Lesson 8: Represent all the number pairs of 10 as number bonds from a given scenario, and generate all expressions equal to 10.

EUREKA
MATH

Mathematics Curriculum

GRADE 1 • MODULE 1

Topic C
Addition Word Problems

1.OA.1, 1.OA.6, 1.OA.5

Focus Standard:	1.OA.1	Use addition and subtraction within 20 to solve word problems involving situations of adding to, taking from, putting together, taking apart, and comparing, with unknowns in all positions, e.g., by using objects, drawings, and equations with a symbol for the unknown number to represent the problem.
	1.OA.6	Add and subtract within 20, demonstrating fluency for addition and subtraction within 10. Use strategies such as counting on; making ten (e.g., $8 + 6 = 8 + 2 + 4 = 10 + 4 = 14$); decomposing a number leading to a ten (e.g., $13 - 4 = 13 - 3 - 1 = 10 - 1 = 9$); using the relationship between addition and subtraction (e.g., knowing that $8 + 4 = 12$, one knows $12 - 8 = 4$); and creating equivalent but easier or known sums (e.g., adding $6 + 7$ by creating the known equivalent $6 + 6 + 1 = 12 + 1 = 13$).
Instructional Days:	5	
Coherence -Links from:	GK–M4	Number Pairs, Addition and Subtraction to 10
-Links to:	G2–M4	Addition and Subtraction Within 200 with Word Problems to 100

In Topic C, students develop a more robust understanding of addition word problems, moving beyond the Kindergarten problem types (**K.OA.2**) by reviewing *put together with result unknown* and *add to with result unknown* problems, and then moving to the more complex *change unknown* version of the earlier problem types.

In Lesson 9, students solve both *add to with result unknown* and *put together with result unknown* problems with their classmates. The lesson begins with a cadre of students engaged in a dance party, and then a number of students join them—how fun! Students then record this action-based problem as an equation, and move on to the *put together with result unknown* problem type, where they are faced with a set of students whose characteristics invite decomposition, much like in Topic B. Students end with a Student Debrief in which they explore the connections between these two problem types, ultimately understanding that they used the operation of addition to solve both problem types.

Lesson 10 has students using 5-group cards to solve *put together with result unknown* problems that are represented by stories stemming from pictures. The 5-group cards again make the expectation clear that students will be practicing counting on (Level 2 strategy), but may use the strategy of counting all (Level 1 strategy) if necessary.

The introduction of the *add to with change unknown* problem type (**1.OA.6**) occurs in Lesson 11. This lesson allows students explorations with problems where the *action*, which represents the *change*, is unknown. For example, "Ben has 5 pencils. He got some more from his mother. Now, he has 9 pencils. How many pencils did Ben get from his mother?" Students physically add more to the starting quantity, counting on until they reach the total; for the first time in Module 1, students simply must use the valuable Level 2 strategy of counting on in order to determine the unknown part.

Lesson 12 continues with solving *add to with change unknown* problems, as students use their 5-group cards to count on to find the unknown change in quantity. Throughout these two lessons, students explore the symbol for the unknown (**1.OA.1**) as both a question mark and an open box. The topic ends with students creating their own *put together with result unknown*, *add to with result unknown*, and *add to with change unknown* problems from equations, and then having their peers solve them through drawings and discussions. These problems set the foundation early in the module for relating addition to subtraction in Topic G (**1.OA.4**).[1]

A Teaching Sequence Toward Mastery of Addition Word Problems

Objective 1: Solve *add to with result unknown* and *put together with result unknown* math stories by drawing, writing equations, and making statements of the solution.
(**Lesson 9**)

Objective 2: Solve *put together with result unknown* math stories by drawing and using 5-group cards.
(**Lesson 10**)

Objective 3: Solve *add to with change unknown* math stories as a context for counting on by drawing, writing equations, and making statements of the solution.
(**Lesson 11**)

Objective 4: Solve *add to with change unknown* math stories using 5-group cards.
(**Lesson 12**)

Objective 5: Tell *put together with result unknown*, *add to with result unknown*, and *add to with change unknown* stories from equations.
(**Lesson 13**)

---

[1] For an analysis of addition and subtraction word problem types used in Grades K–2 please refer to the Counting and Cardinality Progression, pages 7 and 9, and the Common Core State Standards, page 88.

Lesson 9

Objective: Solve *add to with result unknown* and *put together with result unknown* math stories by drawing, writing equations, and making statements of the solution.

Suggested Lesson Structure

■ Fluency Practice   (20 minutes)
▨ Application Problem   (5 minutes)
▢ Concept Development   (25 minutes)
■ Student Debrief   (10 minutes)
   Total Time   **(60 minutes)**

Fluency Practice (20 minutes)

- Sparkle: The Say Ten Way **1.NBT.2**   (5 minutes)
- 5-Group Flash: Partners to 10 **1.OA.6**   (5 minutes)
- X-Ray Vision: Partners to 10 **1.OA.6**   (5 minutes)
- Number Bond Dash: 10 **1.OA.6**   (5 minutes)

Sparkle: The Say Ten Way (5 minutes)

Note: Providing students with ongoing practice with counting throughout the year builds and maintains their counting skills, which are foundational for later Grade 1 work using the Level 3 strategies of making ten and taking from ten when adding and subtracting.

See Lesson 7 for activity instructions.

5-Group Flash: Partners to 10 (5 minutes)

Materials: (T/S) 5-group cards (Lesson 5 Template 1)

Note: This activity addresses the core fluency objective for Grade 1 of adding and subtracting within 10.

Flash 5-group cards for 2–3 seconds, and then instructs students to say the number at the snap. On the second snap, ask students to identify the partner to 10. Remind students they can use their fingers to help. Flash higher numbers first to facilitate finding the partner to 10 so that all students can feel successful.

Next, assign students partners, and instruct them to take turns flashing their 5-group cards with each other.

Lesson 9:   Solve *add to with result unknown* and *put together with result unknown* math stories by drawing, writing equations, and making statements of the solution.

©2015 Great Minds. eureka-math.org
G1-M1-TE-BK1-1.3.1-01.2016

133

X-Ray Vision: Partners to 10 (5 minutes)

Materials: (T) 10 counters, container

Note: This activity addresses the core fluency objective for Grade 1 of adding and subtracting within 10.

1.   Tell students there is a rumor that some of the children in the class are superheroes, and some of them may have x-ray vision. Place 10 counters on the floor next to a container.
2.   Tell students to close their eyes.
3.   Put 1 of the items into the container
4.   Tell students to open their eyes and identify how many counters were put inside it.
5.   When a student figures it out, deem her a superhero with x-ray vision!
6.   Continue the game, eliciting all partners to 10.

Number Bond Dash: 10 (5 minutes)

Materials: (T) Stopwatch or timer (S) Number bond dash 10 (Fluency Template), marker to correct work

Note: By using the same system repeatedly, students can focus on the mathematics alone. The activity addresses the core fluency objective for Grade 1 of adding and subtracting within 10.

Follow the procedure for the Number Bond Dash (see Lesson 5 Fluency Practice).

Application Problem (5 minutes)

Kira was making a number bracelet with a total of 10 beads on it. She has put on 3 red beads so far. How many more beads does she need to add to the bracelet? Explain your thinking in a picture and number sentence.

Extension: If Kira wants to use 5 red beads and 5 yellow beads for her bracelet, how many red beads and how many yellow beads does she need to add?

Note: This problem is designed to serve as a bridge from the previous lesson's focus on decompositions of 10.

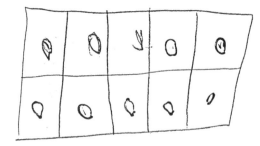

Lesson 9:   Solve *add to with result unknown* and *put together with result unknown* math stories by drawing, writing equations, and making statements of the solution.

EUREKA MATH

Concept Development (25 minutes)

Materials: (S) Personal white board, number bond and two blank equations (Template)

Have students sit in a large semicircle facing the front. Use students to act out the math stories. Draw a number bond on the board. Begin the lesson with *add to* story problems.

- T: Good morning, boys and girls. Welcome to Math Stories Theater! You will be watching some math stories and have a hand at solving them. First, close your eyes. When I tap you on the shoulder, quietly come up to the front.
- S: (Close eyes.)
- T: (Tap 5 students to come up. Have 1 of the students hide behind the bookcase.)
- T: Open your eyes. How many students do you see?
- S: 4 students.
- T: There are 4 students dancing at a party. After a little while, along came their dancing friend, [name of the hiding student]. How many students are dancing at the dance party now?
- S: 5 students.
- T: This is the total number of students at the party. Let's show the total in the number bond. (Write 5 in the total portion of the number bond.)
- T: How many students were dancing at first?
- S: 4 students.
- T: (Record on the number bond.) How many more students came over to dance?
- S: 1 more student.
- T: (Record on the number bond.) Think about the math story you just watched. Turn and tell your partner the number sentence that tells how many students were dancing in all.
- S: (Turn and talk.)
- T: Say the number sentence.
- S: 4 + 1 = 5.
- T: (Write on the board below the completed number bond.) What is the total?
- S: 5.

NOTES ON MULTIPLE MEANS FOR ACTION AND EXPRESSION:

When choosing numbers to use in a story, start at a simple level, and after students have solved it with easy numbers, change to harder numbers. Here is a suggested sequence starting from simple to more complex:

Add within 5 (e.g., 4 + 1 = 5).

Add adding 1 (e.g., 8 + 1 = 9).

Add using 5 (e.g., 5 + 2 = 7).

Add with the smaller addend first (e.g., 3 + 5 = 8).

Add to 9 and 10 (e.g., 7 + 3 = 10).

Add to 9 and 10 with smaller addend first (e.g., 3 + 7 = 10).

Add including 0 (e.g., 0 + 8 = 8 or 8 + 0 = 8).

NOTES ON MULTIPLE MEANS FOR ACTION AND EXPRESSION:

Ask those students who have moved into abstract thinking to solve the subsequent problems without drawing. Ensure that they are still making sense of the problems by having them write or talk about how they solved each one.

Lesson 9: Solve *add to with result unknown* and *put together with result unknown* math stories by drawing, writing equations, and making statements of the solution.

135

©2015 Great Minds. eureka-math.org
G1-M1-TE-BK1-1.3.1-01.2016

T: What does 5 equal? What are the two parts that make 5?

S: 4 and 1.

T: Say the number sentence starting with *5 equals*. (Write number sentence on the board.)

S: 5 = 4 + 1.

Analyze the referents for each number, ensuring that students understand what each number represents in the story. Possibly continue with 8 + 1 = 9 but without writing in the number bond on the board.

Choose a group of new actors to act out *put together* math stories (e.g., 5 students sitting, 2 students standing: 5 + 2 = 7; 3 students facing sideways, 5 students facing forward: 3 + 5 = 8).

T: We will now make math drawings. (Distribute personal white boards.)

T: I will tell you a story and you draw. There are 4 inchworms on a giant leaf.

S: (Draw 4 worms on a leaf.)

T: Three more inchworms crawled onto the leaf.

S: (Draw 3 more worms.)

T: Does your drawing show the two parts of our story clearly? (Have students share how to make their drawings match the story by drawing two distinct groups.)

T: Write a number sentence to show what happened in your picture and find the total.

MP.2   S: (Write 4 + 3 = 7.)

T: Turn and talk to your partner about what each number tells about the story.

S: (Share with their partners.)

T: Write the rest of the number sentences that go with your story.

Possibly continue with the following suggested sequence: 7 + 3 = 10, 3 + 6 = 9, and 0 + 2 = 2.

T: This time, I will only write the number sentence on the board. Your job is to draw a picture with math drawings to match the number sentence. (Write 5 + 2 = 7.)

S: (Draw 5 circles with one color and 2 circles with another color and write 5 + 2 = 7.)

Repeat the process for 6 + 4 = 10, 2 + 7 = 9, and 4 + 0 = 4.

Problem Set (10 minutes)

Students should do their personal best to complete the Problem Set within the allotted 10 minutes. For some classes, it may be appropriate to modify the assignment by specifying which problems they work on first. Some problems do not specify a method for solving. Students solve these problems using the RDW approach used for Application Problems.

Lesson 9:   Solve *add to with result unknown* and *put together with result unknown* math stories by drawing, writing equations, and making statements of the solution.

©2015 Great Minds. eureka-math.org
G1-M1-TE-BK1-1.3.1-01.2016

Student Debrief (10 minutes)

Lesson Objective: Solve *add to with result unknown* and *put together with result unknown* math stories by drawing, writing equations, and making statements of the solution.

The Student Debrief is intended to invite reflection and active processing of the total lesson experience.

Invite students to review their solutions for the Problem Set. They should check work by comparing answers with a partner before going over answers as a class. Look for misconceptions or misunderstandings that can be addressed in the Debrief. Guide students in a conversation to debrief the Problem Set and process the lesson.

Any combination of the questions below may be used to lead the discussion.

- How are the Problem Set stories the same? What did we do to solve them? How are the ball and frog problems different from the flag and flower problems?

- Which of our Math Story Theater situations was like the ball and frog problem? Which situations were like the flag and flower problem?

- Use your picture from your personal white board or think of your own story for us to act out for Math Stories Theater!

- How was today's lesson related to our lesson on ways to make 9? (You may also cite the lessons on ways to make 6, 7, 8, or 10.)

Exit Ticket (3 minutes)

After the Student Debrief, instruct students to complete the Exit Ticket. A review of their work will help with assessing students' understanding of the concepts that were presented in today's lesson and planning more effectively for future lessons. The questions may be read aloud to the students

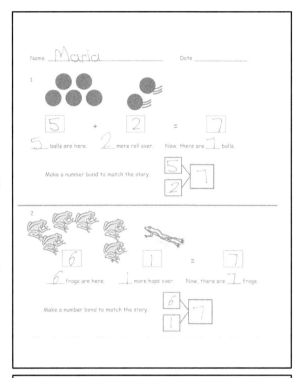

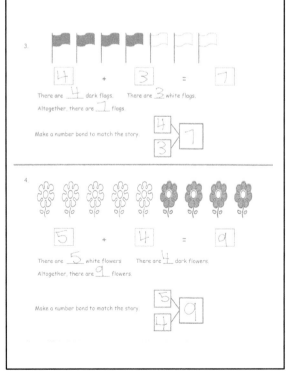

Lesson 9:   Solve *add to with result unknown* and *put together with result unknown* math stories by drawing, writing equations, and making statements of the solution.

137

©2015 Great Minds. eureka-math.org
G1-M1-TE-BK1-1.3.1-01.2016

Name _____   Date _____

1.

$\boxed{}$ **+** $\boxed{}$ **=** $\boxed{}$

_____ balls are here.   _____ more roll over.   Now, there are _____ balls.

Make a number bond to match the story.

2.

$\boxed{}$ **+** $\boxed{}$ **=** $\boxed{}$

_____ frogs are here.   _____ more hops over.   Now, there are _____ frogs.

Make a number bond to match the story.

Lesson 9:   Solve *add to with result unknown* and *put together with result unknown* math stories by drawing, writing equations, and making statements of the solution.

©2015 Great Minds. eureka-math.org
G1-M1-TE-BK1-1.3.1-01.2016

EUREKA
MATH™

3.

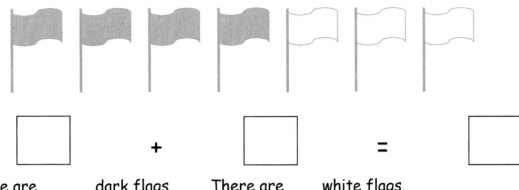

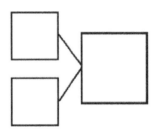

There are _____ dark flags.   There are ____ white flags.

Altogether, there are _____ flags.

Make a number bond to match the story.

4.

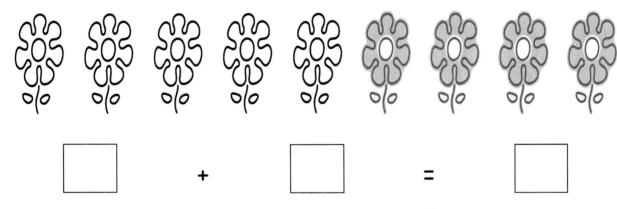

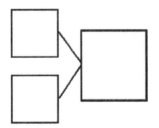

There are _____ white flowers.   There are ____ dark flowers.

Altogether, there are _____ flowers.

Make a number bond to match the story.

Lesson 9:   Solve *add to with result unknown* and *put together with result unknown* math stories by drawing, writing equations, and making statements of the solution.

139

©2015 Great Minds. eureka-math.org
G1-M1-TE-BK1-1.3.1-01.2016

Name _____   Date _____

Draw a picture and write a number sentence to match the story.

Ben has 3 red balls and gets 5 green balls. How many balls does he have now?

$$\boxed{}$$

$\boxed{}$ **+** $\boxed{}$ **=** $\boxed{}$ Ben has _____ balls.

Lesson 9:   Solve *add to with result unknown* and *put together with result*
unknown math stories by drawing, writing equations, and making
statements of the solution.

©2015 Great Minds. eureka-math.org
G1-M1-TE-BK1-1.3.1-01.2016

**EUREKA
MATH**™

Name _____   Date _____

1. Use the picture to tell a math story.

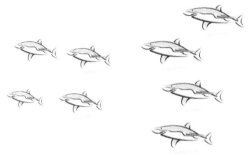

Write a number bond to
match your story.

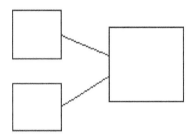

Write a number sentence to tell the story.

    =

There are _____ sharks.

2. Use the picture to tell a math story.

Write a number bond to
match your story.

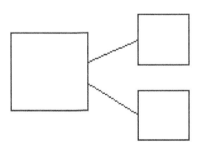

Write a number sentence to tell the story.

  =   +

There are _____ students.

Lesson 9:   Solve *add to with result unknown* and *put together with result*
unknown math stories by drawing, writing equations, and making
statements of the solution.
©2015 Great Minds. eureka-math.org
G1-M1-TE-BK1-1.3.1-01.2016

Draw a picture to match the story.

3. Jim has 4 big dogs and 3 small dogs. How many dogs does Jim have?

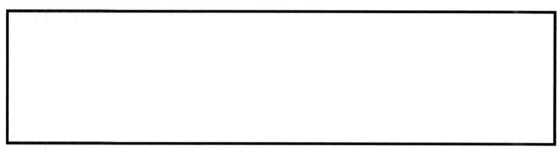

Jim has _____ dogs.

4. Liv plays at the park. She plays with 3 girls and 6 boys. How many kids does she play with at the park?

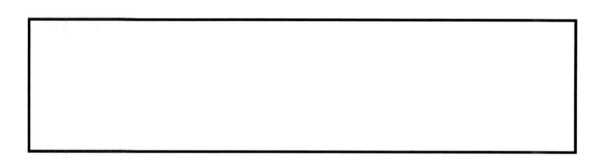

Liv plays with _____ kids.

Lesson 9:   Solve *add to with result unknown* and *put together with result unknown* math stories by drawing, writing equations, and making statements of the solution.

EUREKA
MATH™

Name _____

Date _____

Do as many as you can in 90 seconds. Write the number of bonds you finished here:

1.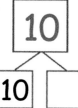

2.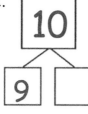

3.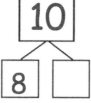

4.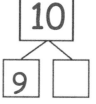

5.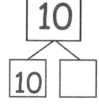

6.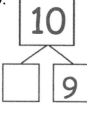

7.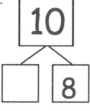

8.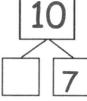

9.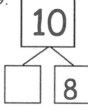

10.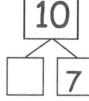

11.

12.

13.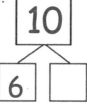

14.

15.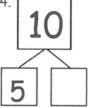

16.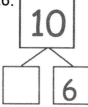

17.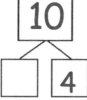

18.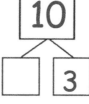

19.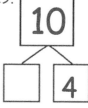

20.

21.

22.

23.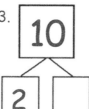

24.

25.

_____

number bond dash 10

EUREKA MATH™

Lesson 9: Solve *add to with result unknown* and *put together with result unknown* math stories by drawing, writing equations, and making statements of the solution.

©2015 Great Minds. eureka-math.org
G1-M1-TE-BK1-1.3.1-01.2016

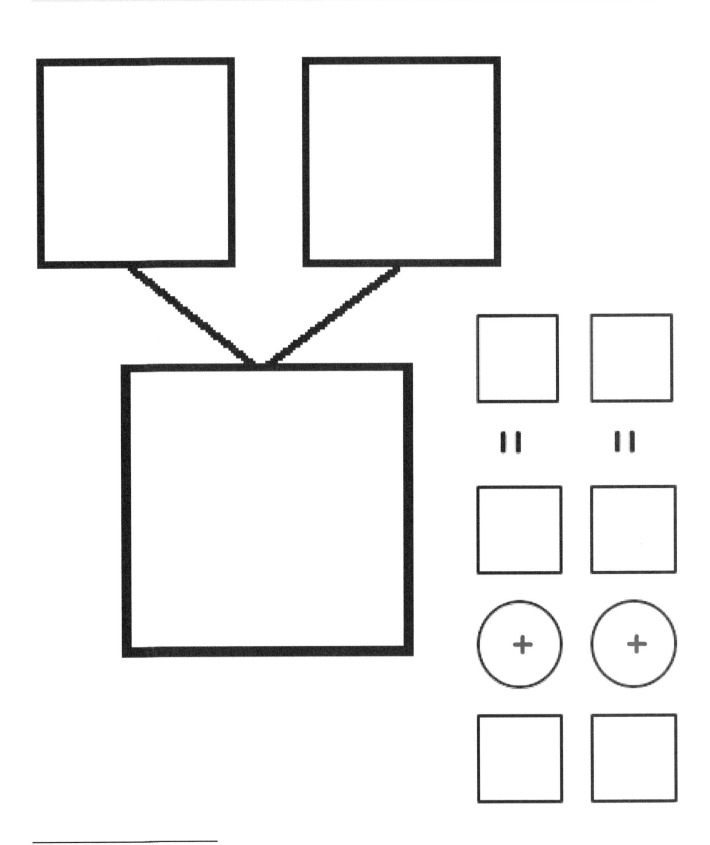

number bond and two blank equations

Lesson 9: Solve *add to with result unknown* and *put together with result unknown* math stories by drawing, writing equations, and making statements of the solution.

EUREKA
MATH™

Lesson 10

Objective: Solve *put together with result unknown* math stories by drawing and using 5-group cards.

Suggested Lesson Structure

■ Fluency Practice   (15 minutes)
▨ Application Problem   (10 minutes)
▨ Concept Development   (25 minutes)
■ Student Debrief   (10 minutes)

Total Time   **(60 minutes)**

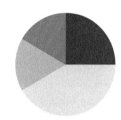

Fluency Practice (15 minutes)

- Happy Counting the Say Ten Way **1.NBT.2**   (2 minutes)
- Cold Call: 1 More **1.OA.5**   (2 minutes)
- Target Practice: 5 and 6 **1.OA.6**   (11 minutes)

Happy Counting the Say Ten Way (2 minutes)

Note: Providing students with ongoing practice with counting throughout the year builds and maintains their counting skills, which are foundational for later Grade 1 work using the Level 3 strategy of making ten and taking from ten to add and subtract.

Repeat the Happy Counting activity from Lesson 3 Fluency Practice counting from 15 to 25 and back the Say Ten Way.

Cold Call: 1 More (2 minutes)

Note: This activity supports the connection of counting on 1 to adding 1.

Tell students a number will be said aloud, and instruct them to think about the number that is 1 more. Cold call one student to say the number aloud as quickly as possible.

Target Practice: 5 and 6 (11 minutes)

Materials: (S) Per set of partners: personal white board, target practice (Fluency Template), 6 counters, 1 die

Note: This activity addresses the core fluency objective for Grade 1 of adding and subtracting within 10.

See directions on the Target Practice board. First, use 5 as the target number, and then distribute 1 more counter and use 6 as the target number.

Application Problem (10 minutes)

The class is collecting canned food to help those in need. The teacher brings in 3 cans to start the collection. On Monday, Becky brings in 2 cans. On Tuesday, Talia brings in 2 cans. On Wednesday, Brendan brings in 2 cans. How many cans were there at the end of each day?

Draw a picture to show your thinking. What do you notice about what happened each day?

Extension: If this pattern continues, how many cans will the class have on Friday?

Note: This problem serves as a bridge from the previous lesson, in which students solved *add to* problems. Students discuss their strategies during the Debrief and connect the work with today's lesson of using drawings and 5-group cards to solve.

Concept Development (25 minutes)

Materials: (T) 7 children picture card (Lesson 5 Template 2), 10 children on playground picture card (Lesson 8 Template) (S): 5-group cards (Lesson 5 Template 1), personal white boards, number bond and two blank equations (Lesson 9 Template), 10 children on playground picture card (Lesson 8 Template) per pair

T: When I tell the math story from the picture, you draw a picture to match it. In a first-grade classroom, some students are sitting down and learning. Use simple math drawings like circles to draw how many students are sitting down.

S: (Draw 5 circles.)

T: Some students are standing up and learning. Draw this part of the story.

S: (Draw 2 circles.)

T: How many students are there in all? (Give time for students to count on.)

NOTES ON MULTIPLE MEANS OF REPRESENTATION:

As the math story is told, make sure to have it written on the board or on a handout for students who need information presented visually. Presenting material in more than one way helps different styles of learners. In this part of the lesson, auditory and visual learners will benefit.

Lesson 10:   Solve *put together with result unknown* math stories by drawing and using 5-group cards.

A STORY OF UNITS

Lesson 10 1•1

S: 7 students!

T: Write the number sentence to match your drawing.

T: (Have students identify what each number represents.)

Using the same picture, generate one or two story problems for students to draw and solve (e.g., 3 + 4 = 7, 1 + 6 = 7).

T: (Distribute 5-group cards to each student.) Let's look at the picture of children playing on the playground. I'll make up a math story, and you use your 5-group cards to match the story. At recess, 3 students are having fun on the swings. Show me with your 5-group card, using the numeral side.

S: (Show the number 3.)

T: Three students are having fun playing with the jump rope. Show me with your 5-group card, using the dot side.

S: (Show 3 dots.)

T: Count on to find out how many students are playing on the swings and how many students are playing with the jump rope. (Give time for students to solve.)

T: Write the number sentence using numbers to match your drawing.

S: (Write 3 + 3 = 6.)

T: (Have students identify what each number represents.)

div style="float:right">**NOTES ON MULTIPLE MEANS OF REPRESENTATION:**

Circulate as students are telling their story problems and solving using 5-group cards. Guide and encourage students to use math vocabulary in discussion. When students use these words, it is apparent that they are applying what they are learning.

Using the same picture, generate one or two story problems for students to solve using their 5-group cards. You might continue with the following suggested examples: 5 + 5 = 10 (children in the air, children on the ground), 3 + 7 = 10 (sitting kids, standing kids).

T: (Write 8 + 2 on the board.) Now, it's your turn to be the storyteller. Study the picture card carefully! Work with your partner to come up with a story that matches my expression.

Lesson 10:   Solve *put together with result unknown* math stories by drawing and using 5-group cards.

147

©2015 Great Minds. eureka-math.org
G1-M1-TE-BK1-1.3.1-01.2016

Circulate and choose pairs to share their stories. There are multiple ways to represent 8 + 2 in the picture. Distribute a picture of the playground to each pair of students. Have them work together to make up story problems and solve them by using 5-group cards. Circulate and then choose a pair of students to share their story for the class to solve at the end of this lesson.

Problem Set (10 minutes)

Students should do their personal best to complete the Problem Set within the allotted 10 minutes. For some classes, it may be appropriate to modify the assignment by specifying which problems they work on first. Some problems do not specify a method for solving. Students solve these problems using the RDW approach used for Application Problems.

Student Debrief (10 minutes)

Lesson Objective: Solve *put together with result unknown* math stories by drawing and using 5-group cards.

The Student Debrief is intended to invite reflection and active processing of the total lesson experience.

Invite students to review their solutions for the Problem Set. They should check work by comparing answers with a partner before going over answers as a class. Look for misconceptions or misunderstandings that can be addressed in the Debrief. Guide students in a conversation to debrief the Problem Set and process the lesson.

Any combination of the questions below may be used to lead the discussion.

- In our lesson, we used simple math drawings like circles to draw the students in our problem. Why would we use circles instead of drawing the students?

- Look at your Problem Set and your Application Problem. What strategies have you been using to tell and solve our stories today?

- What patterns do you see in your Application Problem?

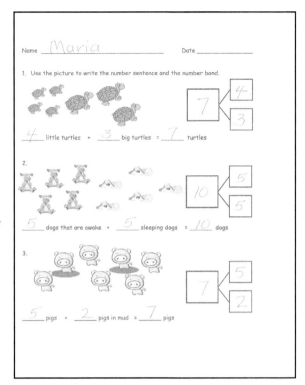

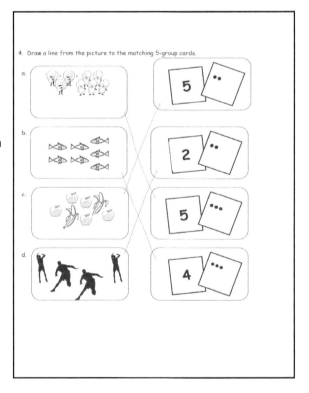

Lesson 10:   Solve *put together with result unknown* math stories by drawing and using 5-group cards.

- Share with a partner how you solved the Application Problem. In what ways did you solve it differently? In what ways did you solve it similarly?

- What do you think was an efficient strategy to use to solve the Application Problem? What made that strategy efficient?

- I heard many of you say that you counted on 2 each time. Help me write a number sentence that shows what happened on Monday. (3 + 2 = 5.) Let's circle the part that shows that we counted on 2.

- How could we use 5-group cards to show how to solve this?

- Was counting on the same as adding today? How do you know? (The numbers were increasing; we were counting up, etc.)

Exit Ticket (3 minutes)

After the Student Debrief, instruct students to complete the Exit Ticket. A review of their work will help with assessing students' understanding of the concepts that were presented in today's lesson and planning more effectively for future lessons. The questions may be read aloud to the students.

Lesson 10:   Solve *put together with result unknown* math stories by drawing and using 5-group cards.

149

©2015 Great Minds. eureka-math.org
G1-M1-TE-BK1-1.3.1-01.2016

Name _____   Date _____

1. Use the picture to write the number sentence and the number bond.

_____ little turtles + _____ big turtles = _____ turtles

2.

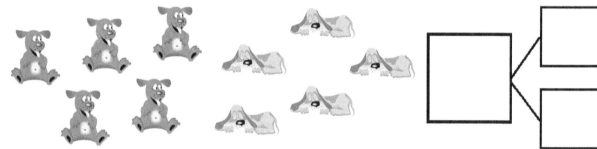

_____ dogs that are awake + _____ sleeping dogs = _____ dogs

3.

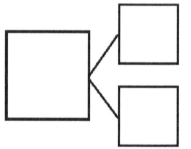

_____ pigs   + _____ pigs in mud = _____ pigs

Lesson 10:   Solve *put together with result unknown* math stories by drawing and
                  using 5-group cards.

EUREKA
MATH™

4. Draw a line from the picture to the matching 5-group cards.

a.
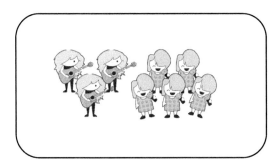 

b.
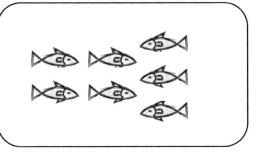 

c.
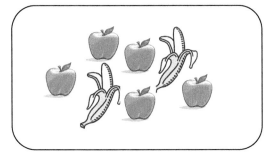 

d.

EUREKA MATH

Lesson 10: Solve *put together with result unknown* math stories by drawing and using 5-group cards.

151

©2015 Great Minds. eureka-math.org
G1-M1-TE-BK1-1.3.1-01.2016

Name _____   Date _____

1. Draw to show the story. There are 3 large balls and 4 small balls.

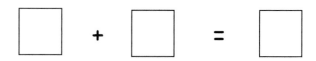

How many balls are there? There are _____ balls.

2. Circle the set of tiles that match your picture.

Lesson 10:   Solve *put together with result unknown* math stories by drawing and
using 5-group cards.

EUREKA
MATH™

Name _____ Date _____

1. Use your 5-group cards to solve.

☐ + ☐ = ☐

Draw the other 5-group card to show what you did.

2. Use your 5-group cards to solve.

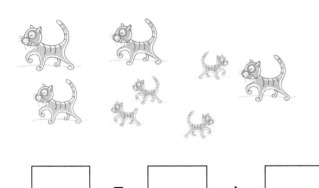

☐ = ☐ + ☐

Draw the other 5-group card to show what you did.

 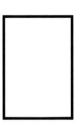

EUREKA MATH™

Lesson 10: Solve *put together with result unknown* math stories by drawing and using 5-group cards.

153

©2015 Great Minds. eureka-math.org
G1-M1-TE-BK1-1.3.1-01.2016

3. There are 4 tall boys and 5 short boys. Draw to show how many boys there are in all.

Write a number bond to match the story.

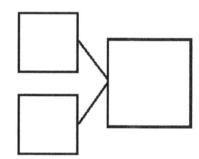

There are _____ boys in all.

Write a number sentence to show what you did.

4. There are 3 girls and 5 boys. Draw to show how many children there are altogether.

Write a number bond to match the story.

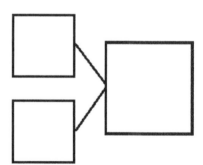

There are _____ children altogether.

Write a number sentence to show what you did.

☐ + ☐ = ☐

Lesson 10: Solve *put together with result unknown* math stories by drawing and using 5-group cards.

EUREKA
MATH™

Target Practice

Target Number:

Choose a *target number* between 6 and 10 and write it in the middle of the circle on the top of the page. Roll a die. Write the number rolled in the circle at the end one of the arrows. Then, make a bull's-eye by writing the number needed to make your target in the other circle.

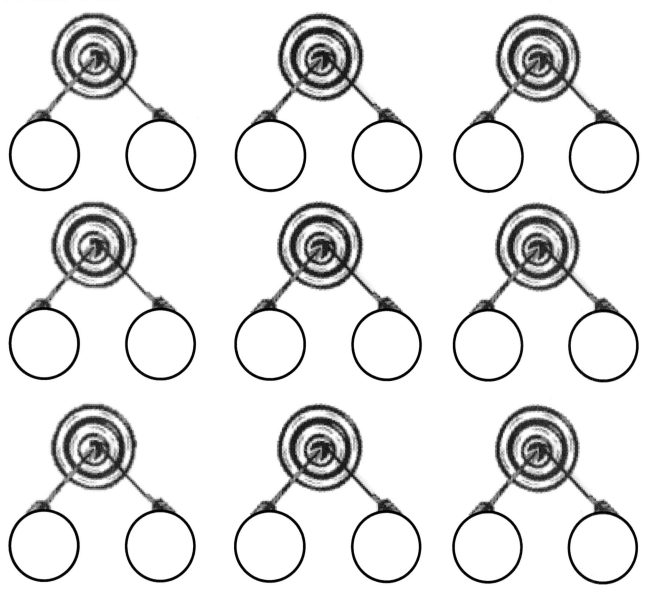

target practice

EUREKA MATH

Lesson 10: Solve *put together with result unknown* math stories by drawing and using 5-group cards.

155

©2015 Great Minds. eureka-math.org
G1-M1-TE-BK1-1.3.1-01.2016

Lesson 11

Objective: Solve *add to with change unknown* math stories as a context for counting on by drawing, writing equations, and making statements of the solution.

Suggested Lesson Structure

■ Fluency Practice	(8 minutes)
■ Application Problem	(5 minutes)
■ Concept Development	(30 minutes)
■ Student Debrief	(17 minutes)
Total Time	**(60 minutes)**

Fluency Practice (8 minutes)

- Count On Cheers: 2 More **1.OA.5**   (3 minutes)
- Number Bond Dash: 6 **1.OA.5**   (5 minutes)

Count On Cheers: 2 More (3 minutes)

Note: This activity supports the connection of counting on by 2 to adding 2.

The teacher says the number aloud. Students repeat the number, touching their heads and counting on as they put their fists in the air, one at a time. Alternately, students can count on with boxing punches.

fiiiive   *six*   *seven*

Number Bond Dash: 6 (5 minutes)

Materials: (T) Stopwatch or timer (S) Number bond dash 6 (Lesson 5 Fluency Template 2), marker to correct work

Note: By using the same system repeatedly, students can focus on the mathematics alone. The activity addresses the core fluency objective for Grade 1 of adding and subtracting within 10.

Follow the procedures for the Number Bond Dash from Lesson 5 Fluency Practice. Tell students to remember how many problems they get correct so they can try to improve their scores tomorrow.

156   Lesson 11:   Solve *add to with change unknown* math stories as a context for counting on by drawing, writing equations, and making statements of the solution.

©2015 Great Minds. eureka-math.org
G1-M1-TE-BK1-1.3.1-01.2016

EUREKA
MATH

Application Problem (5 minutes)

There are 8 children in the afterschool cooking club. How many boys and how many girls might be in the class? Draw a picture and write a number sentence to explain your thinking.

Extension: How many other combinations of boys and girls could be made? Write a number bond for each combination you can think of.

Note: This problem serves as a bridge from the previous lesson's focus on solving *put together* stories. It serves as a context for counting on during the Debrief.

Concept Development (30 minutes)

Materials: (T) Mystery box (shoe box or other box with a question mark on it), counting bears (or another engaging classroom material that lends itself to storytelling), enlarged blank number sentence and number bond (Lesson 6 Template 2), number sentence cards (Template) and 2" × 2" sticky notes labeled with question mark (S) Personal white board; blank number sentence and number bond (Lesson 6 Template 2); yellow colored pencil or a crayon; set of bear counters, paper bag labeled with question marks on the front per pair

Before the lesson, privately place 2 counting bears in a mystery box. Set the box out of sight. Have students bring their personal white boards and sit in a semi-circle. Display 3 counting bears in front of the enlarged number sentence template.

T: Once upon a time, 3 little bears went to play tag in the forest. (Place 3 bear counters on the template on the floor.) Then, some more bears came over. (Place the box with the question mark next to the bears.) In the end, there were 5 little bears playing tag in the woods altogether.

T: How many bears do you think came to play (point to the box)? Turn and talk to a partner. (Circulate and listen to student discussions.)

S: (Discuss.)

T: How many bears joined the group to play tag? (Have students share ideas.) What strategy did you use to decide? (Ask a few students to share varying ideas.) Let's use counting on to test our ideas.

S/T: (Gesture over the 3.) Threeeee, (tap the box while drawing dots below the box for each count) 4, 5.

MP.2

T: How many more bears came to play?

S: 2 bears!

T: Let's find out if we were right. (Open up the box and reveal 2 bears.) You were right! There were 2 more bears that came to play tag. (Close the box and place the 2 bears on top of the box.)

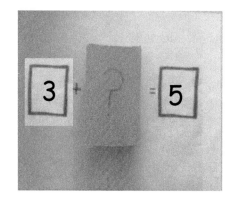

T: Write the number sentence and number bond for the story. (Circulate.)

Lesson 11:   Solve *add to with change unknown* math stories as a context for counting on by drawing, writing equations, and making statements of the solution.

157

S: (Write the number sentence and number bond.)

T: Let's replace our bears with numbers to see our number sentence. (Replace the 3 bears with the number 3 and the 2 bears with the number 2. Add the number 5 after the equal sign as the total.)

Analyze the referents for each number, ensuring that students understand what each number represents in the story. Emphasize the unknown in the number sentence and number bond as being the change.

Repeat this process with a decomposition number sentence such as 9 = 6 + ?. Nine bears were playing tag. At first, there were 6 bears playing. How many more bears joined in?

Provide sets of bears and a paper bag to each pair. Then, distribute one to two number sentence cards with a question mark sticky note covering the second addend. Have students use the bears and the paper bag to tell a story that matches their number sentence card and figure out the mystery number. Circulate and listen to students sharing strategies, solutions, and writing the corresponding number sentence on their templates. Encourage students to talk about what's happening in each story so that they can contextualize the numbers in the action of the story.

NOTES ON MULTIPLE MEANS OF ENGAGEMENT:

The mystery number game that was played in class today would be a good game to send to parents to play at home. This game provides a challenging extension for students to practice counting on to find the missing addend. Let those students who are able to work with larger numbers count on from a two-digit number.

Problem Set (10 minutes)

Students should do their personal best to complete the Problem Set within the allotted 10 minutes. For some classes, it may be appropriate to modify the assignment by specifying which problems they work on first. Some problems do not specify a method for solving. Students solve these problems using the RDW approach used for Application Problems.

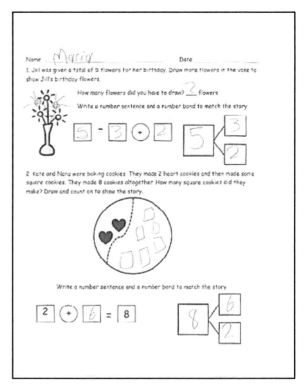

Student Debrief (17 minutes)

Lesson Objective: Solve *add to with change unknown* math stories as a context for counting on by drawing, writing equations, and making statements of the solution.

The Student Debrief is intended to invite reflection and active processing of the total lesson experience.

Invite students to review their solutions for the Problem Set. They should check work by comparing answers with a partner before going over answers as a class. Look for misconceptions or misunderstandings that can be addressed in the Debrief. Guide students in a conversation to debrief the Problem Set and process the lesson.

Lesson 11:   Solve *add to with change unknown* math stories as a context for counting on by drawing, writing equations, and making statements of the solution.
©2015 Great Minds. eureka-math.org
G1-M1-TE-BK1-1.3.1-01.2016

Any combination of the questions below may be used to
lead the discussion. Have students bring their Problem
Sets with a yellow colored pencil or crayon to the meeting
area.

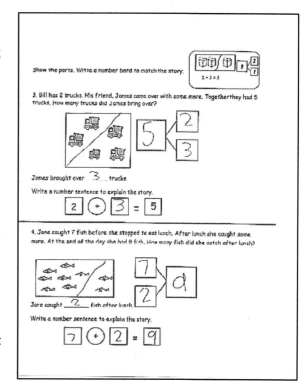

- Look at Problem 1. Where was the mystery
  number in your number sentence? (Have
  students color in the box with a yellow crayon.)
  Repeat the process for the rest of the Problem
  Set.

- What other strategy did you use to solve these
  problems?

- Look at Problem 3. How can you show the
  starting part and the mystery part in the picture?

- How are Problem 1 and Problem 3 different and
  similar?

- How are these number stories different from
  other number stories we've solved?

- (Select student Application Problem samples that
  represent all decompositions of 8.) There are so
  many different answers. Are these all correct?
  How can we figure out if we came up with all of
  the ways to make 8 boys and girls?

- There were 8 boys and girls in our Application Problem, 2 more boys join the cooking club. How can
  we count on to find out how many students are in the club now? How would you change your
  number sentence?

- What if there were still 8 students in the afterschool cooking club, and we knew that there were
  5 boys, but we didn't know how many girls? How can you write that as a new number sentence?

Exit Ticket (3 minutes)

After the Student Debrief, instruct students to complete the Exit Ticket. A review of their work will help with
assessing students' understanding of the concepts that were presented in today's lesson and planning more
effectively for future lessons. The questions may be read aloud to the students.

Name _____   Date _____

1. Jill was given a total of 5 flowers for her birthday. Draw more flowers in the vase to show Jill's birthday flowers.

How many flowers did you have to draw? ____ flowers

Write a number sentence and a number bond to match the story.

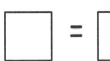 = (+)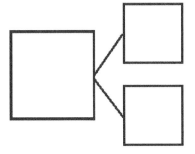

2. Kate and Nana were baking cookies. They made 2 heart cookies and then made some square cookies. They made 8 cookies altogether. How many square cookies did they make? Draw and count on to show the story.

Write a number sentence and a number bond to match the story.

 (+) [ ] = [8]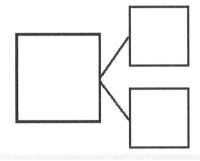

Lesson 11:   Solve *add to with change unknown* math stories as a context for counting on by drawing, writing equations, and making statements of the solution.

EUREKA
MATH

Show the parts. Write a number bond to match the story.

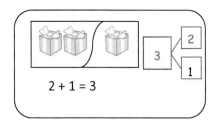

$2 + 1 = 3$

3. Bill has 2 trucks. His friend, James, came over with some more. Together, they had 5 trucks. How many trucks did James bring over?

   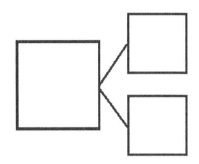

James brought over _____ trucks.

Write a number sentence to explain the story.

$$\boxed{2} \;\bigoplus\; \boxed{} \;=\; \boxed{5}$$

4. Jane caught 7 fish before she stopped to eat lunch. After lunch, she caught some more. At the end of the day, she had 9 fish. How many fish did she catch after lunch?

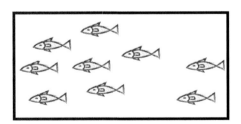   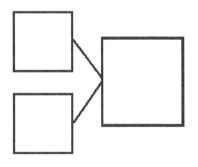

Jane caught _____ fish after lunch.

Write a number sentence to explain the story.

$$\boxed{} \;\bigoplus\; \boxed{} \;=\; \boxed{}$$

Lesson 11:   Solve *add to with change unknown* math stories as a context for counting on by drawing, writing equations, and making statements of the solution.

161

©2015 Great Minds. eureka-math.org
G1-M1-TE-BK1-1.3.1-01.2016

Name _____   Date _____

Draw more bears to show that Jen has 8 bears total.

I added _____ more bears.

Write a number sentence to show how many
bears you drew.

Lesson 11:   Solve *add to with change unknown* math stories as a context for
                    counting on by drawing, writing equations, and making statements of
                    the solution.

©2015 Great Minds. eureka-math.org
G1-M1-TE-BK1-1.3.1-01.2016

EUREKA
MATH

Name _____   Date _____

1. Use the 5-group cards to count on to find the missing number in the number sentences.

a. | 2 | + | | = | 7 |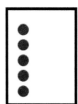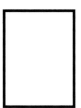

b. | 8 | = | 5 | + | |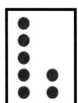

c. | 9 | = | 7 | + | |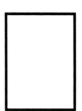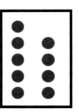

d. | 9 | = | | + | 9 |

EUREKA MATH™

Lesson 11:   Solve *add to with change unknown* math stories as a context for counting on by drawing, writing equations, and making statements of the solution.

©2015 Great Minds. eureka-math.org
G1-M1-TE-BK1-1.3.1-01.2016

163

2. Match the number sentence to the math story. Draw a picture or use your 5-group cards to solve.

a. Scott has 3 cookies. His mom gives him some more. Now, he has 8 cookies. How many cookies did his mom give him?

6 + $?$ = 9

Scott's mom gave him _____ cookies.

3 + $?$ = 8

b. Kim sees 6 birds in the tree.

Some more birds fly in.

Kim sees 9 birds in the tree. How many birds flew to the tree?

4 + $?$ = 8

_____ birds flew to the tree.

Lesson 11: Solve *add to with change unknown* math stories as a context for counting on by drawing, writing equations, and making statements of the solution.

©2015 Great Minds. eureka-math.org
G1-M1-TE-BK1-1.3.1-01.2016

EUREKA MATH

| 3 | + | 2 | = | 5 |

| 7 | + | 1 | = | 8 |

| 6 | + | 1 | = | 7 |

| 4 | + | 2 | = | 6 |

| 6 | = | 5 | + | 1 |

| 10 | = | 7 | + | 3 |

| 8 | = | 6 | + | 2 |

| 7 | = | 5 | + | 2 |

number sentence cards

Lesson 11: Solve *add to with change unknown* math stories as a context for counting on by drawing, writing equations, and making statements of the solution.

©2015 Great Minds. eureka-math.org
G1-M1-TE-BK1-1.3.1-01.2016

Lesson 12

Objective: Solve *add to with change unknown* math stories using 5-group cards.

Suggested Lesson Structure

- ■ Fluency Practice   (15 minutes)
- ▨ Application Problem   (5 minutes)
- ▢ Concept Development   (30 minutes)
- ■ Student Debrief   (10 minutes)

     Total Time   **(60 minutes)**

Fluency Practice (15 minutes)

- Slam: Partners to 6 **1.OA.6**   (10 minutes)
- Number Bond Dash: 6 (Day 2) **1.OA.6**   (5 minutes)

Slam: Partners to 6 (10 minutes)

Materials: (T/S) 5-group cards (Lesson 5 Template 1)

Note: This activity addresses the core fluency objective for Grade 1 of adding and subtracting within 10. In this engaging context, be sure to help students focus on the mathematics of this activity.

Tell students to order cards 0–6 on their desks, beginning with 0. Flash a 5-group card, and instruct students to "slam" the card with the partner to 6 (students carefully slap the card on the table). Tell students to say the partners they found when they hear a snap, beginning with the card they just slammed (5 and 1 make 6). Then, tell them to say it again, beginning with the card that was flashed (1 and 5 make 6). Continue playing until students have found all possible partners to 6. Then, give them time to play the game with partners.

NOTES ON MULTIPLE MEANS FOR ACTION AND EXPRESSION:

When playing games, provide a variety of ways for students to respond. Oral fluency games should be adjusted for students who are deaf or students with hearing impairments. This can be done in many ways, including showing the answer with fingers, using student boards to write answers, or using a visual signal or vibration.

EUREKA MATH™

Number Bond Dash: 6 (5 minutes)

Materials: (T) Stopwatch or timer (S) Number bond dash 6 (Lesson 5 Fluency Template 2), marker to correct work

Note: By using the same system repeatedly, students can focus on the mathematics alone. The activity addresses the core fluency objective for Grade 1 of adding and subtracting within 10.

Follow the procedure for the Number Bond Dash from Lesson 5 Fluency Practice. Remember that today is the second day with making 6. Students should recall their scores from the previous lesson to celebrate improvement.

Application Problem (5 minutes)

Tanya has 7 books on her shelf. She borrowed some books from the library, and now there are 9 books on her shelf. How many books did she get at the library? Explain your thinking in pictures, words, or with a number sentence. Draw a box around the mystery number in your number sentence.

Note: This problem is designed both as a bridge and a lead-up in that it focuses students on solving a *change unknown* problem. Students come back to the problem in the Debrief, applying the use of 5-group cards as another resource for problem solving as they count on to solve.

Concept Development (30 minutes)

Materials: (T) Mystery box (Lesson 11), counting bears (or another engaging classroom material that allows for story telling), enlarged blank number sentence and number bond (Lesson 6 Template 2)
(S) Personal white board, blank number sentence and number bond (Lesson 6 Template 2), 5-group cards including blank (Lesson 5 Template 1), number sentence cards (Lesson 11 Template) with sticky notes labeled with question marks per pair

Before the lesson, privately place 3 counting bears in the mystery box. Have students sit in a semi-circle with their 5-group cards and number sentence template.

- T: Use the number side of your 5-group cards to help me solve a story. Once upon a time, 5 little bears came out of hibernation. (Place 5 bear counters above the first addend space on the teacher number sentence template.)
- S: (Place the numeral 5 card on number sentence.)
- T: Then, some more bears came out of hibernation. (Bring out mystery box.)
- T: What should we do in our number sentence here? Turn and talk to your partner and show it on your number sentence.
- S: (Discuss. Acceptable responses are leaving the second square blank or inserting a question mark.)
- T: Here's a blank card for everyone. (Distribute a blank card.) Place it in your number sentence to show that this part is a mystery.

Lesson 12:   Solve *add to with change unknown* math stories using 5-group cards.

167

T: At the end, there were 8 little bears out of hibernation. Where should we show that number of bears in our number sentence? (Give students time to discuss and place the 8 card in the final box. Then, place the numeral 8 in the teacher equation template.)

T: How can we use the 5-group cards to figure out how many more bears came out of hibernation? With your partner, use your cards to show how many bears are in the box. (Circulate.)

S: (Discuss and solve. For example, students may turn the 8 over to the dot side, gesture to the five and count on, "Fiiiive, 6, 7, 8.")

T: How many bears joined the group?

S: (Share ideas.)

T: How did you use your 5-group cards to figure this out? (Ask students with cards dot side up to demonstrate. Some students may use the cards to check their solution by creating the number sentence 5 + 3 = 8 with the numeral cards and then flipping the 3 to the dot side to count on.)

T: Let's count on as we point to each dot.

S/T: Fiiiiive, 6, 7, 8.

T: How many more bears came out of hibernation?

S: 3 bears!

T: Let's open the box and see how many more bears came out of hibernation! Write the number sentence using the 5-group cards in front of you to help.

Explain to the students that this type of a story problem is a *mystery change* problem since the change that results in the total is a mystery (the unknown).

T: (Show 4 + ? = 7.) This time, I want you to think of a mystery change story with your partner. Try to solve the mystery using your 5-group cards.

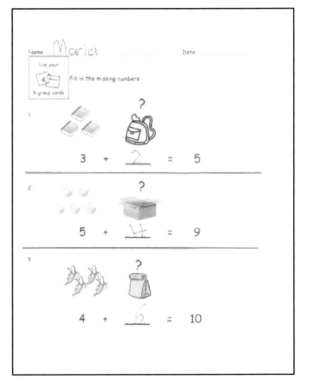

Choose a number sentence card with a sticky note covering the second addend, such as 9 = 5 + ?. Have the students create a mystery change story to go with the number sentence. When the students are ready to work more independently, give partners two or three number sentence cards with sticky notes already covering the second addend to continue telling stories and solving.

Problem Set (10 minutes)

Students should do their personal best to complete the Problem Set within the allotted 10 minutes. For some classes, it may be appropriate to modify the assignment by specifying which problems they work on first. Some problems do not specify a method for solving. Students solve these problems using the RDW approach used for Application Problems.

Student Debrief (10 minutes)

Lesson Objective: Solve *add to with change unknown* math stories using 5-group cards.

The Student Debrief is intended to invite reflection and active processing of the total lesson experience.

Invite students to review their solutions for the Problem Set. They should check work by comparing answers with a partner before going over answers as a class. Look for misconceptions or misunderstandings that can be addressed in the Debrief. Guide students in a conversation to debrief the Problem Set and process the lesson.

Any combination of the questions below may be used to lead the discussion.

- How did the 5-group cards help you with today's work?

- Were some problems faster to solve than others? Why? Share an example.

- Compare the different strategies we used yesterday and today. Which strategy was easier for you, and why?

- How are Problem 3 and Problem 5 different? How are they the same?

- Look at your Application Problem. How can you use 5-group cards to solve this problem?

- Share with your partner an "I can…" statement, based on something you can now do on your own. For example, "I can make up mystery change problems and write number sentences with sticky notes," or "I can use 5-group cards to help me solve mystery change problems."

Exit Ticket (3 minutes)

After the Student Debrief, instruct students to complete the Exit Ticket. A review of their work will help with assessing students' understanding of the concepts that were presented in today's lesson and planning more effectively for future lessons. The questions may be read aloud to the students.

Name _____   Date _____

Use your

5-group cards

Fill in the missing numbers.

1.

   ?

3 + ____ = 5

2.

   ?

5 + ____ = 9

3.

   ?

4 + ____ = 10

Lesson 12:   Solve *add to with change unknown* math stories using 5-group cards.

EUREKA
MATH™

4. Kate and Bob had 6 balls at the park. Kate had 2 of the balls.

How many balls did Bob have?

_____ balls   **=**   _____ balls   **+**   _____ balls

Bob had _____ balls at the park.

_____

5. I had 3 apples. My mom gave me some more. Then, I had 10 apples.

How many apples did my mom give me?

_____ apples   **+**   _____ apples   **=**   _____ apples

Mom gave me _____ apples.

Name _____   Date _____

Draw a picture, and count on to solve the math story.

Bob caught 5 fish. John caught some more fish. They had 7 fish in all. How many fish did John catch?

Write a number sentence to match your picture.

⬜ **+** ⬜ **=** ⬜

John caught _____ fish.

Lesson 12:   Solve *add to with change unknown* math stories using 5-group cards.

EUREKA
MATH™

Name _____   Date _____

 Use your 5-group cards to count on to find the missing number in the number sentences.

1. | 5 | + | ? | = | 7 |

The mystery number is [ ]

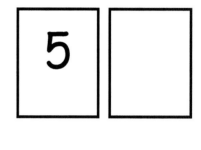

| 5 | |

2. | 2 | + | ? | = | 8 |

The mystery number is [ ]

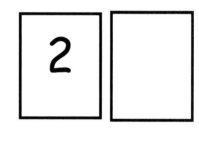

| 2 | |

3. | 6 | + | ? | = | 9 |

The mystery number is [ ]

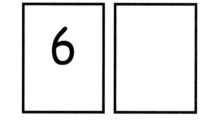

| 6 | |

Use your 5-group cards to count on and solve the math stories. Use the boxes to show your 5-group cards.

4. Jack reads 4 books on Monday. He reads some more on Tuesday. He reads 7 books total. How many books does Jack read on Tuesday?

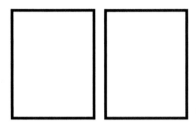

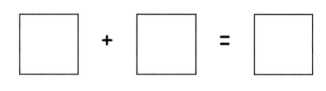

Jack reads _____ books on Tuesday.

5. Kate has 1 sister and some brothers. She has 7 brothers and sisters in all. How many brothers does Kate have?

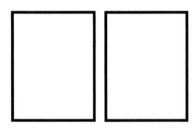

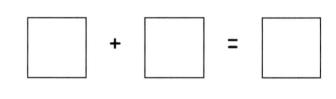

Kate has _____ brothers.

6. There are 6 dogs in the park and some cats. There are 9 dogs and cats in the park altogether. How many cats are in the park?

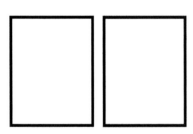

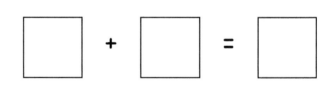

There are _____ cats total.

Lesson 12: Solve *add to with change unknown* math stories using 5-group cards.

EUREKA MATH

Lesson 13

Objective: Tell *put together with result unknown, add to with result unknown,* and *add to with change unknown* stories from equations.

Suggested Lesson Structure

■ Fluency Practice   (20 minutes)
■ Application Problem   (5 minutes)
□ Concept Development   (27 minutes)
■ Student Debrief   (8 minutes)

   Total Time   **(60 minutes)**

Fluency Practice (20 minutes)

- Count by Tens **1.NBT.2**   (5 minutes)
- Ten and Tuck **1.OA.6**, **1.OA.3**   (5 minutes)
- Memory: Partners to 10 **1.OA.6**   (10 minutes)

Count by Tens (5 minutes)

Materials: (T) 5-group cards (Lesson 5 Template 1)

Note: Providing students with ongoing counting practice throughout the year builds and maintains their counting skills, which are foundational for later Grade 1 work with adding and subtracting tens.

Use the tens from your 5-group cards as a visual while students count by tens, first the regular way and then the Say Ten Way.

Next, show students a 3 card and add 10 cards to count on by tens the Say Ten Way, starting at three (three, ten 3, 2 tens 3, 3 tens 3…).

Repeat, starting at various numbers between 1 and 9.

Ten and Tuck (5 minutes)

Note: This activity addresses the core fluency objective for Grade 1.

Tell students to show 10 fingers. Instruct them to tuck 3 (students put down the pinky, ring finger, and middle finger on their right hands). Ask them how many fingers are up (7) and how many are tucked (3). Then, ask them to say the number sentence aloud, beginning with the larger part (7 + 3 = 10), beginning with the smaller part (3 + 7 = 10), and beginning with the whole (10 = 3 + 7 or 10 = 7 + 3).

Lesson 13:   Tell *put together with result unknown, add to with result unknown*
                   add to with change unknown stories from equations.   **175**

©2015 Great Minds. eureka-math.org
G1-M1-TE-BK1-1.3.1-01.2016

Memory: Partners to 10 (10 minutes)

Materials: (S) Per group: 1 set of single-sided 5-group cards, 1 set single-sided numeral cards (Lesson 5 Template 1, single-sided)

Note: This activity addresses the core fluency objective for Grade 1 of adding and subtracting within 10.

Give Partner A a set of single-sided 5-group cards and Partner B a set of single-sided numeral cards. Tell students to sit facing each other and line up their cards in front of them, face down. Instruct students to take turns flipping over one of their cards and one of their partner's cards to try to make a ten. When they make a ten, they place the cards in a separate pile and keep them until the end of the game. The player with the most cards at the end of the game wins.

Application Problem (5 minutes)

Sammi had 6 bunnies. One of them had babies. Now, she has 10 bunnies. How many babies were born? Draw a picture to show how you know. Write a number bond and a number sentence to match your picture.

Note: This problem is designed both as a bridge and a lead-up, in that it focuses students on solving a *change unknown* problem.

Concept Development (27 minutes)

Materials: (S) Number sentence cards (Lesson 11 Template) with sticky notes labeled with a question mark per pair, personal white board, blank number sentence and number bond (Lesson 6 Template 2)

T: (Project 5 + 1 = 6 number sentence card with the 6 covered with a sticky note.) What do we need to find in this number sentence?

S: The total!

T: With your partner, make up a math story using this number sentence. As you make up the story, draw a picture to help you solve for the number that hides under the question mark.

S: (Make up math stories and illustrate.)

T: (Choose two or three pairs to share their stories. After each pair tells the story, invite the class to say the answer and the number sentence. Emphasize the importance of naming the unit: 5 lions + 1 lion = 6 lions.)

> **NOTES ON MULTIPLE MEANS OF REPRESENTATION:**
>
> When asking students to draw an object, check for understanding that they know what it is. If needed, provide a picture of the object for English language learners. At the same time, remind your students they are always to do *math drawings* and not spend time on their illustrations.

> **NOTES ON MULTIPLE MEANS OF REPRESENTATION:**
>
> Never underestimate the use of manipulatives when students are learning a new skill. Students should use their 5-group cards or other manipulatives, such as counting bears, when they need extra support. Allow students to use the extra support as long as they need it.

Lesson 13:   Tell *put together with result unknown, add to with result unknown add to with change unknown* stories from equations.

T: (Project 6 + 2 = 8 number sentence card with the 2 covered with a sticky note.) What do we need to find in this number sentence?

S: The missing part! It's like finding what's in the mystery box.

Repeat the earlier sequence to allow students to share and solve their *change unknown* story problems.

Distribute a set of number sentence cards to each pair of students and assign each student to be A or B.

MP.6

T: You and your partner will take turns being math storytellers. Partners will each pick their own number sentence card and make it special by placing a sticky note either on the total or on the second part of the number sentence. (Model the two different types as they are being presented.) Then, come up with a story that matches your number sentence creation. Tell your partner your story as you show your number sentence. The partner will have to draw a math picture to show what is happening in the story and to solve the problem.

S: (Participate in creating their own math story problems and take turns solving the partner's problem by drawing a picture.)

Problem Set (12 minutes)

Distribute the Problem Set and allow students to work independently or in small groups. While students are working, the teacher circulates and listens. Some students may need encouragement to vary between *add to* and *put together* stories.

Students should do their personal best to complete the Problem Set within the allotted 12 minutes. For some classes, it may be appropriate to modify the assignment by specifying which problems they work on first. Some problems do not specify a method for solving. Students solve these problems using the RDW approach used for Application Problems.

Student Debrief (8 minutes)

Lesson Objective: Tell *put together with result unknown, add to with result unknown,* and *add to with change unknown* stories from equations.

The Student Debrief is intended to invite reflection and active processing of the total lesson experience.

Invite students to review their solutions for the Problem Set. They should check work by comparing answers with a partner before going over answers as a class. Look for misconceptions or misunderstandings that can be addressed in the Debrief. Guide students in a conversation to debrief the Problem Set and process the lesson.

EUREKA MATH™

Lesson 13: Tell *put together with result unknown, add to with result unknown add to with change unknown* stories from equations.

177

©2015 Great Minds. eureka-math.org
G1-M1-TE-BK1-1.3.1-01.2016

Any combination of the questions below may be used to lead the discussion.

- Which two problems from your Problem Set did you think were similar? Why?
- Which two problems from your Problem Set did you think were different? Why?
- Which of your stories was the most difficult for you to make? Which story was the easiest for you? Why?
- (Project a sample of a student Application Problem on the board.)   Which problem was our Application Problem similar to? In what way(s) are they similar?

Exit Ticket (3 minutes)

After the Student Debrief, instruct students to complete the Exit Ticket. A review of their work will help with assessing students' understanding of the concepts that were presented in today's lesson and planning more effectively for future lessons. The questions may be read aloud to the students.

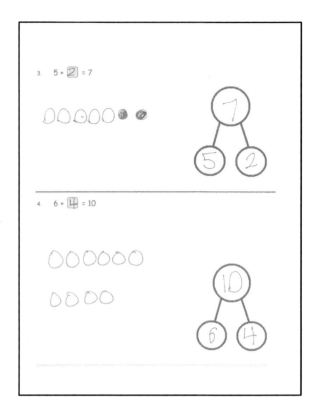

Lesson 13:   Tell *put together with result unknown, add to with result unknown*
                                add to with change unknown stories from equations.

©2015 Great Minds. eureka-math.org
G1-M1-TE-BK1-1.3.1-01.2016

EUREKA
MATH™

Name _____ Date _____

With a partner, create a story for each of the number sentences below. Draw a picture to show. Write the number bond to match the story.

1.   6 + 2 = ☐

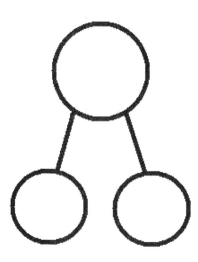

_____

2.   5 + 5 = ☐

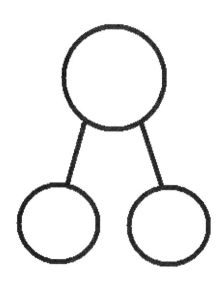

EUREKA
MATH™

Lesson 13:   Tell *put together with result unknown, add to with result unknown add to with change unknown* stories from equations.

179

©2015 Great Minds. eureka-math.org
G1-M1-TE-BK1-1.3.1-01.2016

3. $5 + \boxed{} = 7$

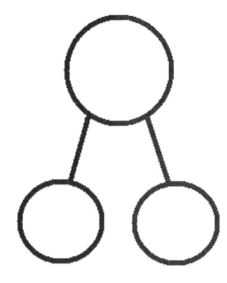

4. $6 + \boxed{} = 10$

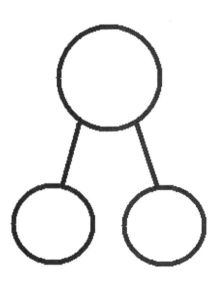

Lesson 13:   Tell *put together with result unknown, add to with result unknown*
                add to with change unknown stories from equations.

EUREKA
MATH™

©2015 Great Minds. eureka-math.org
G1-M1-TE-BK1-1.3.1-01.2016

Name _____   Date _____

Tell a math story for each number sentence by drawing a picture.

1.   5 + 1 = 6

2.   3 + ? = 8

EUREKA MATH™

Lesson 13:   Tell *put together with result unknown, add to with result unknown add to with change unknown* stories from equations.

©2015 Great Minds. eureka-math.org
G1-M1-TE-BK1-1.3.1-01.2016

181

Name _____   Date _____

Use the number sentences to draw a picture, and fill in the number bond to tell a math story.

1.   5 + 2 = 7

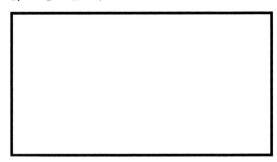 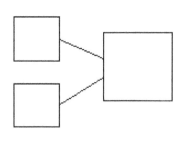

2.   3 + 6 = 9

 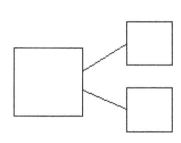

3.   7 + ? = 9

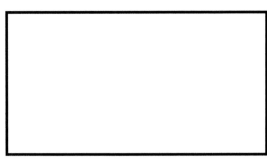 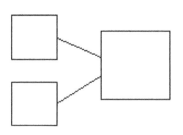

Lesson 13:   Tell *put together with result unknown, add to with result unknown add to with change unknown* stories from equations.

©2015 Great Minds. eureka-math.org
G1-M1-TE-BK1-1.3.1-01.2016

EUREKA
MATH

Mathematics Curriculum

Topic D
Strategies for Counting On

1.OA.5, 1.OA.8, 1.OA.6

Focus Standard:	1.OA.5	Relate counting to addition and subtraction (e.g., by counting on 2 to add 2).
	1.OA.8	Determine the unknown whole number in an addition or subtraction equation relating three whole numbers. *For example, determine the unknown number that makes the equation true in each of the equations 8 + ? = 11, 5 = ☐ − 3, 6 + 6 = ☐.*
Instructional Days:	3	
Coherence -Links from:	GK–M4	Number Pairs, Addition and Subtraction to 10
-Links to:	G2–M4	Addition and Subtraction Within 200 with Word Problems to 100

Topic D affords students the opportunity to solve problems within the simplicity of equations, moving on from the context of story problems. Continuing on the momentum gained with counting on as it relates to addition in Topic C, students begin Topic D with tracking the number of counts on from a given number by using their fingers and 5-group cards (**1.OA.5**).

In Lessons 14 and 15, students begin with an embedded quantity represented by both a picture and a numeral, and then tap pictures, tap the dots on their 5-group cards, draw more, and, finally, replace these pictorial strategies to extending their fingers as an effective strategy for keeping track of the change. They apply these strategies to track changes of 0, 1, 2, and 3, thus limiting their use of tracking to quantities that will maintain efficiency. Students use these same strategies in Lesson 16, in both *result unknown* and the more complex *change unknown* equations, solving problems such as 4 + ___ = 7 as they say, "5, 6, 7" (**1.OA.8**).

A Teaching Sequence Toward Mastery of Strategies for Counting On
Objective 1: **Count on up to 3 more using numeral and 5-group cards and fingers to track the change.** **(Lessons 14–15)**
Objective 2: **Count on to find the unknown part in missing addend equations such as 6 + __ = 9. Answer, "How many more to make 6, 7, 8, 9, and 10?"** **(Lesson 16)**

Lesson 14

Objective: Count on up to 3 more using numeral and 5-group cards and fingers to track the change.

Suggested Lesson Structure

- ■ Fluency Practice   (11 minutes)
- ▨ Application Problem   (4 minutes)
- ☐ Concept Development   (30 minutes)
- ■ Student Debrief   (15 minutes)

  Total Time   **(60 minutes)**

Fluency Practice (11 minutes)

- Skip-Counting Squats: Forward and Back to 20 **1.OA.5**   (2 minutes)
- Count On Cheers: 2 More **1.OA.5**   (3 minutes)
- Missing Part: Make 10 **1.OA.6**   (6 minutes)

Skip-Counting Squats: Forward and Back to 20 (2 minutes)

Note: This activity supports the connection of counting on by 2 to adding 2 and counting back by 2 to subtracting 2.

Have students count from 0 to 20 and back two times, squatting down and touching the floor on odd numbers and standing up for even numbers.

- ■ For the first count, instruct students to whisper when they squat and talk normally when they stand.
- ■ On the second count, encourage students to try to think of the numbers in their heads when they squat and whisper when they stand.

Count On Cheers: 2 More (3 minutes)

Note: This activity supports the connection of counting on by 2 and adding 2 with counting back by 2 and subtracting 2.

The teacher says a number aloud. Students repeat the number, touching their heads and counting on as they put their fists in the air, one at a time. Alternately, students can count on with boxing punches. Extend the game by counting back 2.

fiiiive   *six*   *seven*

Lesson 14:   Count on up to 3 more using numeral and 5-group cards and fingers to track the change.

©2015 Great Minds. eureka-math.org
G1-M1-TE-BK1-1.3.1-01.2016

Missing Part: Make 10 (6 minutes)

Materials: (S) 5-group cards (Lesson 5 Template 1)

Note: This activity addresses the core fluency objective for Grade 1 of adding and subtracting within 10.

Students work with a partner, using 5-group cards. Each student puts a card on his or her forehead. The partner tells how many more to make 10. Students must guess the cards on their foreheads. Partners can play simultaneously, each putting a card on his or her forehead. If appropriate, remind students that they may use their fingers to help.

Application Problem (4 minutes)

Beth went apple picking. She picked 7 apples and put them in her basket. Two more apples fell out of the tree right into her basket! How many apples does she have in her basket now? Draw a math picture and write a number bond and number sentence to match the story.

Note: This serves as a bridge from the *change unknown* stories of the previous topic into the Concept Development of this lesson, which focuses on strategies for counting on.

Concept Development (30 minutes)

Materials: (T) Pictures of crayons and hot dogs (Template) (S) 5-group cards (Lesson 5 Template 1), personal white board

- T: Today, let's try some of those same great strategies to help us solve missing numbers in math sentences. What are some of the ways we figured out the mystery number in our bear stories? Turn and talk with a partner.
- T: (Give time for partner sharing. Then, call on students to share strategies such as counting on, using 5-group cards, and drawing.)
- T: Let's use those strategies with this situation. (Project a picture of a box of crayons labeled 4 on the outside and 2 more crayons.) Look at this picture. How many crayons are outside of the box?
- S: 2.
- T: Let's use our fingers to keep track of these. As I point, put out your fingers to follow along.
- S/T: (Touch crayons on the projection.) Oooneeee (put out one finger), 2 (put out another finger).
- T: How many fingers do you have out?
- S: 2.

NOTES ON
MULTIPLE MEANS
OF REPRESENTATION:

As the class is counting, support those students who may need visual or auditory help. Using physical cues such as body movements (pointing, nodding the head, eye blinking, or foot tapping helps students who need visual help). Using auditory cues such as a snap, clap, or stomp helps those students who need auditory support.

EUREKA MATH™

T: Those 2 fingers match these 2 crayons.

T: Let's count on to find out how many crayons are in the picture. We'll start with the box first. Use your fingers and count with me.

S/T: Fourrrrr (gesture to box), 5, 6. (Put out fingers while counting.)

T: How many crayons are there altogether?

S: 6 crayons!

T: Take out your 5-group cards and build the number sentence using the numeral side.

S: (Share number sentences such as, 4 + 2 = 6, 2 + 4 = 6, 6 = 4 + 2, or 6 = 2 + 4.)

T: Turn over your 2 to show the dot side. We will use the 5-group cards to check our solution.

S/T: Fourrrr (touch 4), 5, 6. (Touch dots while counting.)

T: What is the total when we use the cards?

MP.7

S: 6.

T: What is the total when we counted the crayons with our fingers?

S: 6 crayons!

T: Great job! Let's try another. (Repeat the process with a picture of a package of 6 hot dogs and 2 more hot dogs.)

T: Turn and talk with your partner about the two strategies we just used. How are they similar?

S: When we count on using our fingers, it's just like when we touch the dots. Each finger is like a dot.

T: (Project the following number sentence on the board: 4 + 3 = □.) Let's try to solve one more with a partner. Talk quietly with your partner to decide what number belongs in the box. Remember that you can count on using your fingers or your 5-group cards to help you.

Problem Set (10 minutes)

Students should do their personal best to complete the Problem Set within the allotted 10 minutes. For some classes, it may be appropriate to modify the assignment by specifying which problems they work on first. Some problems do not specify a method for solving. Students solve these problems using the RDW approach used for Application Problems.

NOTES ON MULTIPLE MEANS OF ACTION AND EXPRESSION:

When students are having difficulty counting on with fingers or 5-group cards, continue with more examples together. Some students need to move forward in small steps. Regular opportunities to practice what they are learning will eventually get them to abstract-level thinking.

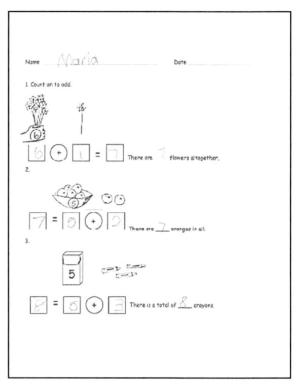

Lesson 14: Count on up to 3 more using numeral and 5-group cards and fingers to track the change.

©2015 Great Minds. eureka-math.org
G1-M1-TE-BK1-1.3.1-01.2016

Student Debrief (15 minutes)

Lesson Objective: Count on up to 3 more using numeral and 5-group cards and fingers to track the change.

The Student Debrief is intended to invite reflection and active processing of the total lesson experience.

Invite students to review their solutions for the Problem Set. They should check work by comparing answers with a partner before going over answers as a class. Look for misconceptions or misunderstandings that can be addressed in the Debrief. Guide students in a conversation to debrief the Problem Set and process the lesson.

Any combination of the questions below may be used to lead the discussion.

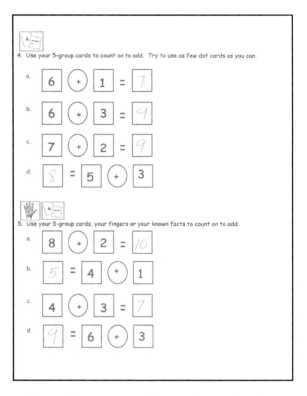

- For which problems did you need to add 1? Let's list those number sentences.

- What do you notice about these problems? Is there a pattern you can find?

- Look at the first three problems. What do you notice about what we are adding each time? Why might we be only counting on 1, 2, or 3 more with our fingers?

- Are there any problems that have the same total? Let's list those number sentences.

- How can the totals be the same if we counted on different amounts?

Exit Ticket (3 minutes)

After the Student Debrief, instruct students to complete the Exit Ticket. A review of their work will help you assess the students' understanding of the concepts that were presented in the lesson today and plan more effectively for future lessons. You may read the questions aloud to the students.

EUREKA MATH™

Lesson 14:   Count on up to 3 more using numeral and 5-group cards and fingers to track the change.

187

©2015 Great Minds. eureka-math.org
G1-M1-TE-BK1-1.3.1-01.2016

Name _____   Date _____

1. Count on to add.

□ ⊕ □ = □   There are _____ flowers altogether.

2.

□ = □ ⊕ □   There are _____ oranges in all.

3.

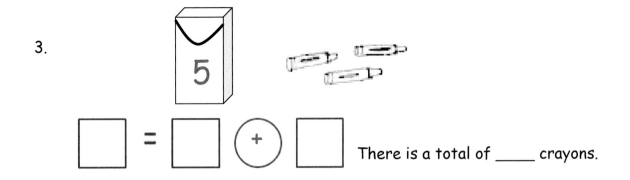

□ = □ ⊕ □   There is a total of _____ crayons.

Lesson 14:   Count on up to 3 more using numeral and 5-group cards and fingers to track the change.

EUREKA
MATH™

4. Use your 5-group cards to count on to add. Try to use as few dot cards as you can.

a. 6 (+) 1 = ☐

b. 6 (+) 3 = ☐

c. 7 (+) 2 = ☐

d. ☐ = 5 (+) 3

5. Use your 5-group cards, your fingers, or your known facts to count on to add.

a. 8 (+) 2 = ☐

b. ☐ = 4 (+) 1

c. 4 (+) 3 = ☐

d. ☐ = 6 (+) 3

EUREKA MATH

Lesson 14: Count on up to 3 more using numeral and 5-group cards and fingers to track the change.

189

©2015 Great Minds. eureka-math.org
G1-M1-TE-BK1-1.3.1-01.2016

Name _____   Date _____

1.

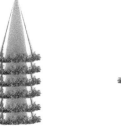

6

6 + 2 = $\boxed{}$

I counted _____ hats in all.

2. Count on to solve the number sentences.

a.

7 + 3 = $\boxed{}$

b.

8 + 2 = $\boxed{}$

Lesson 14:   Count on up to 3 more using numeral and 5-group cards and fingers
to track the change.

EUREKA
MATH

Name _____   Date _____

Count on to add.

a.

5 (+) 1 = ☐

Write what you say
when you count on.

b.

5 (+) 2 = ☐

c.

7 (+) 2 = ☐

d.

☐ = 6 (+) 3

e.

☐ = 7 (+) ☐

EUREKA
MATH™

Lesson 14:   Count on up to 3 more using numeral and 5-group cards and fingers
to track the change.

191

pictures of crayons and hot dogs

Lesson 14: Count on up to 3 more using numeral and 5-group cards and fingers to track the change.

Lesson 15

Objective: Count on up to 3 more using numeral and 5-group cards and fingers to track the change.

Suggested Lesson Structure

■ Fluency Practice   (15 minutes)
■ Application Problem   (5 minutes)
□ Concept Development   (25 minutes)
■ Student Debrief   (15 minutes)

Total Time   **(60 minutes)**

Fluency Practice (15 minutes)

- Happy Counting the Say Ten Way **1.OA.5**   (2 minutes)
- Sprint: Count On **1.OA.5**   (13 minutes)

Happy Counting the Say Ten Way (2 minutes)

Note: Providing students with ongoing counting practice throughout the year builds and maintains their counting skills, which are foundational for later first grade work with adding and subtracting tens.

Repeat the Happy Counting activity from Lesson 3 Fluency Practice, counting by tens the Say Ten Way. First, count from 0 to 50 and back. Then, count from 7 to 77 and back.

Sprint: Count On (13 minutes)

Materials: (S) Count On Sprint

Note: This activity provides continued practice relating counting to addition.

Application Problem (5 minutes)

Joshua and Rebecca were eating raisins. Joshua had 7 raisins and took 2 more from the box. Rebecca had 9 raisins and took 2 more from the box. Who had a greater number of raisins, Joshua or Rebecca? Draw math drawings and write number bonds or number sentences to show how you know.

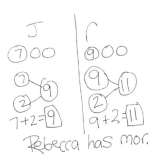

 Lesson 15:   Count on up to 3 more using numeral and 5-group cards and fingers   193
to track the change.

©2015 Great Minds. eureka-math.org
G1-M1-TE-BK1-1.3.1-01.2016

Note: This problem provides a bridge from the previous day's lesson to today's as students solve problems using the Level 2 strategy of counting on.

Concept Development (25 minutes)

Materials: (S) 5-group cards (Lesson 5 Template 1), number sentence cards (Lesson 11 Template) per pair with sticky note covering the total, personal white board

T: Today, let's use our strategies for counting on to play the partner game Count On! We will need to use counting on with our fingers and counting with 5-group cards to play.

T: (Write 6 + 3 = ☐ on the board.) Show how we use counting on with our fingers to solve this.

S: Siiiix, 7, 8, 9. (Extend fingers as they count on.)

T: Show how to use our 5-group cards to solve this.

S: Siiiix, 7, 8, 9. (Put out 5-group cards with 6 on numeral side and 3 on dot side. Touch as they count.)

T: Why did each strategy get to the same answer?

S: Both are ways to keep track of the part we are counting on.

T: This is a type of a *shortcut*. It is a fast or efficient strategy. Today, you will work with a partner to practice using these shortcuts, or strategies, to play Count On!

T: Here are the directions:

1.   Partners A and B, lay all of the number sentence cards in front of you.

2.   Partner A, you touch the card you want to take.

3.   Count on or use the 5-group cards to solve for the total under the sticky note.

4.   When you do, your partner lifts the sticky. If you are right, your partner says, "Go ahead and take it!"

5.   Partner B takes a turn. Continue until all the cards are taken.

S: (Play Count On!)

T: (Circulate, listen, and observe, providing support as necessary.)

NOTES ON
MULTIPLE MEANS
OF REPRESENTATION:

Reading aloud word problems facilitates problem solving for those students who have difficulty reading the text. Hearing the word problem also helps students who are auditory learners.

NOTES ON
MULTIPLE MEANS
OF ENGAGEMENT:

For students who are ready, alter the number sentence cards to include more challenging numbers. For example, 23 + 2 = ? may be more appropriate for some students, as they track the change.

NOTES ON
MULTIPLE MEANS
OF ACTION AND
EXPRESSION:

When a skill is not automatic, provide support so students can practice and refine their skill. Repeated practice with 5-group cards and fingers helps students develop automaticity of their addition facts.

Lesson 15:   Count on up to 3 more using numeral and 5-group cards and fingers to track the change.

Problem Set (10 minutes)

Students should do their personal best to complete the Problem Set within the allotted 10 minutes. For some classes, it may be appropriate to modify the assignment by specifying which problems they work on first. Some problems do not specify a method for solving. Students solve these problems using the RDW approach used for Application Problems.

Review the term *shortcut* with students, if necessary, explaining that this is simply a fast or efficient strategy. If the second page seems overwhelming for students, have them fold the paper in half. This way, they only see seven number sentences at a time.

Student Debrief (15 minutes)

Lesson Objective: Count on up to 3 more using numeral and 5-group cards and fingers to track the change.

The Student Debrief is intended to invite reflection and active processing of the total lesson experience.

Invite students to review their solutions for the Problem Set. They should check work by comparing answers with a partner before going over answers as a class. Look for misconceptions or misunderstandings that can be addressed in the Debrief. Guide students in a conversation to debrief the Problem Set and process the lesson.

Any combination of the questions below may be used to lead the discussion.

- How are Problems 1(a) and 1(b) similar? How are they different? Can one of these help you solve the other? How?

- What shortcuts did you find to add when completing Page 2 of the Problem Set? Explain your thinking.

- How do shortcuts or strategies help us?

- Look at 7 + 1 and 6 + 2. Why is the total the same? How does counting on 1 relate to counting on 2?

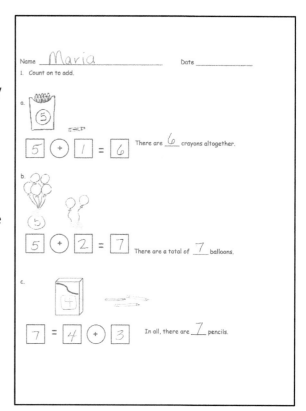

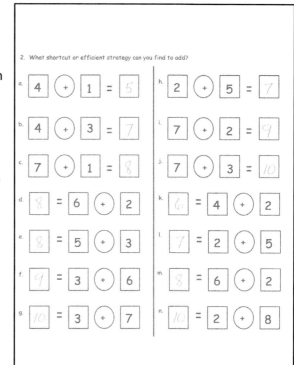

EUREKA MATH™

Lesson 15: Count on up to 3 more using numeral and 5-group cards and fingers to track the change.

195

©2015 Great Minds. eureka-math.org
G1-M1-TE-BK1-1.3.1-01.2016

- Which method do you prefer to use to keep track when you are counting on? Demonstrate what you do, using a number sentence from the Problem Set.

- Is there another way to solve these problems besides counting on? (Visualizing, knowing related facts, just knowing the fact, etc.)

Exit Ticket (3 minutes)

After the Student Debrief, instruct students to complete the Exit Ticket. A review of their work will help with assessing students' understanding of the concepts that were presented in today's lesson and planning more effectively for future lessons. The questions may be read aloud to the students.

Lesson 15: Count on up to 3 more using numeral and 5-group cards and fingers to track the change.

©2015 Great Minds. eureka-math.org
G1-M1-TE-BK1-1.3.1-01.2016

Number Correct:

A

Name _____   Date _____

*Count on to add. Write the number.

1.	1 + 1		16.	4 + 3	
2.	2 + 1		17.	5 + 3	
3.	3 + 1		18.	7 + 3	
4.	3 + 2		19.	7 + 2	
5.	1 + 2		20.	8 + 2	
6.	2 + 2		21.	6 + 2	
7.	2 + 3		22.	6 + 1	
8.	2 + 1		23.	6 + 1	
9.	2 + 2		24.	6 + 2	
10.	3 + 2		25.	7 + 2	
11.	5 + 2		26.	8 + 2	
12.	8 + 2		27.	2 + 8	
13.	8 + 1		28.	2 + 6	
14.	7 + 1		29.	3 + 6	
15.	9 + 1		30.	4 + 5	

EUREKA MATH™

Lesson 15:   Count on up to 3 more using numeral and 5-group cards and fingers to track the change.

197

B

Name _____   Date _____

Number Correct: ⬛

*Count on to add. Write the number.

1.	1 + 1		16.	4 + 2	
2.	2 + 2		17.	3 + 2	
3.	3 + 2		18.	5 + 2	
4.	2 + 2		19.	7 + 2	
5.	2 + 1		20.	7 + 3	
6.	3 + 1		21.	6 + 3	
7.	3 + 2		22.	6 + 2	
8.	3 + 2		23.	6 + 2	
9.	2 + 2		24.	5 + 2	
10.	4 + 2		25.	7 + 2	
11.	1 + 2		26.	6 + 2	
12.	2 + 1		27.	2 + 6	
13.	3 + 1		28.	2 + 7	
14.	5 + 1		29.	3 + 7	
15.	7 + 1		30.	4 + 7	

Lesson 15:   Count on up to 3 more using numeral and 5-group cards and fingers to track the change.

©2015 Great Minds. eureka-math.org
G1-M1-TE-BK1-1.3.1-01.2016

EUREKA MATH™

Name _____ Date _____

1. Count on to add.

a.

 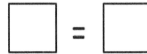 There are ____ crayons altogether.

b.

  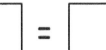 There are a total of ____ balloons.

c.

     In all, there are ____ pencils.

EUREKA
MATH™

Lesson 15:   Count on up to 3 more using numeral and 5-group cards and fingers
to track the change.

199

2. What shortcut or efficient strategy can you find to add?

a. $4 \enspace + \enspace 1 = \boxed{}$

h. $2 \enspace + \enspace 5 = \boxed{}$

b. $4 \enspace + \enspace 3 = \boxed{}$

i. $7 \enspace + \enspace 2 = \boxed{}$

c. $7 \enspace + \enspace 1 = \boxed{}$

j. $7 \enspace + \enspace 3 = \boxed{}$

d. $\boxed{} = 6 \enspace + \enspace 2$

k. $\boxed{} = 4 \enspace + \enspace 2$

e. $\boxed{} = 5 \enspace + \enspace 3$

l. $\boxed{} = 2 \enspace + \enspace 5$

f. $\boxed{} = 3 \enspace + \enspace 6$

m. $\boxed{} = 6 \enspace + \enspace 2$

g. $\boxed{} = 3 \enspace + \enspace 7$

n. $\boxed{} = 2 \enspace + \enspace 8$

Lesson 15:   Count on up to 3 more using numeral and 5-group cards and fingers to track the change.

EUREKA MATH

Name _____   Date _____

Use the picture to add.   Show the shortcut you used to add.

☐ +	☐ =	☐

6

There are _____ eggs total.

EUREKA
MATH™

Lesson 15:   Count on up to 3 more using numeral and 5-group cards and fingers
to track the change.

201

©2015 Great Minds. eureka-math.org
G1-M1-TE-BK1-1.3.1-01.2016

Name _____   Date _____

     Use your 5-group cards or your fingers to count on to solve.

Show the shortcut you used to add.

1.   5 (+) 3 = ▢

2.   6 (+) 2 = ▢

3.   7 (+) 3 = ▢

Show the strategy you used to add.

4.   ▢ = 8 (+) 2

5.   ▢ = 6 (+) 3

6.   ▢ = 7 (+) 2

EUREKA MATH™

Lesson 16

Objective: Count on to find the unknown part in missing addend equations such as 6 + __ = 9. Answer, "How many more to make 6, 7, 8, 9, and 10?"

Suggested Lesson Structure

■ Fluency Practice	(11 minutes)
▨ Application Problem	(5 minutes)
▨ Concept Development	(33 minutes)
▨ Student Debrief	(11 minutes)
Total Time	**(60 minutes)**

Fluency Practice (11 minutes)

- Shake Those Disks: 7 **1.OA.6**   (6 minutes)
- Count On Drums: 3 More **1.NBT.1**   (3 minutes)
- 10 Bowling Pins **1.NBT.1**   (2 minutes)

Shake Those Disks: 7 (6 minutes)

Materials: (S) 7 disks (e.g., counters, two-color beans or pennies), per set of partners, personal white board, shake those disks 7 board (Fluency Template)

Note: This activity addresses the core fluency objective for Grade 1 of adding and subtracting within 10.

Assign students partners. Give each set of partners 7 two-color beans. Instruct them to take turns as the Shaker and the Recorder. The Shaker shakes the disks and tosses them on the table. The Recorder then records the roll on the Shake Those Disks graph. (For example, if the Shaker rolls 3 red and 4 white, the Recorder puts an X on the graph above the 3 and 4 number bond.)

> **NOTES ON MULTIPLE MEANS OF ENGAGEMENT:**
>
> Encourage students who are ready to explore place value to imagine each disk has a value of 10. Adjust the recording sheet so that students can complete the number bonds as they initially identify the combinations of 70 created as they play.

Count On Drums: 3 More (3 minutes)

Note: This activity supports the connection of counting on to addition and counting back to subtraction.

The teacher says a number aloud. Students repeat the number, drumming on the table to count on 3 and matching one drum tap with each consecutive number counted on. Extend the game by counting back 3.

Lesson 16:   Count on to find the unknown part in missing addend equations such as 6 + __ = 9. Answer, "How many more to make 6, 7, 8, 9, and 10?"

10 Bowling Pins (2 minutes)

Note: A prepared set of bowling pins is a wonderful configuration of 10 (4 in the back, then 3, then 2, then 1). This activity supports students creating compositions of 10 in multiple ways.

Show a bird's eye picture of the configuration. Have students look at the arrangement and discuss with a partner how many pins they see and how they know. Share different ways of knowing it is 10.

Application Problem (5 minutes)

There were 10 bowling pins standing. Finn knocked over some bowling pins, and 7 were still standing. How many did he knock over? Use a simple math drawing to show what you did to solve. Write a number sentence with a box to show the mystery or unknown number.

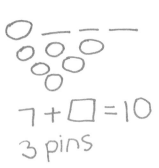

Note: This problem prepares students for this lesson's focus on solving for a missing addend.

Concept Development (33 minutes)

Materials: (T) 5-group cards (Lesson 5 Template 1), mystery box, enlarged blank number sentence and number bond (Lesson 6 Template 2), set of 7 beans from Shake Those Disks
(S) Personal white board, blank number sentence and number bond (Lesson 6 Template 2), 5-group cards (Lesson 5 Template 1), number sentence cards (Lesson 11 Template), sticky notes with question marks

While students are putting away fluency materials, take one set of the 7 beans from Shake Those Disks and bring it to the carpet. Hide 2 of the beans under the carpet without students noticing. Gather students on the carpet with their personal white boards.

> **NOTES ON**
> **MULTIPLE MEANS**
> **OF ENGAGEMENT:**
>
> When using words that may complicate language acquisition in English language learners, be sure to model as much as possible. Hearing teacher-talk along with math-they-can-see helps these students comprehend the skills they are learning. Teaching in multiple modalities also helps other learners in the class.

- T: While we were cleaning up, some of the beans fell on the carpet. I picked most of them up, but I think I am still missing some. We had 7 beans in total, right?
- S: Right!
- T: Now, I have 5 beans. (Show beans to the class.)
- T: How many am I missing? Talk with your partner to solve this.
- S: (Discuss.)
- **MP.7** T: Let's try to count on to check how many I'm missing.
- S/T: Fivvvve (gesture to beans in hand), 6, 7. (Track on fingers.)
- T: How many did we count on to get up to 7? (Keep fingers out to show the two that were used to track.)

S: Two!

T: So, how many beans am I missing?

MP.7 S: Two beans!

T: (Lift edge of carpet to show the 2 beans.)

T: Use your 5-group cards to make the number sentence on your personal white board. Place the numeral side up. If you want to double-check your number sentence, turn the cards to the dot side. Remember, try to turn over the fewest cards you can and count on. (Circulate and check for accuracy.)

S: (Create 5 + 2 = 7 on white boards with 5-group cards. Some students flip to dot side to count on and check.)

Repeat the process using the mystery box, concealing 3 of the 7 beans in the box so that students only see 4 beans. Encourage them to use their 5-group cards or track on their fingers to decide how many beans are in the mystery box. Students use the cards to make a corresponding number sentence.

T: How many beans did I place in the box?

S: 3 beans!

T: What is the number sentence you recorded?

S: 4 + 3 = 7.

T: Circle the part that was the mystery, or unknown part.

T: (Write 5 + □ = 8.) Use your cards to make and solve this number sentence.

S: (Discuss and solve using cards or finger tracking to confirm.)

T: What is the mystery, or unknown part, of this number sentence?

S: 3.

Repeat the process with the following sequence:

a. 5 + __ = 6   4 + __ = 6   3 + __ = 6

b. 6 + __ = 7   5 + __ = 7   4 + __ = 7

c. 7 + __ = 8   6 + __ = 8   5 + __ = 8

d. 8 + __ = 9   7 + __ = 9   6 + __ = 9

e. 9 + __ = 10   8 + __ = 10   7 + __ = 10

Leave the sets of number sentences on the board so that students can notice the patterns within the sequence. Explore the resulting patterns.

▪ What do you notice is happening?

▪ Imagine there is a fourth column (point to where it would be). What number sentence do you think I will add next in each row?

▪ How do the parts change from one number sentence to the next?

▪ What strategies did you use?

Problem Set (10 minutes)

Distribute Problem Set and allow students to work independently or in small groups.

Students should do their personal best to complete the Problem Set within the allotted 10 minutes. For some classes, it may be appropriate to modify the assignment by specifying which problems they work on first. Some problems do not specify a method for solving. Students solve these problems using the RDW approach used for Application Problems.

Student Debrief (11 minutes)

Lesson Objective: Count on to find the unknown part in missing addend equations such as 6 + __ = 9.
Answer, "How many more to make 6, 7, 8, 9, and 10?"

Student Debrief is intended to invite reflection and active processing of the total lesson experience.

Invite students to review their solutions for the Problem Set. They should check work by comparing answers with a partner before going over answers as a class. Look for misconceptions or misunderstandings that can be addressed in the Debrief. Guide students in a conversation to debrief the Problem Set and process the lesson.

Any combination of the questions below may be used to lead the discussion.

- Look at Problems 3 and 4 on the Problem Set. What do you notice is the same about these problems? What do you notice is different?

- How can it be true that all the unknown numbers, the mystery numbers, are the same on the first page?

Have students look at their work from the Application Problem with Finn's bowling pins and the last problem on their Problem Set.

- What strategies did you use to solve these problems? How are these problems the same? How are they different? How can the parts from the bowling pin problem help you solve the last Problem Set problem?

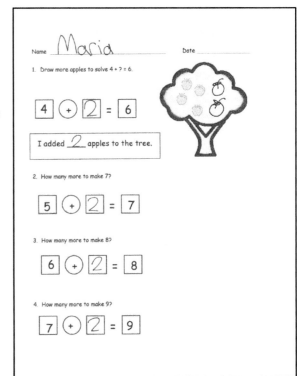

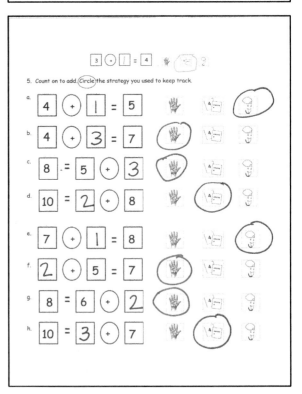

EUREKA
MATH™

- On the Problem Set, you could pick from lots of tools or strategies. You could have kept track on your fingers, used 5-group cards, or known it in your head. Share with your partner: What do you notice about how you solved most of your problems? Why did you pick that tool or strategy the most?

Exit Ticket (3 minutes)

After the Student Debrief, instruct students to complete the Exit Ticket. A review of their work will help with assessing students' understanding of the concepts that were presented in today's lesson and planning more effectively for future lessons. The questions may be read aloud to the students.

Lesson 16:   Count on to find the unknown part in missing addend equations such as 6 + __ = 9. Answer, "How many more to make 6, 7, 8, 9, and 10?"

207

©2015 Great Minds. eureka-math.org
G1-M1-TE-BK1-1.3.1-01.2016

Name _____   Date _____

1. Draw more apples to solve 4 + ? = 6.

I added _____ apples to the tree.

2. How many more to make 7?

3. How many more to make 8?

4. How many more to make 9?

Lesson 16:   Count on to find the unknown part in missing addend equations such
                 as 6 + __ = 9. Answer, "How many more to make 6, 7, 8, 9, and 10?"

EUREKA
MATH™

$3 + 1 = 4$

5. Count on to add. Circle the strategy you used to keep track.

a.     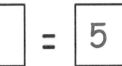

$4 + \square = 5$

b.   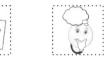

$4 + \square = 7$

c.

$8 = 5 + \square$

d.

$10 = \square + 8$

e.

$7 + \square = 8$

f.   

$\square + 5 = 7$

g.

$8 = 6 + \square$

h.

$10 = \square + 7$

Name _____ Date _____

Solve the number sentences. (Circle) the tool or strategy you used.

a. $5 + \boxed{} = \boxed{7}$

I counted on using

Or

I just knew

b. $6 + \boxed{} = \boxed{9}$

I counted on using

Or

I just knew

Lesson 16:   Count on to find the unknown part in missing addend lequations such
as 6 + __ = 9. Answer, "How many more to make 6, 7, 8, 9, and 10?"

EUREKA
MATH

Name _____ Date _____

1. Use simple math drawings. Draw more to solve 4 + ? = 6.

= 6

4 + [ ] = 6

2. Use your 5-group cards to solve 6 + ? = 8

6

= 8

6 + [ ] = 8

3. Use counting on to solve 7 + ? = 10

7...

7 + [ ] = 10

EUREKA
MATH

Lesson 16: Count on to find the unknown part in missing addend equations such as 6 + __ = 9. Answer, "How many more to make 6, 7, 8, 9, and 10?"

211

©2015 Great Minds. eureka-math.org
G1-M1-TE-BK1-1.3.1-01.2016

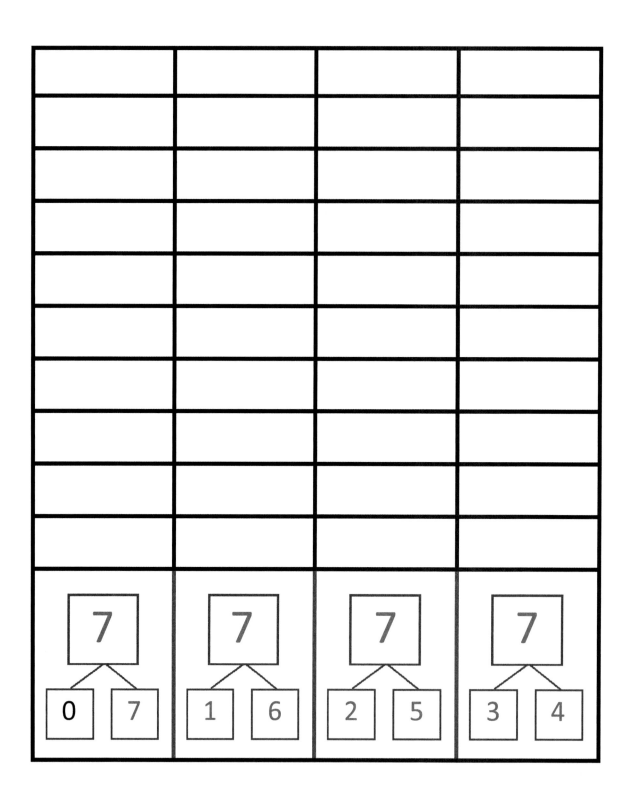

shake those disks 7 board

Lesson 16: Count on to find the unknown part in missing addend equations such as 6 + ___ = 9. Answer, "How many more to make 6, 7, 8, 9, and 10?"

EUREKA MATH™

1
GRADE

Mathematics Curriculum

Topic E

The Commutative Property of Addition and the Equal Sign

1.OA.3, 1.OA.7

Focus Standard:	1.OA.3	Apply properties of operations as strategies to add and subtract. *Examples: If 8 + 3 = 11 is known, then 3 + 8 = 11 is also known. (Commutative property of addition.) To add 2 + 6 + 4, the second two numbers can be added to make a ten, so 2 + 6 + 4 = 2 + 10 = 12. (Associative property of addition.)*
	1.OA.7	Understand the meaning of the equal sign, and determine if equations involving addition and subtraction are true or false. *For example, which of the following equations are true and which are false? 6 = 6, 7 = 8 – 1, 5 + 2 = 2 + 5, 4 + 1 = 5 + 2.*
Instructional Days:	4	
Coherence -Links from:	GK–M4	Number Pairs, Addition and Subtraction to 10
-Links to:	G2–M4	Addition and Subtraction Within 200 with Word Problems to 100

Topic E leads students to a very intentional understanding and application of the equal sign and the commutative property of addition (**1.OA.3** and **1.OA.7**). Lessons 17 and 18 ask students to use pictorial representations (pictures and 5-groups) to write expressions and to demonstrate that they are equivalent by using the equal sign.

This work with the equal sign precedes the lessons on commutativity in order to allow students to construct true number sentences such as 4 + 3 = 3 + 4 without misunderstanding the equal sign to mean that the numbers are the same. Students understand that when added together, two numbers make the same total, regardless of whether one of the numbers appears first or second in equations and expressions.

The topic ends with Lesson 20, where students directly apply their understanding of commutativity by starting with the larger quantity and counting on (a Level 2 strategy) as a matter of efficiency, "I can count on 2 from 7 when I solve 2 + 7!"

A Teaching Sequence Toward Mastery of the Commutative Property of Addition and the Equal Sign

Objective 1: Understand the meaning of the equal sign by pairing equivalent expressions and constructing true number sentences.
(Lessons 17–18)

Objective 2: Represent the same story scenario with addends repositioned (the commutative property).
(Lesson 19)

Objective 3: Apply the commutative property to *count on* from a larger addend.
(Lesson 20)

©2015 Great Minds. eureka-math.org
G1-M1-TE-BK1-1.3.1-01.2016

Lesson 17

Objective: Understand the meaning of the equal sign by pairing equivalent expressions and constructing true number sentences.

Suggested Lesson Structure

■ Fluency Practice   (10 minutes)
▨ Application Problem   (5 minutes)
▢ Concept Development   (35 minutes)
▨ Student Debrief   (10 minutes)

Total Time   **(60 minutes)**

Fluency Practice (10 minutes)

- Penny Drop: 7 **1.OA.6**   (5 minutes)
- Number Bond Dash: 7 **1.OA.6**   (5 minutes)

Penny Drop: 7 (5 minutes)

Materials: (T) 7 pennies, 1 can

Note: This activity addresses the core fluency objective for Grade 1 of adding and subtracting within 10.

Show students 7 pennies. Have students close their eyes and listen. Drop some of the pennies in a can, one at a time. Ask students to open their eyes and guess how many pennies are still in the teacher's hand. Then, have students say how many pennies they heard drop and count on to 7, using the remaining pennies.

NOTES ON
MULTIPLE MEANS
OF ACTION AND
EXPRESSION:

Provide a variety of ways to respond with Fluency Practice when students are not able to complete it the way it is intended. They can be given extra time or allowed to complete the activity orally. The goal of the task is for students to show what they know.

Number Bond Dash: 7 (5 minutes)

Materials: (T) Stopwatch or timer (S) Number bond dash 7 (Lesson 6 Fluency Template), marker to correct work

Note: By using the same system repeatedly, students can focus on the mathematics alone. The activity addresses the core fluency objective for Grade 1 of adding and subtracting within 10.

Follow the procedure for the Number Bond Dash (Lesson 2). Tell students to remember how many problems they get correct so they can try to improve their scores tomorrow.

Lesson 17:   Understand the meaning of the equal sign by pairing equivalent expressions and constructing true number sentences

215

Application Problem (5 minutes)

There are 10 swings on the playground, and 7 students are using the swings. How many swings are empty? Draw or write a number sentence to show your thinking. Use a sentence at the end to answer today's question: How many swings are empty?

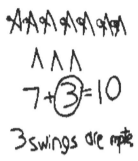

NOTES ON
MULTIPLE MEANS
OF ACTION AND
EXPRESSION:

When asking English language learners to answer a question, support their response with a sentence frame. Write the statement on the board:

_____ swings are empty.

This also helps other students organize their thoughts.

Note: This problem serves as a bridge from the previous lesson's focus on solving for a missing addend.

Concept Development (35 minutes)

Materials: (S) Bag of 20 linking cubes (10 red and 10 yellow), personal white board

Have students sit next to their math partners at their tables.

T: Let's play a game called Make it Equal. Partner B, close your eyes. Partner A, make your linking cubes look exactly like mine. (Show 4 red cubes and 1 yellow cube as a stick.) Hide your stick behind you and close your eyes.

T: Partner B, open your eyes. Make your linking cubes look exactly like mine. (Show 3 red and 2 yellow cubes as a stick.)

T: Partner A, open your eyes. Everyone, write the expression that shows how many cubes you have.

S: (Partner A writes 4 + 1; Partner B writes 3 + 2.)

T: Show each other your linking cube stick. How are they the same? How are they different? (Circulate.)

S: (Discuss.)

T: How are they different?

S: I had 4 red and 1 yellow cube, but my partner had 3 red and 2 yellow cubes.

T: How are they the same?

S: We both have 5 cubes.

T: Even though you have different parts, do you have the same total?

S: Yes.

     Lesson 17:   Understand the meaning of the equal sign by pairing equivalent expressions and constructing true number sentences

T: Put your expressions next to each other. Now, put your sticks in between the expressions by putting them one above the other. What do the two sticks look like now?

S: An equal sign!

T: Hmmm… does this make sense? How many cubes do you have on the left side of the equal sign?

S: 5.

T: How many cubes do you have on the right side of the equal sign?

S: 5.

T: Does 5 equal 5?

S: Yes!

T: Does 4 + 1 equal 3 + 2?

S: Yes!

T: Let's say the number sentence.

T/S: 4 + 1 = 3 + 2.

T: This is called a true number sentence.

Repeat this process. Possibly use the following suggested sequence: 5 + 2 and 6 + 1; 7 + 2 and 6 + 3.

Next, project 3 red and 3 yellow linking cubes and have partners use one board to write the expression. Then, project 1 red and 5 yellow linking cubes. Partners write the expression on the second board. Ask students to give thumbs up if these expressions are equal. If yes, have them draw an imaginary equal sign between the two boards and say the true number sentence. Repeat this process, but be sure to include some expressions that are not equivalent (such as 3 + 5 and 4 + 2).

T: (Project a stick of 6 red and 2 yellow cubes.) Write an expression to match these cubes on one of your white boards.

S: (Write 6 + 2.)

T: With your partner, use your linking cubes to make another stick to show the same total in a different way. Write the expression to match your stick. Then, use your sticks to make the equal sign to help you say the true number sentence.

If students finish early, encourage them to make up as many equivalent expressions as they can. Repeat this process. Possibly use the following suggested sequence: 3 + 4, 4 + 5, and 3 + 7.

Problem Set (10 minutes)

Distribute Problem Set to students, and allow them to work independently or in small groups.

Students should do their personal best to complete the Problem Set within the allotted 10 minutes. For some classes, it may be appropriate to modify the assignment by specifying which problems they work on first. Some problems do not specify a method for solving. Students solve these problems using the RDW approach used for Application Problems.

   Lesson 17:   Understand the meaning of the equal sign by pairing equivalent   217
                                  expressions and constructing true number sentences

                          ©2015 Great Minds. eureka-math.org
                          G1-M1-TE-BK1-1.3.1-01.2016

Student Debrief (10 minutes)

Lesson Objective: Understand the meaning of the equal sign by pairing equivalent expressions and constructing true number sentences.

The Student Debrief is intended to invite reflection and active processing of the total lesson experience.

Invite students to review their solutions for the Problem Set. They should check work by comparing answers with a partner before going over answers as a class. Look for misconceptions or misunderstandings that can be addressed in the Debrief. Guide students in a conversation to debrief the Problem Set and process the lesson.

Any combination of the questions below may be used to lead the discussion.

- Look at Problems 1–4. In Problem 1, we have apples plus oranges, and that equals fruit. What about Problem 2? What about Problem 3? What about Problem 4? How is Problem 3 different from the others? (They are like units.)

- Look at Problem 5(g). Share what you wrote as your true number sentence. What is the total represented by each side of this true number sentence? (10.)

- If both sides equal 10, is 6 + 4 = 5 + 5 the same as 10 = 10? (Write this on the board.) Talk with your partner about why or why not.

- Look at the true number sentence you wrote for Problem 6(g). Think about what we just decided about Problem 5(g). What is another way you can write the true number sentence? (8 = 8.)

- Think about the goal of today's lesson. What does the equal sign tell us?

Exit Ticket (3 minutes)

After the Student Debrief, instruct students to complete the Exit Ticket. A review of their work will help with assessing students' understanding of the concepts that were presented in today's lesson and planning more effectively for future lessons. The questions may be read aloud to the students.

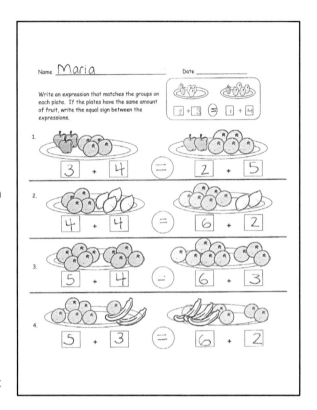

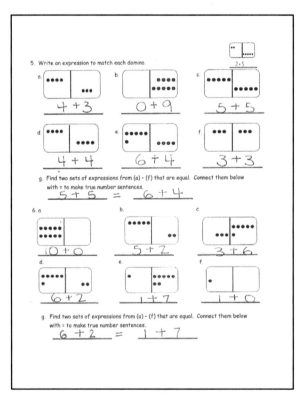

Lesson 17:   Understand the meaning of the equal sign by pairing equivalent
                             expressions and constructing true number sentences

©2015 Great Minds. eureka-math.org
G1-M1-TE-BK1-1.3.1-01.2016

Name _____   Date _____

Write an expression that matches the groups on each plate. If the plates have the same amount of fruit, write the equal sign between the expressions.

[ ] + [ ] (=) [ ] + [ ]
2   3   1   4

1.

[ ] + [ ]   ( )   [ ] + [ ]

2.

[ ] + [ ]   ( )   [ ] + [ ]

3.

[ ] + [ ]   ( )   [ ] + [ ]

4.

[ ] + [ ]   ( )   [ ] + [ ]

EUREKA MATH™

Lesson 17:   Understand the meaning of the equal sign by pairing equivalent expressions and constructing true number sentences

219

©2015 Great Minds. eureka-math.org
G1-M1-TE-BK1-1.3.1-01.2016

5. Write an expression to match each domino.

2+5

a.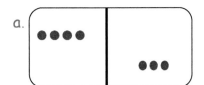

b.

c.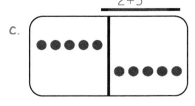

_____

d.

e.

f.

_____

g. Find two sets of expressions from (a)–(f) that are equal. Connect them below with = to make true number sentences.

_____   _____

6. a.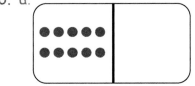

b.

c.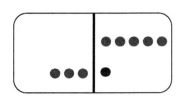

_____

d.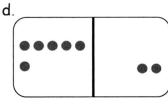

e.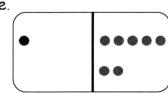

f.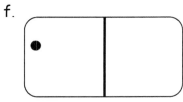

_____

g. Find two sets of expressions from (a)–(f) that are equal. Connect them below with = to make true number sentences.

_____   _____

Lesson 17: Understand the meaning of the equal sign by pairing equivalent expressions and constructing true number sentences

EUREKA MATH

©2015 Great Minds. eureka-math.org
G1-M1-TE-BK1-1.3.1-01.2016

Name _____ Date _____

1. Use math drawings to make the pictures equal. Connect them below with = to make true number sentences.

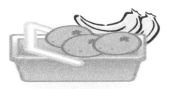   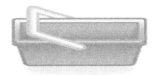

_____   _____

2. Shade the equal dominoes. Write a true number sentence.

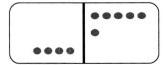   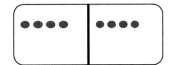   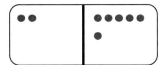

_____   _____

EUREKA
MATH™

Lesson 17:   Understand the meaning of the equal sign by pairing equivalent
              expressions and constructing true number sentences

221

©2015 Great Minds. eureka-math.org
G1-M1-TE-BK1-1.3.1-01.2016

Name _____   Date _____

1. Match the equal dominoes. Then, write true number sentences. 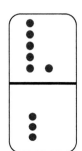 4+4=5+3

a. 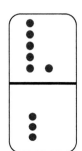 _____   _____

b. 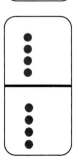 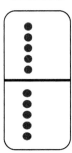 _____   _____

c. 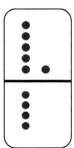 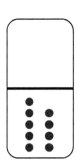 _____   _____

2. Find the expressions that are equal. Use the equal expressions to write true number sentences.

a. _____   _____

b. _____   _____

Lesson 17:   Understand the meaning of the equal sign by pairing equivalent
                    expressions and constructing true number sentences

EUREKA
MATH™

Lesson 18

Objective: Understand the meaning of the equal sign by pairing equivalent expressions and constructing true number sentences.

Suggested Lesson Structure

■ Fluency Practice   (13 minutes)
▨ Application Problem   (7 minutes)
▢ Concept Development   (30 minutes)
■ Student Debrief   (10 minutes)

   Total Time   **(60 minutes)**

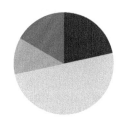

Fluency Practice (13 minutes)

- Red Light/Green Light: Counting by Tens **K.CC.2**   (5 minutes)
- Missing Part: Make 7 **1.OA.6**   (3 minutes)
- Number Bond Dash: 7 **1.OA.6**   (5 minutes)

Red Light/Green Light: Counting by Tens (5 minutes)

Note: Providing students with ongoing practice with counting throughout the year builds and maintains their counting skills.

Begin with 0. Say "green light," after which students begin running in place and counting aloud together by tens, until they reach 100. Say "red light." Students stop counting and freeze. Students who are still moving or counting after "red light" sit down until the next game. Once students reach 100, continue to play, counting back by tens until students arrive at 0. The last student (or few students) standing wins.

For the first game, start at 0 to ensure every child feels success. Then, try playing the game again beginning with 4 and 8, respectively.

Missing Part: Make 7 (3 minutes)

Materials: (S) 5-group cards (0–7 only) (Lesson 5 Template 1)

Note: This activity addresses the core fluency objective for Grade 1 of adding and subtracting within 10.

Students work with a partner, using 5-group cards. Each student puts a card to his or her forehead. The partner tells how many more to make 7. Students must guess the cards on their foreheads. Partners can play simultaneously.

Lesson 18:   Understand the meaning of the equal sign by pairing equivalent expressions and constructing true number sentences.

223

©2015 Great Minds. eureka-math.org
G1-M1-TE-BK1-1.3.1-01.2016

Number Bond Dash: 7 (5 minutes)

Materials: (T) Stopwatch or timer (S) Number bond dash 7 (Lesson 6 Fluency Template), marker to correct work

Note: By using the same system repeatedly, students can focus on the mathematics alone. The activity addresses the core fluency objective for Grade 1 of adding and subtracting within 10.

Follow the procedure for the Number Bond Dash (Lesson 2). Remember today is the second day with making 7. Students should recall their scores from yesterday to see and celebrate improvement.

Application Problem (7 minutes)

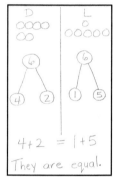

Dylan has 4 cats and 2 dogs at home. Laura has 1 dog and 5 fish at home. Laura says she and Dylan have an equal number of pets. Dylan thinks he has more pets than Laura. Who is right? Draw a picture, write two number bonds, and use a number sentence to show if Dylan and Laura have an equal amount of pets.

Note: This problem serves as both a bridge and as a lead-up to the current lesson's Concept Development, focusing students on using the equal sign to create true number sentences.

Concept Development (30 minutes)

Materials: (S) 5-group cards (Lesson 5 Template 1), personal white board, true and false number sentence cards (Template), red and green markers per pair

Have students sit next to their math partners in the meeting area or at their tables.

- T: (Write $7 + 1 = \underline{\quad} + \underline{\quad}$. Read the number sentence aloud with students.) Talk with your partner, and use this incomplete number sentence to finish writing a true number sentence.

- S: (Write any combination that makes 8, for example, $6 + 2$, $5 + 3$, etc.)

- T: Hold up your true number sentences. Look around the class. Did everyone use the same numbers to make 8 on both sides?

- S: No!

- T: They don't all use the same numbers, but are all of them equal to 8?

- S: Yes!

- T: Yesterday, you made a lot of true number sentences. Use your 5-group cards to tell me why this number sentence is NOT true. (Project $4 + 2 = 5 + 3$.)

- S: (Build $4 + 2 = 5 + 3$ with 5-group cards, and solve for each side.)

NOTES ON MULTIPLE MEANS OF REPRESENTATION:

Connect calculations to 5-group cards to encourage counting on. Students use one numeral side and one dot side and touch the dots with their fingers as they count on. Some students will be able to do the calculations in their head while others will use the 5-group cards for as long as needed.

Lesson 18:   Understand the meaning of the equal sign by pairing equivalent expressions and constructing true number sentences.

©2015 Great Minds. eureka-math.org
G1-M1-TE-BK1-1.3.1-01.2016

T: Is 4 + 2 = 5 + 3 true or false?

S: False!

T: Talk with your partner. How do you know that 4 + 2 = 5 + 3 is *not* equal, or false?
     (As students share, circulate and listen. Then, call on one student.)

S: 4 + 2 is 6, and 5 + 3 is 8, so they are not equal because 6 is not the same as 8.

T: Talk with your partner. How can you fix this number sentence to make it equal, or true?
     (As students share, circulate and listen. Then, call on a couple of students.)

S: Change 4 + 2 to 4 + 4 to make it equal 8. → Change 5 + 3 to 5 + 1 to make it equal 6.

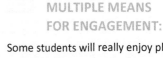

T: Is there more than one way to fix this number
     sentence to make it true?

S: Yes!

T: Today, you will be playing True or False Number
     Sentences, like we just did, with a partner. Here are
     the directions:

     1. Read the number sentence together.

     2. Use your 5-group cards to solve each side of the
         number sentence together.

     3. If the sentence is true, Partner A uses your green marker to put a check on it.

     4. If the sentence is false, work together to use your 5-group cards to change one number to fix the
         number sentence to make it equal, using your red marker.

     5. Then, Partner B checks it, and it becomes her turn to pick a card.

Circulate and support students as they play.

NOTES ON
MULTIPLE MEANS
FOR ENGAGEMENT:

Some students will really enjoy playing
True or False Number Sentences.
Provide challenging extensions
(e.g., 14 + 2 = 15 + 1) and give these
students more problems to figure out
and solve.

Problem Set (10 minutes)

Distribute the Problem Set and allow students to work independently or in small groups.

Students should do their personal best to complete the Problem Set within the allotted 10 minutes. For some
classes, it may be appropriate to modify the assignment by specifying which problems they work on first.
Some problems do not specify a method for solving. Students solve these problems using the RDW approach
used for Application Problems.

Student Debrief (10 minutes)

Lesson Objective: Understand the meaning of the equal sign by pairing equivalent expressions and constructing
true number sentences.

The Student Debrief is intended to invite reflection and active processing of the total lesson experience.

Lesson 18:   Understand the meaning of the equal sign by pairing equivalent
               expressions and constructing true number sentences.

225

©2015 Great Minds. eureka-math.org
G1-M1-TE-BK1-1.3.1-01.2016

Invite students to review their solutions for the Problem Set. They should check work by comparing answers with a partner before going over answers as a class. Look for misconceptions or misunderstandings that can be addressed in the Debrief. Guide students in a conversation to debrief the Problem Set and process the lesson.

Any combination of the questions below may be used to lead the discussion.

- Look at Problem 2(b). How did you and your partner rewrite this to make a true number sentence? How were your number sentences the same and different?

- Look at Problem 2(f). Can we rewrite this to be 10 = 10? Why or why not? (If appropriate, ask the same about Problem 2(g) rewritten as 9 = 9.)

- Think about the goal of today's lesson and the work we have been doing with the equal sign. Imagine an alien came down from outer space and asked you what the equal sign means. Tell your partner what you would say to that alien to describe it! Be sure to use examples.

- Look at your Application Problem. Dylan and Laura have a friend Simon who has the same number of pets they have. If Simon has 6 guinea pigs, how many other pets does he have? Show with a number sentence or number bond to prove your answer.

Exit Ticket (3 minutes)

After the Student Debrief, instruct students to complete the Exit Ticket. A review of their work will help with assessing students' understanding of the concepts that were presented in today's lesson and planning more effectively for future lessons. The questions may be read aloud to the students.

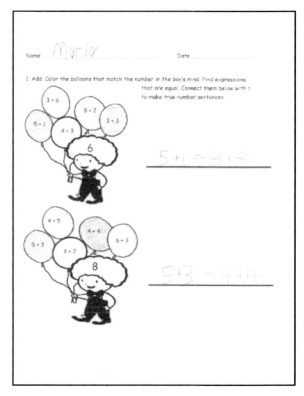

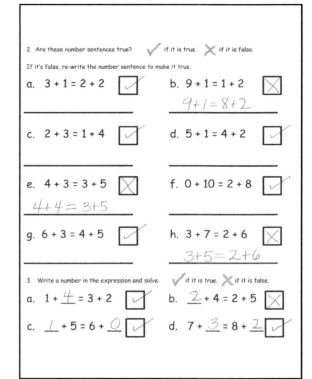

Understand the meaning of the equal sign by pairing equivalent
         expressions and constructing true number sentences.

©2015 Great Minds. eureka-math.org
G1-M1-TE-BK1-1.3.1-01.2016

EUREKA
MATH™

Name _____   Date _____

1. Add. Color the balloons that match the number in the boy's mind. Find expressions that are equal. Connect them below with = to make true number sentences.

a.

_____

b.

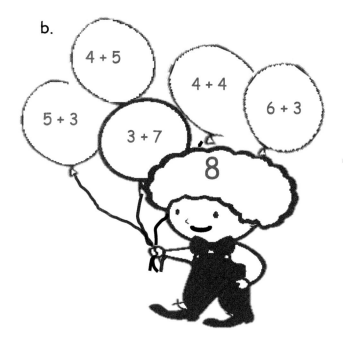

_____

EUREKA
MATH™

Lesson 18:   Understand the meaning of the equal sign by pairing equivalent
expressions and constructing true number sentences.

227

©2015 Great Minds. eureka-math.org
G1-M1-TE-BK1-1.3.1-01.2016

2. Are these number sentences true? if it is true. if it is false.

If it is false, rewrite the number sentence to make it true.

a. 3 + 1 = 2 + 2

_____

b. 9 + 1 = 1 + 2

_____

c. 2 + 3 = 1 + 4 ☐

_____

d. 5 + 1 = 4 + 2 ☐

_____

e. 4 + 3 = 3 + 5 ☐

_____

f. 0 + 10 = 2 + 8 ☐

_____

g. 6 + 3 = 4 + 5 ☐

_____

h. 3 + 7 = 2 + 6 ☐

_____

3. Write a number in the expression and solve. if it is true. ✗ if it is false.

a. 1 + ___ = 3 + 2 ☐

b. ___ + 4 = 2 + 5

c. ___ + 5 = 6 + ___ ☐

d. 7 + ___ = 8 + ___ ☐

Lesson 18: Understand the meaning of the equal sign by pairing equivalent expressions and constructing true number sentences.

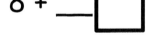

©2015 Great Minds. eureka-math.org
G1-M1-TE-BK1-1.3.1-01.2016

Name _____   Date _____

Find two ways to fix each number sentence to make it true.

a. | 7 + 3 = 6 + 2 |

b. | 8 + 1 = 3 + 5 |

7 + 3 = 6 + 4

_____   _____

_____   _____

_____   _____

_____   _____

EUREKA
MATH™

Lesson 18:   Understand the meaning of the equal sign by pairing equivalent
                    expressions and constructing true number sentences.

229

©2015 Great Minds. eureka-math.org
G1-M1-TE-BK1-1.3.1-01.2016

Name _____   Date _____

1. The pictures below are not equal. Make the pictures equal, and write a true number sentence.

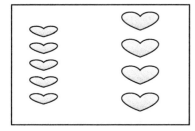   

_____   _____

2. Circle the true number sentences, and rewrite the false sentences to make them true.

a.
$$4 = 4$$

_____

b.
$$5 + 1 = 6 + 1$$

_____

c.
$$3 + 2 = 5 + 0$$

_____

d.
$$6 + 2 = 4 + 4$$

_____

e.
$$3 + 3 = 6 + 2$$

_____

f.
$$9 + 0 = 7 + 2$$

_____

g.
$$4 + 3 = 2 + 4$$

_____

h.
$$8 = 8 + 0$$

_____

i.
$$6 + 3 = 5 + 4$$

_____

Lesson 18:   Understand the meaning of the equal sign by pairing equivalent expressions and constructing true number sentences.

©2015 Great Minds. eureka-math.org
G1-M1-TE-BK1-1.3.1-01.2016

EUREKA
MATH™

3. Find the missing part to make the number sentences true.

a.

8 + 0 = ___ + 4

b.

7 + 2 = 9 + ___

c.

5 + 2 = 4 + ___

d.

5 + ___ = 6 + 0

e.

6 + ___ = 4 + 3

f.

5 + 4 = ___ + 3

EUREKA
MATH™

Lesson 18:   Understand the meaning of the equal sign by pairing equivalent
expressions and constructing true number sentences.

231

©2015 Great Minds. eureka-math.org
G1-M1-TE-BK1-1.3.1-01.2016

4 + 1 = 2 + 2	2 + 5 = 8 + 2
3 + 2 = 4 + 1	9 + 1 = 4 + 6
6 + 2 = 3 + 3	3 + 4 = 6 + 3
1 + 7 = 4 + 4	5 + 4 = 3 + 7
2 + 5 = 4 + 3	5 + 5 = 6 + 3
5 + 1 = 4 + 2	8 + 2 = 3 + 7

true and false number sentence cards

Lesson 18: Understand the meaning of the equal sign by pairing equivalent expressions and constructing true number sentences.

©2015 Great Minds. eureka-math.org
G1-M1-TE-BK1-1.3.1-01.2016

EUREKA MATH

Lesson 19

Objective: Represent the same story scenario with addends repositioned (the commutative property).

Suggested Lesson Structure

■ Fluency Practice   (13 minutes)
▨ Application Problem   (7 minutes)
▢ Concept Development   (25 minutes)
■ Student Debrief   (15 minutes)
Total Time   **(60 minutes)**

Fluency Practice (13 minutes)

- 5-Group Addition **1.OA.3**   (3 minutes)
- Sprint: +1, 2, 3 **1.OA.6**   (10 minutes)

5-Group Addition (3 minutes)

Materials: (T) 5-group cards 1–5 only (Lesson 5 Template 1)

Note: This activity prepares students for working with the commutative property in today's lessons. It also addresses the core fluency objective for Grade 1 of adding and subtracting within 10.

The teacher holds up a 5-group card and asks students to identify the quantity. The teacher holds up a second 5-group card and asks students to identify that quantity. The teacher holds the cards side by side and asks students a series of addition questions: What is the total? What is the number sentence, starting with the bigger part? What is the number sentence, starting with the smaller part? Continue the game with various number combinations.

NOTES ON MULTIPLE MEANS OF REPRESENTATION:

While using vocabulary words such as *total* and *part* is important for students' understanding of a concept, it is essential that students understand them. This is particularly important for English language learners. When using the words, point, gesture, or label these parts of the number sentence. Encourage students to use these words when talking about number sentences, too. Using them correctly demonstrates students' level of understanding.

Sprint: +1, 2, 3 (10 minutes)

Materials: (S) +1, 2, 3 Sprint

Note: This activity addresses the core fluency objective for Grade 1 of adding and subtracting within 10.

Lesson 19:   Represent the same story scenario with addends repositioned (the commutative property).

233

©2015 Great Minds. eureka-math.org
G1-M1-TE-BK1-1.3.1-01.2016

Application Problem (7 minutes)

Dylan has 4 cats and 2 dogs at home. Sammy has 1 mama bunny and 6 baby bunnies at home. Draw a number bond showing the total number of pets of each household. Write a statement to tell if the two households have an equal number of pets.

Note: This problem serves as a bridge from the previous lesson's focus on using the equal sign to write true number sentences.

Concept Development (25 minutes)

Materials: (S) Personal white board, bag of 7 counters (4 red, 3 white)

Invite students to sit on the carpet with their personal white boards, facing the front of the room. Choose 5 girls and 3 boys (or 3 girls and 5 boys) to stand in a row in front of the class.

T: How many girls are standing here?

S: 5 girls!

T: How many boys are standing here?

S: 3 boys!

T: Write a number sentence on your board to show 5 girls plus 3 boys.

S: (Write 5 + 3 = 8 on their boards.)

T: Starting with the boys, write the number sentence on your boards.

S: (Write 3 + 5 = 8.)

T: How many children do we have when we add 3 boys and 5 girls?

S: 8 children!

T: Is that the same total or a different total of children as we had the last time we added the boys and girls?

S: The same!

T: Take 4 red and 3 white counters out of your bag. Put them in a line starting with the red counters.

T: Tell your friend two number sentences that match your materials.

MP.7

S: 4 + 3 = 7 and 3 + 4 = 7.

T: Can you start with the whole amount?

S: Yes! 7 = 4 + 3 and 7 = 3 + 4.

T: Now, switch the red and white counters, putting the white first in your line. Tell your partner four number sentences that match your new arrangement.

S: (Do so.)

NOTES ON MULTIPLE MEANS OF ACTION AND EXPRESSION:

Though some think of the commutative property as "switch arounds," it is the addends that switch not the referents. When the placement of the materials changes when adding, the exact same four number sentences also describe the materials in different positions.

      Lesson 19:   Represent the same story scenario with addends repositioned (the commutative property).

©2015 Great Minds. eureka-math.org
G1-M1-TE-BK1-1.3.1-01.2016

T: Is this the same set of number sentences?

S: Yes!

T: Why? Turn and talk with your partner. (Circulate and listen.)

S: (Talk with partner.) The number of reds and whites did not change. We can add them in any order, as long as we include them all.

MP.7

T: On your board, write a number sentence showing that 4 plus 3 is the same as 3 plus 4.

S: (Write 3 + 4 = 4 + 3.)

T: On your board, draw 6 circles and 3 hearts in a line. Write four number sentences to match your picture. Share your work with a partner. What are you noticing?

Problem Set (10 minutes)

Distribute the Problem Set and allow students to work independently or in small groups.

Students should do their personal best to complete the Problem Set within the allotted 10 minutes. For some classes, it may be appropriate to modify the assignment by specifying which problems they work on first. Some problems do not specify a method for solving. Students solve these problems using the RDW approach used for Application Problems.

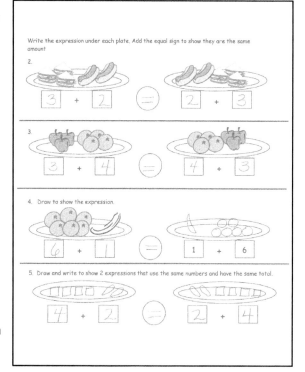

Student Debrief (15 minutes)

Lesson Objective: Represent the same story scenario with addends repositioned (the commutative property).

The Student Debrief is intended to invite reflection and active processing of the total lesson experience.

Invite students to review their solutions for the Problem Set. They should check work by comparing answers with a partner before going over answers as a class. Look for misconceptions or misunderstandings that can be addressed in the Debrief. Guide students in a conversation to debrief the Problem Set and process the lesson.

Any combination of the questions below may be used to lead the discussion.

- What do you notice about the number sentences you made for Problem 1? Why do you think that happens?
- Why does the total stay the same, even though you are adding in a different order?
- Try adding two amounts in different orders. See if you get the same total each time. You can draw and use number sentences as you try it.
- Look at Problem 1(c). Which number sentence represents the easier way for you to add 2 and 8? How does choosing a certain order make adding easier?
- How will this strategy help you add more quickly next time, especially during a Number Bond Dash or a Sprint?

Exit Ticket (3 minutes)

After the Student Debrief, instruct students to complete the Exit Ticket. A review of their work will help with assessing students' understanding of the concepts that were presented in today's lesson and planning more effectively for future lessons. The questions may be read aloud to the students.

©2015 Great Minds. eureka-math.org
G1-M1-TE-BK1-1.3.1-01.2016

Number Correct:

A

Name _____   Date _____

*Count on to add.

1.	1 + 1		16.	4 + 3	
2.	2 + 1		17.	3 + 3	
3.	3 + 1		18.	4 + 3	
4.	3 + 2		19.	3 + 4	
5.	2 + 2		20.	2 + 4	
6.	3 + 2		21.	4 + 2	
7.	2 + 2		22.	5 + 2	
8.	3 + 0		23.	2 + 5	
9.	3 + 1		24.	2 + 6	
10.	3 + 2		25.	6 + 3	
11.	5 + 2		26.	3 + 6	
12.	5 + 3		27.	2 + 7	
13.	5 + 2		28.	3 + 7	
14.	5 + 3		29.	2 + 8	
15.	6 + 3		30.	3 + 6	

EUREKA MATH™

Lesson 19:   Represent the same story scenario with addends repositioned (the commutative property).

237

B

Number Correct: ⭐

Name _____ Date _____

*Count on to add.

1.	2 + 1		16.	4 + 3	
2.	1 + 1		17.	3 + 3	
3.	2 + 1		18.	2 + 3	
4.	2 + 2		19.	1 + 3	
5.	3 + 2		20.	0 + 3	
6.	2 + 2		21.	1 + 3	
7.	3 + 2		22.	2 + 5	
8.	3 + 1		23.	5 + 2	
9.	5 + 1		24.	2 + 6	
10.	6 + 1		25.	6 + 2	
11.	6 + 2		26.	3 + 6	
12.	5 + 2		27.	3 + 7	
13.	6 + 2		28.	2 + 7	
14.	6 + 3		29.	2 + 6	
15.	5 + 3		30.	3 + 6	

Lesson 19:   Represent the same story scenario with addends repositioned (the commutative property).

EUREKA MATH™

©2015 Great Minds. eureka-math.org
G1-M1-TE-BK1-1.3.1-01.2016

Name _____ Date _____

1. Write the number bond to match the picture. Then, complete the number sentences.

a.

b.

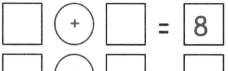   

c.

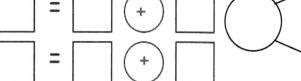

EUREKA
MATH™

Lesson 19:   Represent the same story scenario with addends repositioned (the commutative property).

239

©2015 Great Minds. eureka-math.org
G1-M1-TE-BK1-1.3.1-01.2016

Write the expression under each plate. Add the equal sign to show they are the same amount.

2.

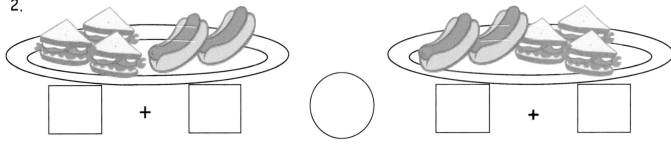

☐ + ☐ ◯ ☐ + ☐

3.

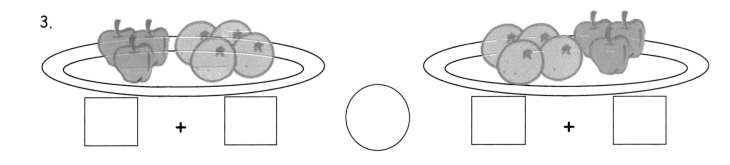

☐ + ☐ ◯ ☐ + ☐

4. Draw to show the expression.

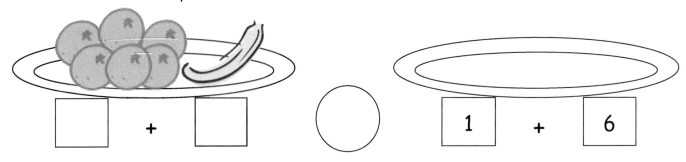

☐ + ☐ ◯ 1 + 6

5. Draw and write to show 2 expressions that use the same numbers and have the same total.

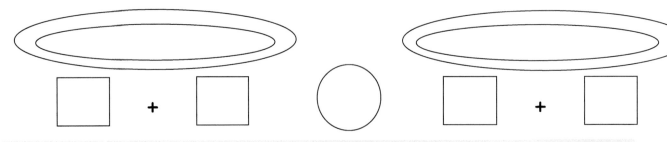

☐ + ☐ ◯ ☐ + ☐

Lesson 19: Represent the same story scenario with addends repositioned (the commutative property).

©2015 Great Minds. eureka-math.org
G1-M1-TE-BK1-1.3.1-01.2016

Name _____   Date _____

Use the picture and write the number sentences to show the parts in a different order.

_____ + _____ = _____   _____ = _____ + _____

_____ + _____ = _____   _____ = _____ + _____

Lesson 19:   Represent the same story scenario with addends repositioned (the commutative property).

241

Name _____   Date _____

1. Use the picture to write a number bond. Then, write the matching number sentences.

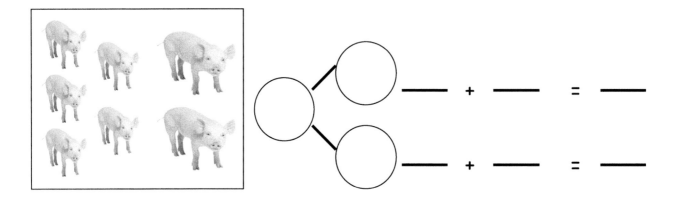

_____ + _____ = _____

_____ + _____ = _____

2. Write the number sentences to match the number bonds.

a.

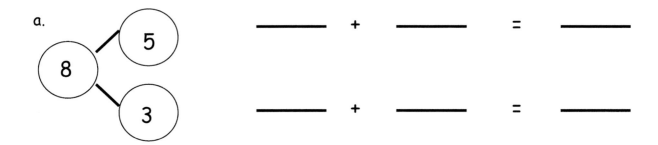

_____ + _____ = _____

_____ + _____ = _____

b.

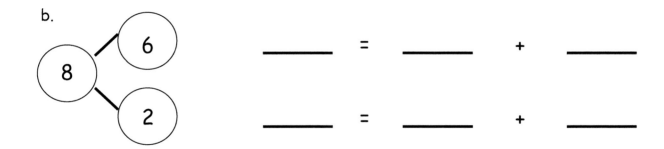

_____ = _____ + _____

_____ = _____ + _____

Lesson 19:   Represent the same story scenario with addends repositioned (the commutative property).

©2015 Great Minds. eureka-math.org
G1-M1-TE-BK1-1.3.1-01.2016

EUREKA MATH

c.

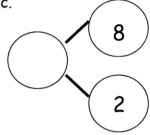

_____ + _____ = _____

_____ + _____ = _____

d.

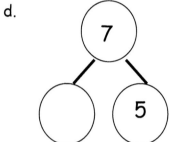

_____ + _____ = _____

_____ + _____ = _____

e.

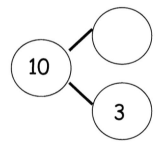

_____ = _____ + _____

_____ = _____ + _____

f.

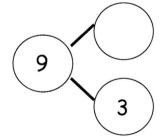

_____ + _____ = _____

_____ + _____ = _____

EUREKA
MATH™

Lesson 19: Represent the same story scenario with addends repositioned (the commutative property).

243

©2015 Great Minds. eureka-math.org
G1-M1-TE-BK1-1.3.1-01.2016

Lesson 20

Objective: Apply the commutative property to count on from a larger addend.

Suggested Lesson Structure

■ Fluency Practice   (15 minutes)
░ Application Problem   (7 minutes)
░ Concept Development   (28 minutes)
■ Student Debrief   (10 minutes)
  Total Time   **(60 minutes)**

Fluency Practice (15 minutes)

- Sparkle: Count by Tens, Starting at 5 **K.CC.5**   (5 minutes)
- Linking Cube Partners: 10 **1.OA.6**   (10 minutes)

Sparkle: Count By Tens, Starting at 5 (5 minutes)

Note: Providing students with ongoing counting practice throughout the year builds and maintains their counting skills, which are foundational for later first grade work with adding and subtracting tens.

Play two games of Sparkle, counting by tens, starting at 5. For the first game, count the regular way: 5, 15, 25, 35… For the second game, count by tens the Say Ten Way: 5, 1 ten 5, 2 tens 5, 3 tens 5…

Linking Cube Partners: 10 (10 minutes)

Materials: (S) 10 linking cubes (5 cubes one color, 5 cubes another color) per pair, personal white board

Note: This activity provides continued practice with the commutative property and prepares students for today's objective. It also addresses the core fluency objective for Grade 1 of adding and subtracting within 10.

Show students 10 linking cubes in a stick with a color change at the 5, and then remove it from sight. Break off a part and show the part to students. Students make a number bond and two number sentences to match the part shown and the part hidden (commutative property).

Application Problem (7 minutes)

Laura had 5 fish. Her mother gave her 1 more. Laura's brother Frank
had 1 fish. Their mother gave Frank 5 more. Laura cried, "That's not
fair! He has more fish than I do!"

Use number bonds and a number sentence to show Laura the truth.
If you can, write a sentence with words that would help Laura
understand.

Note: This problem is designed to support student understanding of
the commutative property to enable them to apply this property for
the sake of efficiency in the upcoming Concept Development.

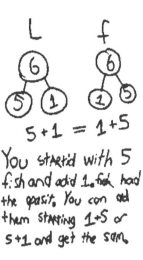

$5 + 1 = 1 + 5$

You started with 5
fish and add 1. fish had
the oppasit. You can add
them starting 1+5 or
5+1 and get the sam.

Concept Development (28 minutes)

Materials: (S) Expression cards (Template 1), equal signs (Template 2) per pair

Note: There are enough expression cards for 34 students. Multiple copies of the equal signs sheet will be
needed to accommodate the number of students in the class.

While students are still at their seats, give them expression cards, and ask each student to hold his card so the
class cannot see it.

T: Find someone who has an expression card with a total equal to yours. When you find your partner,
take an equal sign from the pile in front of the room, sit with your partner, and write a number
sentence with your expression cards.

S: (Look for a partner, take an equal sign, sit together, and make a number sentence such as
3 + 2 = 2 + 3.)

T: Great job finding your partner. Here is one of the number sentences a partnership made.
(Write 1 + 7 = 7 + 1 on the board.)

T: Does everyone agree that 1 plus 7 is the same amount
as 7 plus 1?

S: Yes!

T: (Write the two expressions underneath each other:
1 + 7 and 7 + 1)

T: If I wanted to count on to solve this, which would be
faster, starting with 1 and counting on 7 or starting
with 7 and counting on 1? Talk with a partner.

S: (Discuss.)

T: Let's try counting on with both to decide together.

S/T: Onnnnnne (gesture to first addend), 2, 3, 4, 5, 6, 7, 8.
(Keep track on fingers.)

NOTES ON
MULTIPLE MEANS
OF ACTION AND
EXPRESSION:

Some students may still be developing
their ability to decide which number is
bigger within a number sentence.
Offer students the choice to respond
by first circling or coloring the bigger
number. Then, have them write the
number sentence using the circled or
colored number first.

T: Now, let's try the second expression.

S/T: Seveeeennnnn (gesture to first addend), 8. (Keep track on fingers.)

Repeat the process with 3 + 5 and 5 + 3. Collect the expressions, redistribute them, and allow students to play again.

NOTES ON
MULTIPLE MEANS
OF ENGAGEMENT:

Adjust the lesson structure to suit specific learning needs, remembering that some students will need to keep counting all (by using objects or their 5-group cards to expose all of the dots).

T: Which way was the faster way to count on?

S: 5 + 3.

T: Why?

S: When you start with the bigger number, you don't have to count on as much.

T: What about when we solved 7 + 1 and 1 + 7? Discuss which was faster and why with your partner.

S: (Discuss with partner.)

Problem Set (10 minutes)

Distribute Problem Set to students, and allow them to work independently or in small groups.

Students should do their personal best to complete the Problem Set within the allotted 10 minutes. For some classes, it may be appropriate to modify the assignment by specifying which problems they work on first. Some problems do not specify a method for solving. Students solve these problems using the RDW approach used for Application Problems.

Student Debrief (10 minutes)

Lesson Objective: Apply the commutative property to count on from a larger addend.

The Student Debrief is intended to invite reflection and active processing of the total lesson experience.

Invite students to review their solutions for the Problem Set. They should check work by comparing answers with a partner before going over answers as a class. Look for misconceptions or misunderstandings that can be addressed in the Debrief. Guide students in a conversation to debrief the Problem Set and process the lesson.

Any combination of the questions below may be used to lead the discussion.

- Look at your Application Problem. How does it relate to today's lesson?

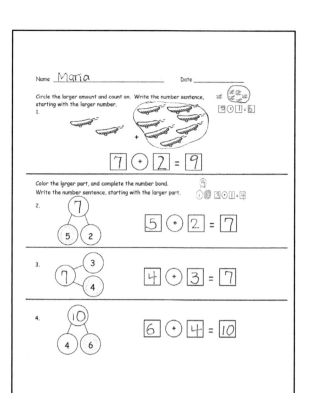

Lesson 20:   Apply the commutative property to count on from a larger addend.

©2015 Great Minds. eureka-math.org
G1-M1-TE-BK1-1.3.1-01.2016

- Which problems on your Problem Set required you to rewrite the number sentence to count on from the larger number?
- When does switching the order to count on from the larger number help you the most?
- If I gave you a really challenging expression like 1 + 51, how could you use what you learned today to make it an easier expression to solve?

Exit Ticket (3 minutes)

After the Student Debrief, instruct students to complete the Exit Ticket. A review of their work will help with assessing students' understanding of the concepts that were presented in today's lesson and planning more effectively for future lessons. The questions may be read aloud to the students.

Color the larger part of the bond. Count on from that part to find the total, and fill in the number bond. Complete the first number sentence, and then rewrite the number sentence to start with the larger part.

5.

$2 + 7 = 9$

$7 + 2 = 9$

6.

$3 + 6 = 9$

$6 + 3 = 9$

Circle the larger number, and count on to solve.

7. $1 + ⑤ = \underline{6}$ 8. $2 + ⑥ = \underline{8}$

9. $④ + 3 = \underline{4}$ 10. $3 + ⑥ = \underline{9}$

EUREKA MATH

Lesson 20:   Apply the commutative property to count on from a larger addend.

247

©2015 Great Minds. eureka-math.org
G1-M1-TE-BK1-1.3.1-01.2016

Name _____ Date _____

Circle the larger amount and count on. Write the number sentence, starting with the larger number.

1.

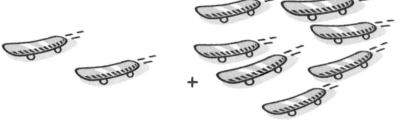

9 + 1 = 5

☐ + ☐ = ☐

Color the larger part, and complete the number bond.
Write the number sentence, starting with the larger part.

3 + 1 = 4

2.

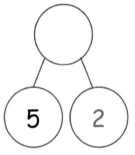

☐ + ☐ = ☐

3.

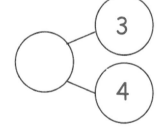

☐ + ☐ = ☐

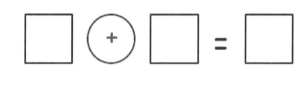

4.

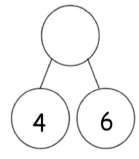

☐ + ☐ = ☐

Lesson 20: Apply the commutative property to count on from a larger addend.

EUREKA MATH™

©2015 Great Minds. eureka-math.org
G1-M1-TE-BK1-1.3.1-01.2016

Color the larger part of the bond. Count on from that part to find the total, and fill in the number bond. Complete the first number sentence, and then rewrite the number sentence to start with the larger part.

5.

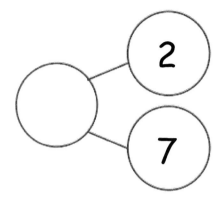

| 2 | + | | = | |

| | + | | = | |

6.

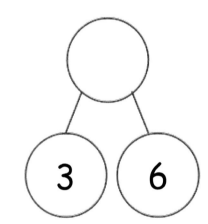

| 3 | + | | = | |

| | + | | = | |

Circle the larger number, and count on to solve.

7. 1 + 5 = _____

8. 2 + 6 = _____

9. 4 + 3 = _____

10. 3 + 6 = _____

EUREKA
MATH™

Lesson 20: Apply the commutative property to count on from a larger addend.

249

©2015 Great Minds. eureka-math.org
G1-M1-TE-BK1-1.3.1-01.2016

Name _____ Date _____

Circle the larger part, and complete the number bond. Write the number sentence, starting with the larger part.

a.

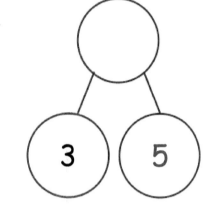

b.

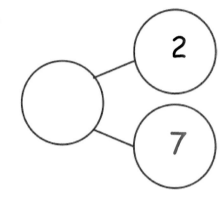

 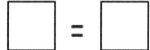 =

Lesson 20:   Apply the commutative property to count on from a larger addend.

©2015 Great Minds. eureka-math.org
G1-M1-TE-BK1-1.3.1-01.2016

EUREKA MATH™

Name _____ Date _____

Color the larger part, and complete the number bond.
Write the number sentence, starting with the larger part.

1.

2.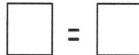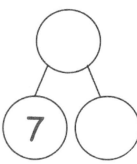

3.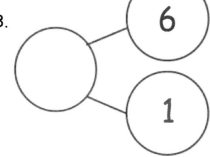

_____ + _____ = _____

4.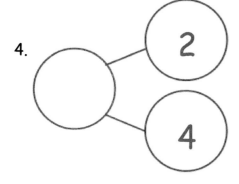

_____ + _____ = _____

EUREKA MATH

Lesson 20:   Apply the commutative property to count on from a larger addend.

251

5.

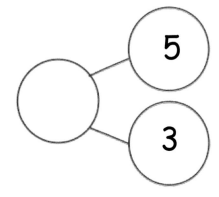

_____ + _____ = _____

6.

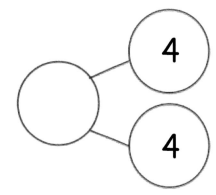

_____ + _____ = _____

7.

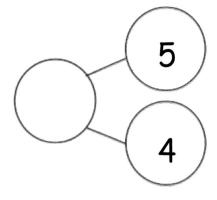

_____ + _____ = _____

Lesson 20:   Apply the commutative property to count on from a larger addend.

EUREKA
MATH™

©2015 Great Minds. eureka-math.org
G1-M1-TE-BK1-1.3.1-01.2016

$7 + 3$	$3 + 7$
$8 + 2$	$2 + 8$
$9 + 0$	$0 + 9$
$8 + 1$	$1 + 8$
$6 + 3$	$3 + 6$
$7 + 1$	$1 + 7$

expression cards

Lesson 20:   Apply the commutative property to count on from a larger addend.   **253**

©2015 Great Minds. eureka-math.org
G1-M1-TE-BK1-1.3.1-01.2016

6 + 2	2 + 6
5 + 3	3 + 5
4 + 3	3 + 4
5 + 2	2 + 5
5 + 1	1 + 5
4 + 2	2 + 4

expression cards

Lesson 20:   Apply the commutative property to count on from a larger addend.

EUREKA
MATH™

4 + 1	1 + 4
2 + 3	3 + 2
4 + 0	0 + 4
3 + 1	1 + 3
2 + 1	1 + 2

expression cards

EUREKA MATH™

Lesson 20:   Apply the commutative property to count on from a larger addend.

255

©2015 Great Minds. eureka-math.org
G1-M1-TE-BK1-1.3.1-01.2016

equal signs

Lesson 20: Apply the commutative property to count on from a larger addend.

EUREKA
MATH™

Mathematics Curriculum

Topic F

Development of Addition Fluency Within 10

1.OA.3, 1.OA.6

Focus Standard:	1.OA.3	Apply properties of operations as strategies to add and subtract. *Examples: If 8 + 3 = 11 is known, then 3 + 8 = 11 is also known. (Commutative property of addition.) To add 2 + 6 + 4, the second two numbers can be added to make a ten, so 2 + 6 + 4 = 2 + 10 = 12. (Associative property of addition.)*
	1.OA.6	Add and subtract within 20, demonstrating fluency for addition and subtraction within 10. Use strategies such as counting on; making ten (e.g., 8 + 6 = 8 + 2 + 4 = 10 + 4 = 14); decomposing a number leading to a ten (e.g., 13 − 4 = 13 − 3 − 1 = 10 − 1 = 9); using the relationship between addition and subtraction (e.g., knowing that 8 + 4 = 12, one knows 12 − 8 = 4); and creating equivalent but easier or known sums (e.g., adding 6 + 7 by creating the known equivalent 6 + 6 + 1 = 12 + 1 = 13).
Instructional Days:	4	
Coherence -Links from:	GK–M4	Number Pairs, Addition and Subtraction to 10
-Links to:	G2–M4	Addition and Subtraction Within 200 with Word Problems to 100

Topic F continues with the theme of more efficient strategies coupled with deep understanding to solve addition problems within 10. In Lesson 21, students begin to internalize doubles and doubles plus 1 as they work with visual representations of these problems (**1.OA.6**).

As students almost take a mental picture of these doubles and doubles plus 1 dot configurations, they can call on these images to quickly assist them when faced with these problems in the future. Students explore patterns on the addition chart within the context of familiar facts in Lessons 22 and 23 (MP.7, MP.8).

1 + 0	1 + 1	1 + 2	1 + 3	1 + 4	1 + 5	1 + 6	1 + 7	1 + 8	1 + 9
2 + 0	2 + 1	2 + 2	2 + 3	2 + 4	2 + 5	2 + 6	2 + 7	2 + 8	
3 + 0	3 + 1	3 + 2	3 + 3	3 + 4	3 + 5	3 + 6	3 + 7		
4 + 0	4 + 1	4 + 2	4 + 3	4 + 4	4 + 5	4 + 6			
5 + 0	5 + 1	5 + 2	5 + 3	5 + 4	5 + 5				
6 + 0	6 + 1	6 + 2	6 + 3	6 + 4					
7 + 0	7 + 1	7 + 2	7 + 3						
8 + 0	8 + 1	8 + 2							
9 + 0	9 + 1								
10 + 0									

EUREKA MATH™

Topic F: Development of Addition Fluency Within 10.

257

©2015 Great Minds. eureka-math.org
G1-M1-TE-BK1-1.3.1-01.2016

Lesson 22 focuses on having students look for common addends and discuss how those addends affect the total in systematic ways. For example, "I see 3 + 2 = 5, 4 + 2 = 6, 5 + 2 = 7, and 6 + 2 = 8. Even though we're adding 2 each time and that stays the same, the totals are increasing by 1, because we're adding a number that's 1 more each time!" Building upon this, Lesson 23 has students using the facts they know, such as those from Topic B's decomposition posters, to explore patterns in problems where the totals are the same. The topic closes with Lesson 24's addition fact practice, where students actually get to practice their facts in an engaging, supportive environment with their peers (**1.OA.6**).

A Teaching Sequence Toward Mastery of Development of Addition Fluency Within 10
Objective 1: Visualize and solve doubles and doubles plus 1 with 5-group cards. (Lesson 21)
Objective 2: Look for and make use of repeated reasoning on the addition chart by solving and analyzing problems with common addends. (Lesson 22)
Objective 3: Look for and make use of structure on the addition chart by looking for and coloring problems with the same total. (Lesson 23)
Objective 4: Practice to build fluency with facts to 10. (Lesson 24)

©2015 Great Minds. eureka-math.org
G1-M1-TE-BK1-1.3.1-01.2016

Lesson 21

Objective: Visualize and solve doubles and doubles plus 1 with
5-group cards.

Suggested Lesson Structure

- ■ Fluency Practice   (12 minutes)
- ▨ Application Problem   (5 minutes)
- ▢ Concept Development   (28 minutes)
- ▨ Student Debrief   (15 minutes)
- **Total Time**   **(60 minutes)**

Fluency Practice (12 minutes)

- Stand on Even Numbers **1.OA.5**   (3 minutes)
- Target Practice: 8 **1.OA.6**   (9 minutes)

Stand on Even Numbers (3 minutes)

Note: Counting on allows students to maintain fluency with this strategy as they solve addition problems.

Students sit in a circle and count by ones, each student saying one number to count up. When a student says an even number, she stands: 1, 2 (student stands), 3, 4 (student stands)... Continue around the circle until all students are standing. Those who are standing do not continue counting. Then, continuing in the same direction around the circle, students count backwards, beginning with the last number said and sitting on even numbers.

Play the game a second time, instructing students who stay still to whisper their numbers and students who stand or sit to use a normal voice.

Target Practice: 8 (9 minutes)

Materials: (S) Per set of partners: personal white board, target practice (Lesson 10 Fluency Template),
              8 counters, 1 die

Note: This activity addresses the core fluency objective for Grade 1 of adding and subtracting within 10.

Follow the directions on the Target Practice template. Use 8 as the target number.

Lesson 21:   Visualize and solve doubles and doubles plus 1 with 5-group cards.   **259**

©2015 Great Minds. eureka-math.org
G1-M1-TE-BK1-1.3.1-01.2016

Application Problem (5 minutes)

Jordan is holding a container with 3 pencils. His teacher gives him 4 more pencils for the container. How many pencils will be in the container? Write a number bond, number sentence, and statement to show the solution.

Note: This problem is an application of the commutative property to count on from the larger addend from Lesson 20. It is also relevant to the Concept Development of the current lesson as a doubles plus 1 problem.

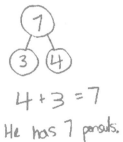

$4 + 3 = 7$

He has 7 pencils.

Concept Development (28 minutes)

Materials: (T) 5-group cards (1–6) (Lesson 5 Template 1), addition chart (Template), colored pencils (yellow, orange) (S) Personal white board

Have students sit next to their math partners in the meeting area or at their tables.

T: Let's count by twos using our fingers. Watch me first.

T/S: (Show fingers.) 2, 4, 6, 8, 10, 10, 8, 6, 4, 2.

T: Show me 1 and 1 with your pinkies like me. (See image below.) How many fingers are you holding up?

S: 2.

T: What is the number sentence?

S: $1 + 1 = 2$.

T: Show me 2 and 2 fingers, your pinkies and ring fingers. Say the number sentence to tell how many fingers you're holding up.

S: $2 + 2 = 4$.

Continue with 3 + 3, 4 + 4, 5 + 5, and back down to 1 + 1.

T: What did you notice about the numbers we added each time?

S: We added the same number two times.

T: We call those **doubles.**

NOTES ON
MULTIPLE MEANS
OF ENGAGEMENT:

To help students recognize the doubles they are creating, encourage them to wiggle their fingers as they hold up doubles. For instance, to solve 3 + 3, have students wiggle pinkies and say "two," wiggle pinkies and ring fingers and say "four," and finally wiggle pinky, ring, and middle fingers and say "six."

260   Lesson 21:   Visualize and solve doubles and doubles plus 1 with 5-group cards.

EUREKA
MATH

©2015 Great Minds. eureka-math.org
G1-M1-TE-BK1-1.3.1-01.2016

Give 2 minutes for students to work with a partner and practice making doubles number sentences. Partner A flashes doubles fingers; Partner B says the number sentence. They switch roles after 1 minute.

T: (Show two 5-group cards showing 3 dots.) Without counting all, tell how many dots there are.

S: 6.

T: How did you know?

S: I saw doubles. Three and 3. That makes 6.

Continue with 2 + 2, 4 + 4, and 5 + 5, ensuring students use the term *doubles* to explain what they see and eventually naming it as a strategy. Congratulate them on getting better at mastering their doubles facts.

T: (Show 3 dots card and 4 dots card.) Without counting all, tell how many dots there are.

S: 7.

T: How did you know so quickly? Turn and talk to your partner. (Circulate and listen.)

T: Bobbie said she saw 3 and 3 plus another dot! Give thumbs up if you see 3 dots hiding inside these 4 dots.

S: (Show thumbs.)

T: She used her doubles fact to help. Three plus 3 (circle 3 dots and 3 dots), that's….

S: 6.

T: Plus another dot?

S: 7.

T: How is 3 + 4 related to 3 + 3?

S: It's making doubles and adding 1 more.

T: This is called **doubles plus 1**. Let's see if we can find more doubles facts hiding inside another expression.

Continue with 1 + 2, 3 + 2, and 4 + 5.

T: (Project the numerals 4 and 5.) How would you solve 4 + 5 using what you learned in today's lesson? Turn and talk to your partner, and solve on your board.

MP.8

S: (Write 4 + 5 = 9.) Use our doubles facts. 4 + 4 = 8. Add 1 more, and you get 9.

T: (Project 3 + __ = 6.) What number is missing here? Talk with your partner to decide. Tell each other how you know.

S: (Discuss with partner.)

T: What is the missing number in 3 + __ = 6?

S: 3.

T: How do you know?

S: I know that 3 + 3 = 6. I thought of the doubles. If I have 3 (holds up 3 fingers on one hand), I need 3 more to make 6.

T: (Project 3 + __ = 7.) What number is missing here? Discuss with your partner. Remember to use words or your boards to explain your thinking.

NOTES ON
MULTIPLE MEANS
OF ENGAGEMENT:

For students who have reached mastery with larger doubles, consider using other doubles facts within their repertoire. This helps motivate those students and keep them actively engaged in the objective.

Lesson 21:   Visualize and solve doubles and doubles plus 1 with 5-group cards.

261

©2015 Great Minds. eureka-math.org
G1-M1-TE-BK1-1.3.1-01.2016

S: (Discuss with partner.)

T: What is the missing number in 3 + __ = 7?

S: 4.

T: How could the last problem, 3 + 3 = 6, help you with this one?

S: If you know 3 + 3 is 6, and you need to have 7, you know you need 1 more than last time, so now it's 3 + 4.

Continue with 4 + 4 and 4 + 5.

Problem Set (10 minutes)

Students should do their personal best to complete the Problem Set within the allotted 10 minutes. For some classes, it may be appropriate to modify the assignment by specifying which problems they work on first. Some problems do not specify a method for solving. Students solve these problems using the RDW approach used for Application Problems.

In this Problem Set, students should begin with Problem 1, Problem 2, Problem 5, Problem 6, and possibly leave Problem 7(d) and 7(e), Problem 8, and Problem 9 to the end if there is still time.

Student Debrief (15 minutes)

Lesson Objective: Visualize and solve doubles and doubles plus 1 with 5-group cards.

The Student Debrief is intended to invite reflection and active processing of the total lesson experience.

Invite students to review their solutions for the Problem Set. They should check work by comparing answers with a partner before going over answers as a class. Look for misconceptions or misunderstandings that can be addressed in the Debrief. Guide students in a conversation to debrief the Problem Set and process the lesson.

Any combination of the questions below may be used to lead the discussion.

- (Post the addition chart.) Can you find all the **doubles** facts? (Color them red.) What do you notice about these numbers?

- Can you find all the **doubles plus 1** facts? (Color them using blue.) What do you notice about the two parts in doubles plus 1 facts? (They are the numbers next to each other when we count.)

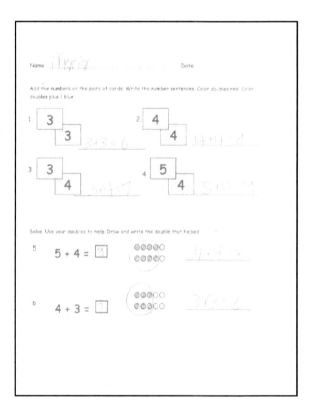

EUREKA MATH

©2015 Great Minds. eureka-math.org
G1-M1-TE-BK1-1.3.1-01.2016

- Is 4 + 3 a doubles plus 1? Why? How is this related to another math lesson from before? Can you find any more doubles plus 1 facts like this one? (Color them blue if you find any more.)

- Look at Problem 7 in your Problem Set. What do you notice about all the answers to the doubles facts? (They are all even numbers.) What do you notice about all the answers to the doubles plus 1 facts? (They are all odd numbers.) Is this always true? Explain your thinking.

- Look at Problem 7(e) and (f) in your Problem Set. How could you use the pictures in your mind or your knowledge of doubles facts to help you solve these problems?

- Look at your Application Problem. If you used counting on to solve this, which number did you start with in your number sentence? Can you use the strategy from today's lesson to solve this? How?

7. Solve the doubles and the doubles plus 1 number sentences.

a. 0 + 0 = $\boxed{0}$ 0 + 1 = $\boxed{1}$

b. 2 + 2 = $\boxed{4}$ 2 + 3 = $\boxed{5}$

c. 3 + 3 = $\boxed{6}$ 3 + 4 = $\boxed{7}$

d. 4 + 4 = $\boxed{8}$ 4 + 5 = $\boxed{9}$

e. 3 + $\boxed{3}$ = 6   3 + $\boxed{4}$ = 7

f. 5 + $\boxed{5}$ = 10   4 + $\boxed{5}$ = 9

8. Show how this strategy can help you solve: 5 + 6 = $\boxed{11}$

5+5=10   00000 0   5+6 is one
          00000   more.

9. Write a set of 4 related addition facts for the number sentences at Problem 7(d).

4 + 4 = 8   8 = 4 + 4
4 + 5 = 9   9 = 4 + 5

Exit Ticket (3 minutes)

After the Student Debrief, instruct students to complete the Exit Ticket. A review of their work will help with assessing students' understanding of the concepts that were presented in today's lesson and planning more effectively for future lessons. The questions may be read aloud to the students.

Name _____ Date _____

Add the numbers on the pairs of cards. Write the number sentences. Color doubles red. Color doubles plus 1 blue.

1.
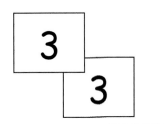
_____

2.
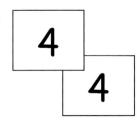
_____

3.
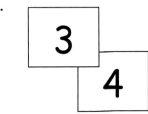
_____

4.
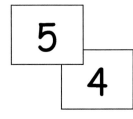
_____

Solve. Use your doubles to help. Draw and write the double that helped.

5.   5 + 4 = ☐   OOOOO
                 OOOOO   _____

6.   4 + 3 = ☐   OOOOO
                 OOOOO   _____

Lesson 21:   Visualize and solve doubles and doubles plus 1 with 5-group cards.

EUREKA MATH

7. Solve the doubles and the doubles plus 1 number sentences.

a. $0 + 0 = \boxed{}$ $0 + 1 = \boxed{}$

b. $2 + 2 = \boxed{}$ $2 + 3 = \boxed{}$

c. $3 + 3 = \boxed{}$ $3 + 4 = \boxed{}$

d. $4 + 4 = \boxed{}$ $4 + 5 = \boxed{}$

e. $3 + \boxed{} = 6$ $3 + \boxed{} = 7$

f. $5 + \boxed{} = 10$ $4 + \boxed{} = 9$

8. Show how this strategy can help you solve $5 + 6 = \boxed{}$

9. Write a set of 4 related addition facts for the number sentences of Problem 7(d).

Lesson 21: Visualize and solve doubles and doubles plus 1 with 5-group cards.

265

Name _____   Date _____

Write the double and double plus 1 number sentence for each 5-group card.

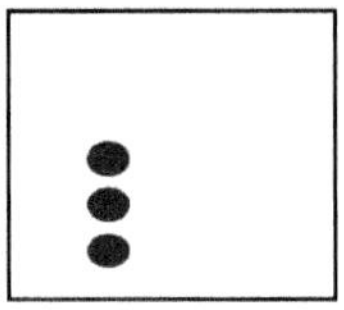

:··	4	5

_____   _____   _____

_____   _____   _____

Name _____   Date _____

1. Draw the 5-group card to show a double. Write the number sentence to match the cards.

a.

b.

c.

2. Fill in the 5-group cards in order from least to greatest, double the number, and write the number sentences.

a.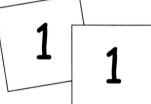

b.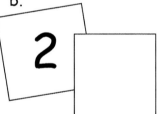

c.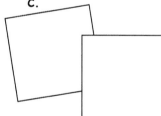

d.

e.

EUREKA
MATH™

Lesson 21:   Visualize and solve doubles and doubles plus 1 with 5-group cards.

267

©2015 Great Minds. eureka-math.org
G1-M1-TE-BK1-1.3.1-01.2016

3. Solve the number sentences.

a. 3 + 3 = ____

b. 5 + ____ = 10

c. 1 + ____ = 2

d. 4 = ____ + 2

e. 8 = 4 + ____

4. Match the top cards to the bottom cards to show doubles plus 1.

a. 1

b. 4

c. 3

d. 2

5

2

3

4

5. Solve the number sentences. Write the double fact that helped you solve the double plus 1.

a.

2 + 3 = ____

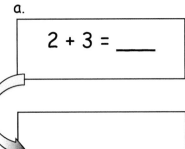

b.

3 + ____ = 7

c.

4 + ____ = 9

Lesson 21:   Visualize and solve doubles and doubles plus 1 with 5-group cards.

1 + 9									
1 + 8	2 + 8								
1 + 7	2 + 7	3 + 7							
1 + 6	2 + 6	3 + 6	4 + 6						
1 + 5	2 + 5	3 + 5	4 + 5	5 + 5					
1 + 4	2 + 4	3 + 4	4 + 4	5 + 4	6 + 4				
1 + 3	2 + 3	3 + 3	4 + 3	5 + 3	6 + 3	7 + 3			
1 + 2	2 + 2	3 + 2	4 + 2	5 + 2	6 + 2	7 + 2	8 + 2		
1 + 1	2 + 1	3 + 1	4 + 1	5 + 1	6 + 1	7 + 1	8 + 1	9 + 1	
1 + 0	2 + 0	3 + 0	4 + 0	5 + 0	6 + 0	7 + 0	8 + 0	9 + 0	10 + 0

addition chart

Lesson 21: Visualize and solve doubles and doubles plus 1 with 5-group cards.

269

Lesson 22

Objective: Look for and make use of repeated reasoning on the addition chart by solving and analyzing problems with common addends.

Suggested Lesson Structure

■ Fluency Practice   (13 minutes)
▨ Application Problem   (5 minutes)
░ Concept Development   (32 minutes)
▨ Student Debrief   (10 minutes)
   Total Time   **(60 minutes)**

Fluency Practice (13 minutes)

- Sparkle: Counting by Twos **1.OA.5**   (5 minutes)
- Penny Drop: 8 **1.OA.5, 1.OA.6**   (3 minutes)
- Number Bond Dash: 8 **1.OA.6**   (5 minutes)

Sparkle: Counting by Twos (5 minutes)

Note: Practicing counting up allows students to maintain fluency with the strategy as it relates to addition.

Play Sparkle, counting by twos from 0 to 20. (Refer to game directions in Lesson 7.) While practicing the counting sequence before the game, model the say–think–say skip-counting strategy: say 0, think 1, say 2, think 3…

Penny Drop: 8 (3 minutes)

Materials: (T) 8 pennies, 1 can

Note: This activity addresses the core fluency objective for Grade 1 of adding and subtracting within 10.

Show students 8 pennies. Have students close their eyes and listen. Drop some of the pennies in a can, one at a time. To prepare students for the upcoming subtraction lessons, instruct them to count back from 8 in their heads as they hear each penny drop. Ask students to open their eyes and say how many pennies are still in the teacher's hand.

NOTES ON
MULTIPLE MEANS
OF ACTION AND
EXPRESSION:

Not all students are comfortable being timed while completing Fluency Practice activities. Allow these students extra time for completion so that they feel successful and strive to do their best during these exercises.

EUREKA
MATH™

©2015 Great Minds. eureka-math.org
G1-M1-TE-BK1-1.3.1-01.2016

Number Bond Dash: 8 (5 minutes)

Materials: (T) Stopwatch or timer (S) Number bond dash 8 (Lesson 7 Fluency Template 2), marker to correct work

Note: By using the same system repeatedly, students can focus on the mathematics alone. This activity addresses the core fluency objective for Grade 1 of adding and subtracting within 10. Teachers may want to take note of students who are using finger counting. This may help identify students who require additional time or support to solve partners of 8.

Follow the procedure for the Number Bond Dash in Lesson 5 Fluency Practice. Tell students to remember how many problems they get correct so they can try to improve their scores tomorrow.

Application Problem (5 minutes)

May and Kay are twins. Whatever May has, Kay has it, too. May has 2 dolls. How many dolls do May and Kay have together? May has 3 stuffed animals. How many stuffed animals do they have together? Write a number bond, number sentence, and statement to show your solution.

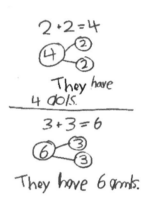

Extension: If all the dolls and all the stuffed animals were put together for an imaginary tea party, how many toys would there be? Draw or write to explain your thinking.

Note: This problem is designed as a bridge from the previous lesson, which focused on doubles. Students will also have the opportunity to locate the expressions within their number sentences on the chart and begin to recognize other ways to use repeated reasoning as they explore the addition chart. Teachers may want to take note of students who are using finger counting for doubles. This may help identify students who require additional time or support to utilize doubles as a strategy.

Concept Development (32 minutes)

Materials: (T) Addition chart with sums to 10 (Lesson 21 Template), cover paper

- T: (Post or project addition chart, reveal only the +0 column.) Mathematicians, today you need to especially put on your noticing ears and eyes! Read the expressions aloud with me.
- S/T: 1 + 0, 2 + 0, 3 + 0, 4 + 0, 5 + 0, 6 + 0, 7 + 0, 8 + 0, 9 + 0, 10 + 0.
- T: What did you notice was the same as you read each of these expressions?
- S: We said "plus zero" every time!

Addition Chart with +0 Revealed

                    Lesson 22:   Look for and make use of repeated reasoning on the addition chart by
EUREKA MATH   solving and analyzing problems with common addends.   271

©2015 Great Minds. eureka-math.org
G1-M1-TE-BK1-1.3.1-01.2016

T: What did you notice was different as you read each of these expressions?

S: The first number went up by 1 each time!

T: Good. Now, let's solve each problem together.

As students solve the problems, transform the expressions into equations as the teacher or student volunteers write the solutions. Be sure to have students read the equations aloud. Next, reveal the +1 column, and go through the same process of having students read, notice the similarities and differences, and then solve.

T: (Point to 1 + 0 and 2 + 0.) You said that all of these problems add zero each time. How does adding zero change this first **addend**, or part? (Point.)

S: The first addend doesn't change, because we're just adding zero!

T: So, it's zero more than the first number? Is this true of all of the facts in this area? (Gesture to the + 0 column.)

S: Yes!

T: (Point to 8 + 1 and 9 + 1.) You said that all of these problems add 1 each time. How does adding 1 change this first addend?

S: The total goes up by 1, because we're adding on! → It's just the next counting number!

Continue this process with the +2 column, focusing on the common addends.

Problem Set (15 minutes)

Note: Explain to students to complete one color at a time. Students do not need to overlap colors. For example, 1 + 2 will already be colored red. Students do not need to color it orange.

Students should do their personal best to complete the Problem Set within the allotted 10 minutes. For some classes, it may be appropriate to modify the assignment by specifying which problems they work on first. Some problems do not specify a method for solving. Students solve these problems using the RDW approach used for Application Problems.

NOTES ON MULTIPLE MEANS OF REPRESENTATION:

Some students will benefit from an addition chart colored based on the addend. For example, color all the +0 blue, +1 yellow, +3 green, etc. Using the addition chart in this way will especially help visually impaired students who may find the chart hard to read.

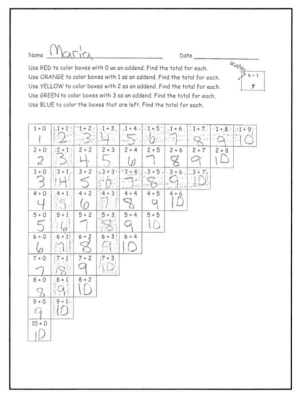

Lesson 22: Look for and make use of repeated reasoning on the addition chart by solving and analyzing problems with common addends.

Student Debrief (10 minutes)

Lesson Objective: Look for and make use of repeated reasoning on the addition chart by solving and analyzing problems with common addends.

The Student Debrief is intended to invite reflection and active processing of the total lesson experience.

Invite students to review their solutions for the Problem Set. They should check work by comparing answers with a partner before going over answers as a class. Look for misconceptions or misunderstandings that can be addressed in the Debrief. Guide students in a conversation to debrief the Problem Set and process the lesson.

Any combination of the questions below may be used to lead the discussion.

- Look at your Problem Set. We talked about how all the problems add 1 each time in this column. (Gesture going up and down on +1 column.) Is that the only place that had problems adding 1 each time?
- How are the second column (n + 1) and the first row (1 + n) related? Does this remind you of another math lesson?
- Which row is the third column related to? What **addend**, or part, do they have in common?
- Look at your Application Problem. Can you find the expressions from your number sentences on the chart? What do you notice about their locations?
- Which colored boxes have the easiest facts for you to solve? Why?
- Which colored boxes have the facts you need the most practice with? Why?
- How can this chart help you learn your facts better?

Exit Ticket (3 minutes)

After the Student Debrief, instruct students to complete the Exit Ticket. A review of their work will help with assessing students' understanding of the concepts that were presented in today's lesson and planning more effectively for future lessons. The questions may be read aloud to the students.

          Lesson 22:   Look for and make use of repeated reasoning on the addition chart by   **273**
                            solving and analyzing problems with common addends.

©2015 Great Minds. eureka-math.org
G1-M1-TE-BK1-1.3.1-01.2016

Name _____   Date _____

1. Use RED to color boxes with 0 as an addend. Find the total for each.
2. Use ORANGE to color boxes with 1 as an addend. Find the total for each.
3. Use YELLOW to color boxes with 2 as an addend. Find the total for each.
4. Use GREEN to color boxes with 3 as an addend. Find the total for each.
5. Use BLUE to color the boxes that are left. Find the total for each.

orange
6 + 1
7

1 + 0	1 + 1	1 + 2	1 + 3	1 + 4	1 + 5	1 + 6	1 + 7	1 + 8	1 + 9
2 + 0	2 + 1	2 + 2	2 + 3	2 + 4	2 + 5	2 + 6	2 + 7	2 + 8	
3 + 0	3 + 1	3 + 2	3 + 3	3 + 4	3 + 5	3 + 6	3 + 7		
4 + 0	4 + 1	4 + 2	4 + 3	4 + 4	4 + 5	4 + 6			
5 + 0	5 + 1	5 + 2	5 + 3	5 + 4	5 + 5				
6 + 0	6 + 1	6 + 2	6 + 3	6 + 4					
7 + 0	7 + 1	7 + 2	7 + 3						
8 + 0	8 + 1	8 + 2							
9 + 0	9 + 1								
10 + 0									

Lesson 22:   Look for and make use of repeated reasoning on the addition chart by solving and analyzing problems with common addends.

EUREKA MATH™

Name _____   Date _____

Some of the addends in this chart are missing! Fill in the missing numbers.

1 + 0	1 + 1	1 + 2	1 + 3	1 + 4	1 + 5	1 + 6	1 + 7	1 + 8	1 + 9
2 + 0	2 + 1	2 + 2	2 + __	2 + 4	2 + 5	2 + 6	2 + 7	2 + 8	
3 + 0	3 + 1	3 + 2	3 + __	3 + 4	3 + 5	3 + 6	3 + 7		
4 + 0	4 + __	4 + 2	4 + 3	__ + 4	__ + 5	__ + 6			
5 + 0	5 + __	5 + 2	5 + 3	5 + 4	5 + 5				
6 + 0	6 + __	6 + 2	6 + 3	6 + 4					
7 + __	7 + 1	7 + 2	7 + 3						
8 + __	8 + 1	8 + 2							
9 + __	9 + 1								
10 + 0									

Lesson 22:   Look for and make use of repeated reasoning on the addition chart by
solving and analyzing problems with common addends.

275

©2015 Great Minds. eureka-math.org
G1-M1-TE-BK1-1.3.1-01.2016

Name _____ Date _____

 Solve the problems without counting all. Color the boxes using the key.

Step 1: Color the problems with "+ 1" or "1 +" blue.

Step 2: Color the remaining problems with "+ 2" or "2 +" green.

Step 3: Color the remaining problems with "+ 3" or "3 +" yellow.

a. 7 + 1 = ___	b. 8 + ___ = 9	c. 3 + 1 = ___	d. 5 + 3 = ___
e. 5 + ___ = 7	f. 4 + ___ = 7	g. 6 + 3 = ___	h. 8 + ___ = 10
i. 2 + 1 = ___	j. 1 + ___ = 2	k. 1 + ___ = 4	l. 6 + 2 = ___
m. 3 + ___ = 6	n. 6 + ___ = 7	o. 3 + 2 = ___	p. 5 + 1 = ___
q. 2 + 2 = ___	r. 4 + ___ = 6	s. 4 + 1 = ___	t. 7 + 2 = ___
u. 2 + ___ = 3	v. 9 + 1 = ___	w. 7 + 3 = ___	x. 1 + ___ = 3

Lesson 22: Look for and make use of repeated reasoning on the addition chart by solving and analyzing problems with common addends.

©2015 Great Minds. eureka-math.org
G1-M1-TE-BK1-1.3.1-01.2016

EUREKA MATH

Lesson 23

Objective: Look for and make use of structure on the addition chart by looking for and coloring problems with the same total.

Suggested Lesson Structure

■ Fluency Practice   (12 minutes)
▨ Application Problem   (8 minutes)
▢ Concept Development   (30 minutes)
■ Student Debrief   (10 minutes)

   Total Time   **(60 minutes)**

Fluency Practice (12 minutes)

- Happy Counting by Twos **1.OA.5**   (2 minutes)
- Missing Part: 8 **1.OA.6**   (5 minutes)
- Number Bond Dash: 8 **1.OA.6**   (5 minutes)

Happy Counting by Twos (2 minutes)

Note: This activity supports the connection between counting on by 2 and adding 2.

Repeat the Happy Counting activity from Lesson 3, counting by twos from 0 to 20 and back.

Missing Part: 8 (5 minutes)

Materials: (S) 5-group cards (0–8 only) (Lesson 5 Template 1)

Note: This activity addresses the core fluency objective for Grade 1 of mastery of sums to 10.

Students work with partners, using 5-group cards. Each student puts a card on his or her forehead. The partner tells how many more to make 8. Students must guess the cards on their foreheads. Partners can play simultaneously.

Number Bond Dash: 8 (5 minutes)

Materials: (T) Stopwatch or timer (S) Number bond dash 8 (Lesson 7 Fluency Template 2), marker to correct work

Note: This activity addresses the core fluency objective for Grade 1 of adding and subtracting within 10.

Follow the procedure for the Number Bond Dash in Lesson 5 Fluency Practice, remembering today is the second day with making 8. Students should recall their scores from Lesson 22 to see and celebrate improvement.

Application Problem (8 minutes)

John has 3 stickers. Mark has 4 stickers. Anna has 5 stickers. They each get two more stickers. How many do they each have now? Write a number bond and number sentence for each student.

Extension: How many stickers do John, Mark, and Anna have together?

Note: This problem is designed as an application of the previous lesson, which focused on common addends on the addition chart. Students continue to explore the addition chart in today's lesson, focusing on expressions with the same total.

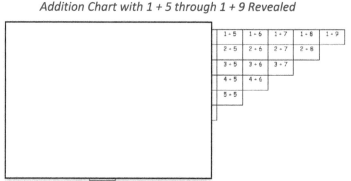

Concept Development (30 minutes)

Materials: (T) Addition chart with sums to 10 to project or post (Lesson 21 Template), cover paper, markers (three different colors) (S) Addition chart with sums to 10 (Lesson 21 Template), pencils (three different colors)

Distribute an addition chart to each student. Have students fold their papers to match the chart below.

T: (Point to 5 + 5.) What is 5 + 5?

S: 10.

T: (Point to 4 + 6.) What is 4 + 6?

S: 10.

T: (Repeat through 1 + 9.) Talk to your partner. What do you notice about the totals?

T: (Circulate and listen. Then, choose students to share with the class.)

Addition Chart with 1 + 5 through 1 + 9 Revealed

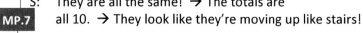

MP.7

S: They are all the same! → The totals are all 10. → They look like they're moving up like stairs!

T: You said all of the totals are 10. Help me color in the expressions that equal 10. (Prompt students to say which to color.)

S: (Lightly color in charts.)

T: What is 4 + 5?

S: 9.

T: Talk with your partner. Find the other expressions that equal 9.

S: (Share with partners to find totals of 9.)

T: Let's color them in. (Using a different color, prompt students to say which to color as they color in their own charts.)

T: Talk with your partner: What do you notice about these problems? (Circulate and listen, and then choose students to share with the class.)

Lesson 23:   Look for and make use of structure on the addition chart by looking for and coloring problems with the same total.

©2015 Great Minds. eureka-math.org
G1-M1-TE-BK1-1.3.1-01.2016

S: They all equal 9. → The totals are all 1 less than the ones we colored in for 10. → They make another staircase!

T: With your partner, look for expressions that equal 8. When you both agree, color them in with your last colored pencil.

S: (Circulate and observe.)

T: Which expressions equal 8? (As students share, color them in on the class chart.)

T: What patterns are you noticing?

S: All the totals of 8 make a slanted line, like a staircase.

NOTES ON
MULTIPLE MEANS
OF ENGAGEMENT:

Offer opportunities for student leadership as "teacher." Have students demonstrate for the class how the staircase works for each total. Listen for the use of math vocabulary in their descriptions.

Problem Set (15 minutes)

Students should do their personal best to complete the Problem Set within the allotted 15 minutes. For some classes, it may be appropriate to modify the assignment by specifying which problems they work on first. Some problems do not specify a method for solving. Students solve these problems using the RDW approach used for Application Problems.

Student Debrief (10 minutes)

Lesson Objective: Look for and make use of structure on the addition chart by looking for and coloring problems with the same total.

The Student Debrief is intended to invite reflection and active processing of the total lesson experience.

Invite students to review their solutions for the Problem Set. They should check work by comparing answers with a partner before going over answers as a class. Look for misconceptions or misunderstandings that can be addressed in the Debrief. Guide students in a conversation to debrief the Problem Set and process the lesson.

Name: Maria _____   Date _____

Use your chart to write a list of number sentences in the spaces below.

Totals of 10	Totals of 9	Totals of 8	Totals of 7
1+9=10	1+8=9	1+7=8	7=1+6
10=2+8	2+7=9	2+6=8	7=2+5
10=3+7	3+6=9	3+5=8	7=3+4
10=4+6	4+5=9	4+4=8	7=4+3
10=5+5	5+4=9	5+3=8	7=5+2
10=6+4	6+3=9	6+2=8	7=6+1
10=7+3	7+2=9	7+1=8	7=7+0
10=8+2	8+1=9	8+0=8	
10=9+1	9+0=9		
10=10+0			

Any combination of the questions below may be used to lead the discussion.

- Look at your Application Problem. What is similar in each of your number bonds? What is different? Could one number bond or number sentence help you solve another one?

- What did you notice about the number of boxes of each color? How many boxes will be colored for the total of 4? 3?

- Why do you think we have more totals for 10 compared to totals for 5?

Lesson 23:   Look for and make use of structure on the addition chart by looking   279
                for and coloring problems with the same total.

©2015 Great Minds. eureka-math.org
G1-M1-TE-BK1-1.3.1-01.2016

- Which totals are the easiest for you to solve? Why?
- Which totals do you think you need to practice the most? What can you do to get better at these expressions?
- (Point to the addition chart from yesterday's work.) How is today's work similar to what we did yesterday? How is it different?

Exit Ticket (3 minutes)

After the Student Debrief, instruct students to complete the Exit Ticket. A review of their work will help with assessing students' understanding of the concepts that were presented in today's lesson and planning more effectively for future lessons. The questions may be read aloud to the students.

Lesson 23:   Look for and make use of structure on the addition chart by looking for and coloring problems with the same total.

©2015 Great Minds. eureka-math.org
G1-M1-TE-BK1-1.3.1-01.2016

Name _____ Date _____

Use your chart to write a list of number sentences in the spaces below.

Totals of 10	Totals of 9	Totals of 8	Totals of 7

Lesson 23:   Look for and make use of structure on the addition chart by looking for and coloring problems with the same total.

281

©2015 Great Minds. eureka-math.org
G1-M1-TE-BK1-1.3.1-01.2016

Name _____   Date _____

1. Circle all the boxes that total 10.
2. Draw an X through all the boxes that total 8.

1 + 0	1 + 1	1 + 2	1 + 3	1 + 4	1 + 5	1 + 6	1 + 7	1 + 8	1 + 9
2 + 0	2 + 1	2 + 2	2 + 3	2 + 4	2 + 5	2 + 6	2 + 7	2 + 8	
3 + 0	3 + 1	3 + 2	3 + 3	3 + 4	3 + 5	3 + 6	3 + 7		
4 + 0	4 + 1	4 + 2	4 + 3	4 + 4	4 + 5	4 + 6			
5 + 0	5 + 1	5 + 2	5 + 3	5 + 4	5 + 5				
6 + 0	6 + 1	6 + 2	6 + 3	6 + 4					
7 + 0	7 + 1	7 + 2	7 + 3						
8 + 0	8 + 1	8 + 2							
9 + 0	9 + 1								
10 + 0									

Lesson 23:   Look for and make use of structure on the addition chart by looking
               for and coloring problems with the same total.

EUREKA
MATH™

Name _____   Date _____

Fill in the missing box, and find the totals for all of the expressions. Use your completed addition chart to help you.

1.

1 + 2	1 + 3
2 + 2	
3 + 2	3 + 3

2.

6 + 1	6 + 2
7 + 1	
	8 + 2
9 + 1	

3.

4 + 4	4 + 5	
5 + 4		
6 + 4		

4.

2 + 4		2 + 6
	3 + 5	

EUREKA MATH™

Lesson 23:   Look for and make use of structure on the addition chart by looking for and coloring problems with the same total.

283

Lesson 24

Objective: Practice to build fluency with facts to 10.

Suggested Lesson Structure

■ Fluency Practice   (15 minutes)
▨ Application Problem   (7 minutes)
▢ Concept Development   (30 minutes)
▨ Student Debrief   (8 minutes)
   Total Time   **(60 minutes)**

Fluency Practice (15 minutes)

- Partner Counting by Twos **1.OA.5**   (2 minutes)
- Cold Call: 2 More and 2 Less **1.OA.5**   (3 minutes)
- Friendly Fact Go Around **1.OA.6**   (10 minutes)

Partner Counting by Twos (2 minutes)

Note: Counting on and back allows students to build and maintain fluency with this strategy as they solve addition and subtraction problems.

Partners alternate saying numbers aloud to count by twos from 0 to 20 and back.

Cold Call: 2 More and 2 Less (3 minutes)

Note: This activity addresses the core fluency objective for Grade 1 of adding and subtracting within 10.

Say a number aloud and instruct students to think about the number that is 2 more. Let them know that the teacher will cold call students to say the number as quickly as possible. Alternate between calling on individual students, the whole class, and groups of students (e.g., only girls, only boys, etc.). Play again, cold calling students to say the number that is 2 less.

Friendly Fact Go Around (10 minutes)

Materials: (T) Friendly Fact Go Around: Addition Strategies Review (Fluency Template)

Note: This activity addresses the core fluency objective for Grade 1 of adding and subtracting within 10.

Project the Friendly Fact Go Around: Addition Strategies Review sheet (or make a poster). Point to a problem and call on a student to answer (e.g., 8 + 0 = ☐). The student answers "8," and then the class says the number sentence aloud, completed with the answer (8 + 0 = 8). If the student gives an incorrect answer, he or she then repeats the correct equation that the class gave. The teacher can adapt the problem to individual students, pointing to easier problems for students who are less fluent.

Application Problem (7 minutes)

The teacher told Henry to get 8 linking cubes. Henry took 4 blue cubes and 3 red cubes. Does Henry have the correct amount of linking cubes? Use pictures or words to explain your thinking.

Note: This problem is designed as a bridge from the previous lesson's focus on common totals on the addition chart. Students also discuss the related facts embedded in the problem during the Debrief.

No. He has 7 cubes

$4 + 3 = 7$

If he needs 8, he needs 4+4. That's a dubble.

Concept Development (30 minutes)

Materials: (T) Friendly Fact Go Around (Fluency Template), Related Fact Ladder (Template 1), 10 expression cards (Template 2) (S) 5–12 expression cards per pair (Template 2)

Materials note: Friendly Fact Go Around and Related Fact Ladder are both to be posted or projected. The suggested set for the expression cards is 3 + 1, 2 + 1, 2 + 2, 3 + 3, 3 + 2, 2 + 3, 4 + 3, 4 + 4, 4 + 5, 5 + 5.

T: (Hold up the expression cards 3 + 1 and 2 + 1. Project ladder picture on the board.) We just found the total of each of the expressions when we played Friendly Fact Go Around. (Tape 3 + 1 on bottom center of board and 2 + 1 directly above it.) How are 3 + 1 and 2 + 1 alike? How are they related to each other?

S: They both are adding 1 to a number.

T: What happens when you add 1 to a number? Use 3 + 1 and 2 + 1 as your examples to explain.

S: You get the next counting number. When you add 1 to 3, you get 4, the next counting number. When you add 1 to 2, you get 3, which is the next counting number after 2. Twooo, 3.

T: We're going to make a Related Fact Ladder. Let's look for an expression that might be related to 2 + 1 in some way. How about 2 + 2? How is 2 + 2 related to 2 + 1?

S: 2 + 2 is one more than 2 + 1.

T: (Place 2 + 2 card on the next ladder rung, above 2 + 1.) Find a card that is related to 2 + 2. Explain how it is related.

S: 3 + 3. It's the next doubles fact.

T: (Add card on the next rung of the ladder.)

NOTES ON
MULTIPLE MEANS
OF REPRESENTATION:

The Related Fact Ladder provides students an opportunity to demonstrate their level of comprehension. This activity facilitates student discovery of patterns and structures in their math work. Encourage students to discover these connections whenever possible.

Repeat the process, having students explain how the expressions are related as cards are added to the ladder rungs in successive order.

Note: There will always be more than one expression that could be an appropriate choice. (For example, appropriate choices to follow 3 + 2 could be 2 + 2 or 3 + 3 as the double that helps solve the expression, or 4 + 1 as an expression with the same total, where 1 is added to the first addend, and 1 is taken away from the second addend.) As long as students are able to discuss the mathematical relationship between the two expressions (i.e., it is the next double, a double plus 1 fact is 1 more than the double fact, or the expression is 1 more than the previous expression), the expression can be used.

Problem Set (10 minutes)

Distribute Problem Sets and expression cards to students. Allow them to play as partners or small groups. Students should do their personal best to complete the Problem Set within the allotted 10 minutes. For some classes, it may be appropriate to modify the assignment by specifying which problems they work on first. Some problems do not specify a method for solving. Students solve these problems using the RDW approach used for Application Problems.

MP.6 & MP.7

To complete the Problem Set, partners begin with the first ladder. They work together to find an expression card that could be the next related fact on the ladder. Partners discuss how the fact is related and write the number sentence on the next rung. When players complete the ladder, they begin the next ladder.

Note: As students play, circulate and ask them to articulate the strategies they used to find the total. This information can be used during the Debrief.

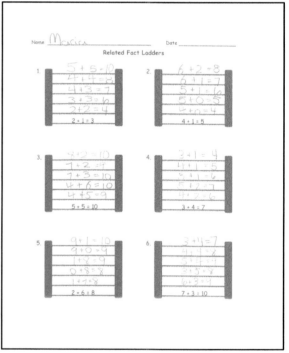

Student Debrief (8 minutes)

Lesson Objective: Practice to build fluency with facts to 10.

The Student Debrief is intended to invite reflection and active processing of the total lesson experience.

Invite students to review their solutions for the Problem Set. They should check work by comparing answers with a partner before going over answers as a class.

Look for misconceptions or misunderstandings that can be addressed in the Debrief. Guide students in a conversation to debrief the Problem Set and process the lesson.

Any combination of the questions below may be used to lead the discussion.

- Share one of your Related Fact Ladders with a partner. Explain how each number sentence is related. What types of relationships did you both use? What was the easiest relationship for you to think of? Why?

©2015 Great Minds. eureka-math.org
G1-M1-TE-BK1-1.3.1-01.2016

- For which facts did you have the hardest time thinking of a related fact? Explain what made it difficult, and what you decided to do.

- Let's look at the addition chart together. How does the chart help us see how facts are related? Use examples to explain your thinking.

- Look at your Application Problem. How could Henry change his number of linking cubes from 4 blue cubes and 3 red cubes so that he has 8 cubes using a related number sentence? Explain how your suggestion is related to 4 + 3 = 7.

Exit Ticket (3 minutes)

After the Student Debrief, instruct students to complete the Exit Ticket. A review of their work will help with assessing students' understanding of the concepts that were presented in today's lesson and planning more effectively for future lessons. The questions may be read aloud to the students.

Name _____   Date _____

Related Fact Ladders

1.
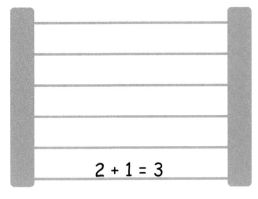
2 + 1 = 3

2.
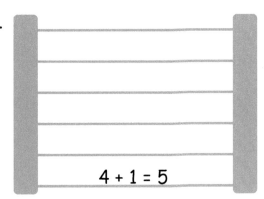
4 + 1 = 5

3.
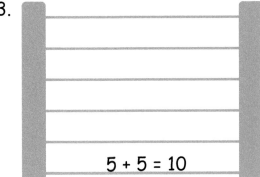
5 + 5 = 10

4.
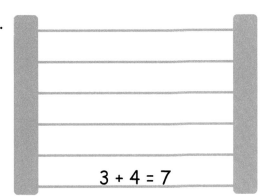
3 + 4 = 7

5.
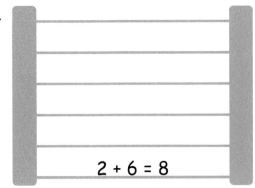
2 + 6 = 8

6.
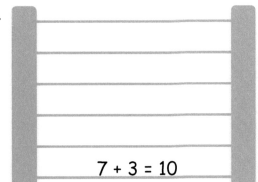
7 + 3 = 10

Lesson 24:   Practice to build fluency with facts to 10.

EUREKA MATH™

©2015 Great Minds. eureka-math.org
G1-M1-TE-BK1-1.3.1-01.2016

Name _____   Date _____

Solve the number sentences. Use the key to color. Once the box is colored, you do not need to color it again.

a. $5 + 2 =$ _____	b. $7 + 2 =$ _____	c. $2 + 3 =$ _____
d. $3 + 3 =$ _____	e. $7 = 1 +$ _____	f. $2 = 1 +$ _____
g. _____ $= 4 + 4$	h. $8 + 2 =$ _____	i. $3 + 4 =$ _____
j. _____ $= 5 + 4$	k. $10 = 1 +$ _____	l. $10 = 5 +$ _____

Color doubles red.

Color +1 blue.

Color +2 green.

Color doubles +1 brown.

Challenge:

List the number sentences that can be colored more than 1 way.

_____   _____

Name _____   Date _____

Solve and sort the number sentences. One number sentence can go in more than one place when you sort.

| 5 + 1 = ___ | 6 + 2 = ____ | 2 + 3 = ____ |

| 3 + 3 = ____ | 7 + 1 = ____ | 2 + 2 = ____ |

| ____ = 4 + 4 | 8 + 2 = ____ | 3 + 4 = ____ |

| ____ = 5 + 4 | 10 = 1 + ____ | ____ = 5 + 2 |

Doubles	Doubles +1	+1	+2	Mentally visualized 5-groups

Write your own number sentences, and add them to the chart.

| | | |

EUREKA MATH

©2015 Great Minds. eureka-math.org
G1-M1-TE-BK1-1.3.1-01.2016

Solve and practice math facts.

1 + 0	1 + 1	1 + 2	1 + 3	1 + 4	1 + 5	1 + 6	1 + 7	1 + 8	1 + 9
2 + 0	2 + 1	2 + 2	2 + 3	2 + 4	2 + 5	2 + 6	2 + 7	2 + 8	
3 + 0	3 + 1	3 + 2	3 + 3	3 + 4	3 + 5	3 + 6	3 + 7		
4 + 0	4 + 1	4 + 2	4 + 3	4+ 4	4 + 5	4 + 6			
5 + 0	5 + 1	5 + 2	5 + 3	5 + 4	5 + 5				
6 + 0	6 + 1	6 + 2	6 + 3	6 + 4					
7 + 0	7 + 1	7 + 2	7 + 3						
8 + 0	8 + 1	8 + 2							
9 + 0	9 + 1								
10 + 0									

$2 + 1 = \square$ $3 + 1 = \square$ $5 + 1 = \square$

$4 + 1 = \square$ $6 + 1 = \square$ $9 + 1 = \square$

$2 + 2 = \square$ $2 + 3 = \square$ $5 + 5 = \square$

$3 + 3 = \square$ $4 + 4 = \square$ $4 + 5 = \square$

$0 + 1 = \square$ $1 + 3 = \square$ $1 + 1 = \square$

$2 + 2 = \square$ $7 + 1 = \square$ $3 + 3 = \square$

$1 + 5 = \square$ $5 + 5 = \square$ $3 + 4 = \square$

$8 + 1 = \square$ $4 + 4 = \square$ $5 + 4 = \square$

friendly fact go around

Lesson 24:   Practice to build fluency with facts to 10.

EUREKA
MATH™

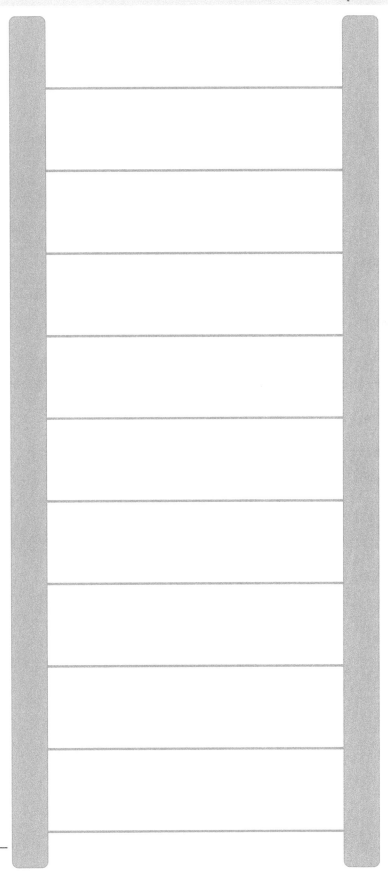

related fact ladder

7 + 3	0 + 7
0 + 2	8 + 2
9 + 0	0 + 3
9 + 1	1 + 8

expression cards

Lesson 24:   Practice to build fluency with facts to 10.

EUREKA
MATH™

6 + 3	4 + 6
7 + 2	1 + 7
6 + 2	4 + 5
6 + 1	0 + 6
4 + 3	4 + 4

expression cards

5 + 2	5 + 5
5 + 1	3 + 5
4 + 2	4 + 4
0 + 8	4 + 1

expression cards

Lesson 24:   Practice to build fluency with facts to 10.

EUREKA
MATH

2 + 3	3 + 3
4 + 0	5 + 0
3 + 1	3 + 4
5 + 4	2 + 2

expression cards

Name _____   Date _____

1. There were 5 boys at Jake's party. Some more came after basketball practice. Then, there were 9. How many boys came to Jake's party after basketball practice?

   a. Draw a picture to help you solve the problem.

   b. Draw a complete number bond that goes with this story.

   c. Write an addition sentence to match this story.

   _____

EUREKA MATH

2. Write the numbers that go in the blanks.

    a. Color all of the partners to 10 blue.
    b. Color all of the +1 facts yellow.
    c. Color all of the +2 facts red.

3 + 7 = _____	_____ = 1 + 4	3 + 2 = _____
_____ = 7 + 2	5 + 1 = _____	_____ = 8 + 1
9 + 1 = _____	_____ = 2 + 6	6 + 4 = _____

3. Look at the party picture!

    a. Write at least two different addition sentences using 3, 6, and 9 that describe the party picture.

        _____   _____

    b. How are these number sentences the same? Explain using pictures and numbers.

4. Monica says that when the unknown is 4, it makes this number sentence true:
5 + 3 = ____ + 4. Terry says she is wrong. He says 8 makes the number sentence true.

a. Who is correct? Explain your thinking using pictures, words, or numbers.

b. Monica says that 3 and 5 is equal to 5 and 3. Terry says she is wrong again. Explain who is correct, using pictures, numbers, or words.

c. Next, Monica tells Terry 8 = 8. Terry says she is wrong one more time. Explain who is correct, using pictures, numbers, or words.

d. Terry decided to give 8 carrot sticks to his friend Monica. Monica put 5 carrot sticks on her plate and some more in her lunch box. How many carrot sticks did Monica put in her lunch box?

EUREKA
MATH

©2015 Great Minds. eureka-math.org
G1-M1-TE-BK1-1.3.1-01.2016

Mid-Module Assessment Task **Standards Addressed**	**Topics A–F**

Represent and solve problems involving addition and subtraction.

1.OA.1   Use addition and subtraction within 20 to solve word problems involving situations of adding to, taking from, putting together, taking apart, and comparing, with unknowns in all positions, e.g., by using objects, drawings, and equations with a symbol for the unknown number to represent the problem. (See Glossary, Table 1.)

Understand and apply properties of operations and the relationship between addition and subtraction.

1.OA.3   Apply properties of operations as strategies to add and subtract. (Students need not use formal terms for these properties.) *Examples: If 8 + 3 = 11 is known, then 3 + 8 = 11 is also known. (Commutative property of addition.) To add 2 + 6 + 4, the second two numbers can be added to make a ten, so 2 + 6 + 4 = 2 + 10 = 12. (Associative property of addition.)*

Add and subtract within 20.

1.OA.5   Relate counting to addition and subtraction (e.g., by counting on 2 to add 2).

1.OA.6   Add and subtract within 20, demonstrating fluency for addition and subtraction within 10. Use strategies such as counting on; making ten (e.g., 8 + 6 = 8 + 2 + 4 = 10 + 4 = 14); decomposing a number leading to a ten (e.g., 13 − 4 = 13 − 3 − 1 = 10 − 1 = 9); using the relationship between addition and subtraction (e.g., knowing that 8 + 4 = 12, one knows 12 − 8 = 4); and creating equivalent but easier or known sums (e.g., adding 6 + 7 by creating the known equivalent 6 + 6 + 1 = 12 + 1 = 13).

Work with addition and subtraction equations.

1.OA.7   Understand the meaning of the equal sign, and determine if equations involving addition and subtraction are true or false. *For example, which of the following equations are true and which are false? 6 = 6, 7 = 8 − 1, 5 + 2 = 2 + 5, 4 + 1 = 5 + 2.*

1.OA.8   Determine the unknown whole number in an addition or subtraction equation relating three whole numbers. *For example, determine the unknown number that makes the equation true in each of the equations 8 + ? = 11, 5 = □ − 3, 6 + 6 = □.*

Evaluating Student Learning Outcomes

A Progression Toward Mastery is provided to describe steps that illuminate the gradually increasing understandings that students develop *on their way to proficiency.* In this chart, this progress is presented from left (Step 1) to right (Step 4). The learning goal for students is to achieve Step 4 mastery. These steps are meant to help teachers and students identify and celebrate what the students CAN do now and what they need to work on next.

A Progression Toward Mastery

Assessment Task Item	STEP 1 Little evidence of reasoning without a correct answer. (1 Point)	STEP 2 Evidence of some reasoning without a correct answer. (2 Points)	STEP 3 Evidence of some reasoning with a correct answer or evidence of solid reasoning with an incorrect answer. (3 Points)	STEP 4 Evidence of solid reasoning with a correct answer. (4 Points)
1 1.OA.1 1.OA.5 1.OA.8	The student is unable to represent the problem with pictures or is disorganized with the symbols, digits, and structure and writes an inaccurate number bond and number sentence.	The student draws an incorrect picture with an equation and number bond that may or may not match the incorrect picture.	The student draws and solves the *add to with change unknown* problem correctly (4 more boys came to the party) but is unable to write an addition equation or number bond to match the problem. OR The student writes an equation and number bond (using 9, 5, and 4) but cannot explain his thinking using pictures to solve the *add to with change unknown* problem.	The student correctly ▪ Draws a picture to solve the *add to with change unknown* problem and determines that 4 more boys came to the party. ▪ Makes a number bond with 9, 5, and 4. ▪ Writes an addition equation (9 = 5 + __, 5 + __ = 9, etc.).
2 1.OA.6	The student is unable to add as evidenced by unanswered problems. The student colors boxes at random with little understanding of partners to 10, +1, and +2.	The student makes several calculation or category coloring errors. The student makes no accommodation for 9 + 1.	The student answers most addition problems correctly and makes some category coloring errors (up to two calculation or color errors combined.) The student makes no accommodation for 9 + 1 or makes an accommodation for 9 + 1 with caluculation or category coloring errors.	The student correctly ▪ Answers all addition problems. ▪ Colors all equations in accordance to the problem type categories. ▪ Makes an accommodation for 9 + 1 as it fits two categories.

Module 1: Sums and Differences to 10

A Progression Toward Mastery				
3 **1.OA.3** **1.OA.6**	The student writes two incorrect number sentences. OR The student is disorganized with the symbols, digits, and structure, and writes an inaccurate equation.	The student writes one correct number sentence and thus cannot explain the similarities between two equations. OR The student writes two number sentences that are exactly the same as one another and explains thinking that does not reflect an understanding of the commutative property.	The student writes two correct and unique addition equations using 3, 6, and 9, but is unable to cite the commutative property in her own words to explain how the equations are same.	The student clearly ▪ Writes two correct and unique addition equations that use 3, 6, and 9 (9 = 6 + 3, or 3 + 6 = 9, or 9 = 3 + 6, etc.). ▪ Demonstrates with pictures, numbers, and words how the number sentences are the same, somehow citing the commutative property in her own words.
4 **1.OA.1** **1.OA.3** **1.OA.5** **1.OA.6** **1.OA.7** **1.OA.8**	The student cannot explain any of the three scenarios clearly using equations, pictures, or words. The student cannot solve the *take apart with addend unknown* problem correctly.	The student explains one of the three scenarios clearly and thoroughly using equations, pictures, or words. The student solves the *take apart with addend unknown* problem incorrectly (something other than 3 carrots were in her lunch box).	The student explains two of the three scenarios clearly and thoroughly using equations, pictures, and/or words. The student solves the *take apart with addend unknown* problem correctly and determines that 3 carrots were in her lunch box.	The student clearly and thoroughly ▪ Explains all three scenarios using equations, pictures, and/or words. ▪ Solves the *take apart with addend unknown* problem correctly and determines that 3 carrots were in her lunch box.

©2015 Great Minds. eureka-math.org
G1-M1-TE-BK1-1.3.1-01.2016

Name _Maria_____   Date _____

1. There were 5 boys at Jake's party. Some more came after basketball practice.
   Then, there were 9. How many boys came to Jake's party after basketball practice?

   a. Draw a picture to help you solve the problem.

   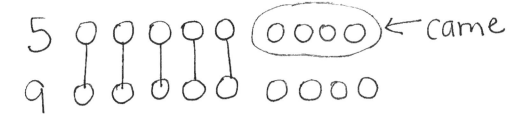

   b. Draw a complete number bond that goes with this story.

   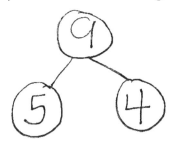

   c. Write an addition sentence to match this story.

   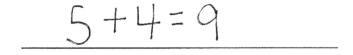

EUREKA
MATH™

2. Write the numbers that go in the blanks.

   a. Color all of the partners to 10 blue.

   b. Color all of the +1 facts yellow.

   c. Color all of the +2 facts red.

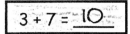 3 + 7 = 10

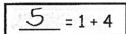 5 = 1 + 4

 3 + 2 = 5

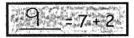 9 = 7 + 2

5 + 1 = 6

9 = 8 + 1

9 + 1 = 10

8 = 2 + 6

6 + 4 = 10

3. Look at the party picture!

   a. Write at least two different addition sentences using 3, 6, and 9 that describe the party picture.

   3 + 6 = 9   6 + 3 = 9

   b. How are these number sentences the same? Explain using pictures and numbers.

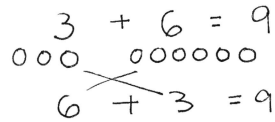
3   +   6   =   9
O O O   O O O O O O

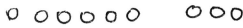
6   +   3   =   9
O O O O O O   O O O

EUREKA
MATH™

Module 1:   Sums and Differences to 10

305

©2015 Great Minds. eureka-math.org
G1-M1-TE-BK1-1.3.1-01.2016

4. Monica says when the unknown is 4, it makes this number sentence true:
5 + 3 = ___ + 4. Terry says she is wrong. He says 8 makes the number sentence true.

a. Who is correct? Explain your thinking using pictures, words, or numbers.

Monica

They are the same so shes rite.

b. Monica says that 3 and 5 is equal to 5 and 3. Terry says she is wrong again. Explain who is correct, using pictures, numbers, or words.

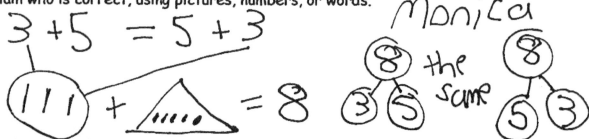

Monica the same

c. Next, Monica tells Terry 8 = 8. Terry says she is wrong one more time. Explain who is correct, using pictures, numbers, or words.

Its true!

d. Terry decided to share 8 carrot sticks with his friend Monica. Monica put 5 carrot sticks on her plate and some more in her lunch box. How many carrot sticks did Monica put in her lunch box?

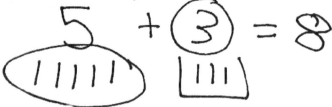

3 carrot sticks

Mathematics Curriculum

Topic G

Subtraction as an Unknown Addend Problem

1.OA.1, 1.OA.4, 1.OA.5

Focus Standard:	1.OA.1	Use addition and subtraction within 20 to solve word problems involving situations of adding to, taking from, putting together, taking apart, and comparing, with unknowns in all positions, e.g., by using objects, drawings, and equations with a symbol for the unknown number to represent the problem.
	1.OA.4	Understand subtraction as an unknown-addend problem. *For example, subtract $10 - 8$ by finding the number that makes 10 when added to 8.*
	1.OA.5	Relate counting to addition and subtraction (e.g., by counting on 2 to add 2).
Instructional Days:	3	
Coherence -Links from:	GK–M4	Number Pairs, Addition and Subtraction to 10
-Links to:	G2–M4	Addition and Subtraction Within 200 with Word Problems to 100

Following the Mid-Module Assessment, Topic G focuses on students understanding the meaning of subtraction as it relates to addition. In Lesson 25, students solve *add to with change unknown* problems as they did in Topic C using addition but now relate that work directly to the act of taking away (**1.OA.4**). The work of this lesson starts with students calling upon their knowledge from previous *add to with change unknown* problems and then applying it in the context of subtraction, using the addend to subtract from the total in order to find the missing addend or part (**1.OA.1**).

In this opening lesson, students use objects to represent discrete counts, which serves as a bridge to the number path used in Lessons 26 and 27. Number bonds will continue to serve as a bridge between prior learning and this new learning.

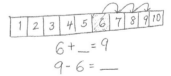

In these concluding lessons, students use the number path, as pictured to the right, in order to find one part, count on to the total, and determine the number of counts it took to get to that total from the part (**1.OA.5**). The teacher engages students in deep discussion about these strategies as they relate to the contextualized situations of story problems, ensuring that students build a solid conceptual understanding of why and how one utilizes counting on to solve subtraction.

EUREKA
MATH™

Topic G: Subtraction as an Unknown Addend Problem

307

A Teaching Sequence Toward Mastery of Subtraction as an Unknown Addend Problem

Objective 1: Solve *add to with change unknown* math stories with addition, and relate to subtraction. Model with materials, and write corresponding number sentences.
(Lesson 25)

Objective 2: Count on using the number path to find an unknown part.
(Lessons 26–27)

Lesson 25

Objective: Solve *add to with change unknown* math stories with addition, and relate to subtraction. Model with materials, and write corresponding number sentences.

Suggested Lesson Structure

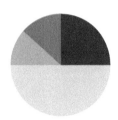

■ Fluency Practice   (15 minutes)
▨ Application Problem   (7 minutes)
▫ Concept Development   (30 minutes)
■ Student Debrief   (8 minutes)

   Total Time   **(60 minutes)**

Fluency Practice (15 minutes)

▪ Race to the Top: Doubles **1.OA.6**   (5 minutes)
▪ X-Ray Vision: Partners to 9 **1.OA.6**   (5 minutes)
▪ Number Bond Dash: 9 **1.OA.6**   (5 minutes)

Race to the Top Doubles (5 minutes)

Materials: (S) Race to the Top (Fluency Template), crayons
             (or pencil), 1 die (replace 6 with 0) per pair

Note: Reviewing doubles permits students continued practice with the facts presented in Lesson 21.

Students take turns rolling a die. Their partner says the double fact and records it on the graph.

X-Ray Vision: Partners to 9 (5 minutes)

Materials: (T) 9 counters, container

Note: Reviewing partners to 9 allows students to gain and maintain fluency with addition and subtraction facts within 10.

1. Place 9 counters on the floor next to an opaque container.

2. Tell students to close their eyes. Put 1 counter in the container.

NOTES ON
MULTIPLE MEANS
OF REPRESENTATION:

Frequent checks for understanding benefit English language learners and other students who may shy away from asking questions. Ask questions for comprehension during this lesson to ensure that students understand the vocabulary and concept.

Lesson 25:   Solve *add to with change unknown* math stories with addition, and
             relate to subtraction. Model with materials, and write corresponding
             number sentences.
             ©2015 Great Minds. eureka-math.org
             G1-M1-TE-BK1-1.3.1-01.2016

309

3. Tell students to open their eyes. Ask, "Who can use their x-ray vision to make a number sentence combining the counters in and outside the container?"

4. Continue the game, eliciting all partners to 9.

Number Bond Dash: 9 (5 minutes)

Materials: (T) Stopwatch or timer (S) Number Bond Dash 9 (Lesson 8 Fluency Template), marker to correct work

Note: By using the same system repeatedly, students can focus on the mathematics alone.

Follow the procedure for the Number Bond Dash in Lesson 5 Fluency Practice. Tell students to remember how many problems they get correct so they can try to improve their scores in Lesson 26.

Application Problem (7 minutes)

Taylor and her sister Reilly each got 4 books from the library. Then, Reilly went back in and checked out another book. How many books do Taylor and Reilly have together? Draw and label a number bond to show the part of the books Taylor took out and the part that Reilly took out. Write a statement to share your answer.

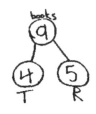

Note: This problem is designed as a bridge from the previous lesson's focus on fluency with facts within 10. This problem also allows students practice with a contextualized double and double plus 1 problem.

Concept Development (30 minutes)

Materials: (T) 10 bear counters, number bond and number sentences (Template) (S) Personal white board, number bond and number sentences (Template), 10 bear counters

Have students bring their personal white boards to the meeting area and sit in a semi-circle. Project the number bond and number sentences template on the board.

T: Once upon a time, 4 little bears went to play tag in the forest. Some more bears came over. In the end, there were 6 little bears playing tag in the woods. (Place 6 bear counters on the floor.)

T: How many more bears came to play? Turn and talk to a partner to share a strategy you used.

Review the strategy of counting on to solve. Ask students to write the number sentence (4 + 2 = 6) and the number bond. Circle the solution in both.

NOTES ON
MULTIPLE MEANS
OF REPRESENTATION:

Post a written copy of the problem for students to consult as the two stories in this lesson are being read aloud. This helps visual learners, in particular, and all students follow along as the story is being told.

Lesson 25:   Solve *add to with change unknown* math stories with addition, and relate to subtraction. Model with materials, and write corresponding number sentences.

©2015 Great Minds. eureka-math.org
G1-M1-TE-BK1-1.3.1-01.2016

T: (Write the number sentence and the number bond on the board.)

T: What does 6 stand for?

S: The number of bears playing at the end.

T: (Gesture over the 6 bears on the floor.)

T: What does 4 stand for?

S: The number of bears playing in the beginning.

T: (Separate 4 bears slightly from the group.)

T: How many bears came over to play? Point to where you see them.

S: 2 bears. (Point to 2 bears.)

T: We can make an imaginary line with our finger to show the two parts. (Draw an imaginary line between the two groups.) Four bears were there first, and then 2 more bears came. (Point to each part accordingly.)

T: Many of you used addition to figure out how many bears came over to play. When we checked our work just now, we separated the 4 bears from the total group of 6 bears. (Write 4 + __ = 6 on the board.) Since we know the whole and one part, we can use subtraction to find the other part. Turn and talk to your partner about how we could write this as a subtraction sentence. (Circulate and listen.)

S: (Discuss.)

T: (Choose a student to demonstrate her subtraction sentence using the bears.)

T: We can write 6 − 4 = 2 to show that we had 6 bears and separated 4 of them from the group, leaving us with 2 bears for the unknown part. You write the subtraction sentence on your board as I write it.

S/T: (Write 6 − 4 = 2.)

T: Circle the answer to our question in the number sentence.

T: What number bond matches the parts and the total for this story? Add that to your board.

S/T: (Draw a number bond of 4 and 2 with the total of 6.)

Tell the following story: Once upon a time, 8 bears were fishing for dinner. Five bears had been fishing all day. The rest of the bears came after lunch. How many bears came after lunch?

Have students solve and write an addition and subtraction number sentence along with a matching number bond.

Place 8 bears on the floor. Invite students to share the number sentences and analyze the referents for each number. Emphasize that there are two parts within the total by drawing an imaginary line between them.

MP.8

T: Do both of your number sentences match the number bond?

S: Yes!

T: How are these number sentences the same? How are they different? Turn and talk to your partner.

S: Both number sentences gave us the answer. Three more bears came to fish. The first time, we used counting on and an addition sentence to solve. The second time, we used subtraction.

Distribute bear counters to each student. Repeat the process by telling other *change unknown* stories for students to solve using their counters. Be sure to have students separate one addend from the other. Consider using the following sequence: 5 +___ = 7, 7 − 5 = ___; 2 + ___ = 8, 8 − 2 = ___; and 4 + ___ = 9, 9 − 4 = ___.

Problem Set (10 minutes)

MP.7

Distribute the Problem Set, and guide students through by reading each word problem and giving sufficient time to complete the task.

Students should do their personal best to complete the Problem Set within the allotted 10 minutes. For some classes, it may be appropriate to modify the assignment by specifying which problems they work on first. Some problems do not specify a method for solving. Students solve these problems using the RDW approach used for Application Problems. On this Problem Set, all students should begin with Problem 1 and possibly leave Problem 4 to the end if they still have time.

Student Debrief (8 minutes)

Lesson Objective: Solve *add to with change unknown* math stories with addition and relate to subtraction. Model with materials, and write corresponding number sentences.

The Student Debrief is intended to invite reflection and active processing of the total lesson experience.

Invite students to review their solutions for the Problem Set. They should check work by comparing answers with a partner before going over answers as a class. Look for misconceptions or misunderstandings that can be addressed in the Debrief. Guide students in a conversation to debrief the Problem Set and process the lesson.

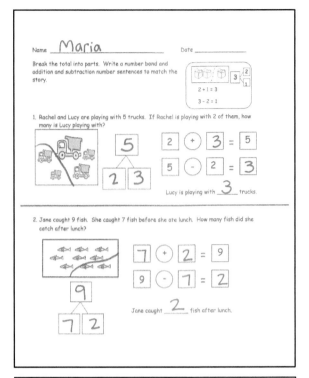

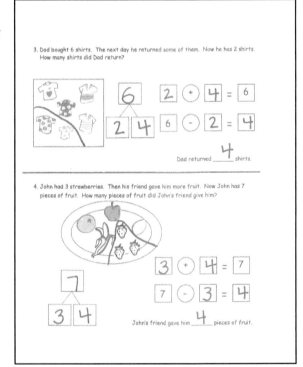

Any combination of the questions below may be used to lead the discussion. Ask students to bring a yellow colored pencil to the Student Debrief.

- With your yellow colored pencil, circle all the numbers that were the unknown in the number bond and in the number sentences. Where do they appear in the number bonds and the number sentences?
- How did the number bond help you come up with the addition and the related subtraction sentence?
- Look at Problem 4. Explain how the addition and subtraction sentences are related. How are addition and subtraction alike?

Exit Ticket (3 minutes)

After the Student Debrief, instruct students to complete the Exit Ticket. A review of their work will help with assessing students' understanding of the concepts that were presented in today's lesson and planning more effectively for future lessons. The questions may be read aloud to the students.

Lesson 25:   Solve *add to with change unknown* math stories with addition, and
relate to subtraction. Model with materials, and write corresponding
number sentences.
©2015 Great Minds. eureka-math.org
G1-M1-TE-BK1-1.3.1-01.2016

313

Name _____   Date _____

Break the total into parts. Write a number bond and addition and subtraction number sentences to match the story.

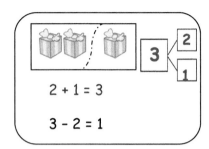

2 + 1 = 3

3 - 2 = 1

1. Rachel and Lucy are playing with 5 trucks. If Rachel is playing with 2 of them, how many is Lucy playing with?

   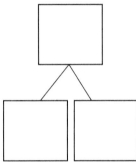

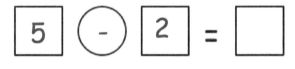

Lucy is playing with _____ trucks.

2. Jane caught 9 fish. She caught 7 fish before she ate lunch. How many fish did she catch after lunch?

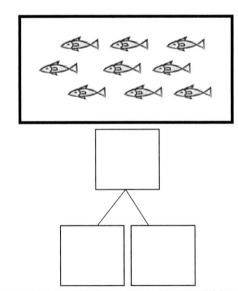

Jane caught _____ fish after lunch.

Lesson 25:   Solve *add to with change unknown* math stories with addition, and relate to subtraction. Model with materials, and write corresponding number sentences.
©2015 Great Minds. eureka-math.org
G1-M1-TE-BK1-1.3.1-01.2016

EUREKA MATH

3. Dad bought 6 shirts. The next day he returned some of them. Now, he has 2 shirts. How many shirts did Dad return?

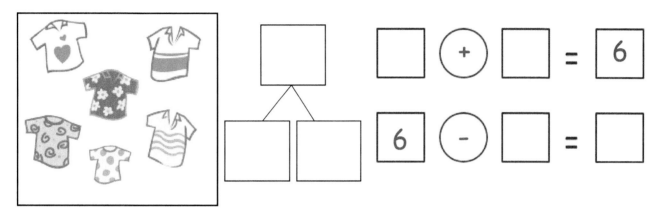

Dad returned _____ shirts.

4. John had 3 strawberries. Then, his friend gave him more fruit. Now, John has 7 pieces of fruit. How many pieces of fruit did John's friend give him?

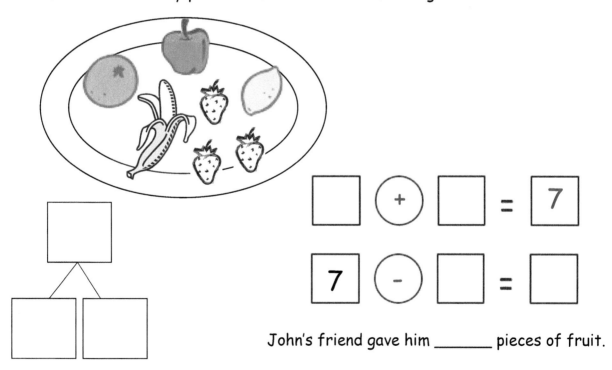

John's friend gave him _____ pieces of fruit.

EUREKA MATH™   Lesson 25:   Solve *add to with change unknown* math stories with addition, and relate to subtraction. Model with materials, and write corresponding number sentences.   315

©2015 Great Minds. eureka-math.org
G1-M1-TE-BK1-1.3.1-01.2016

Name _____   Date _____

Solve the math story. Complete the number bond and number sentences. Color the unknown number yellow.

Rich bought 6 cans of soda on Monday.
He bought some more on Tuesday.
Now, he has 9 cans of soda.
How many cans did Rich buy on Tuesday?

Rich bought _____ cans.

Lesson 25:   Solve *add to with change unknown* math stories with addition, and
                            relate to subtraction. Model with materials, and write corresponding
                            number sentences.
                        ©2015 Great Minds. eureka-math.org
                        G1-M1-TE-BK1-1.3.1-01.2016

EUREKA MATH

Name _____ Date _____

Break the total into parts. Write a number bond and addition and subtraction number sentences to match the story.

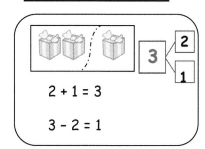

2 + 1 = 3

3 – 2 = 1

1. Six flowers bloomed on Monday. Some more bloomed on Tuesday. Now, there are 8 flowers. How many flowers bloomed on Tuesday?

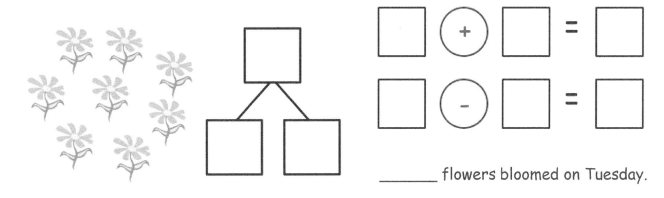

_____ flowers bloomed on Tuesday.

2. Below are the balloons that Mom bought. She bought 4 balloons for Bella, and the rest of the balloons were for Jim. How many balloons did she buy for Jim?

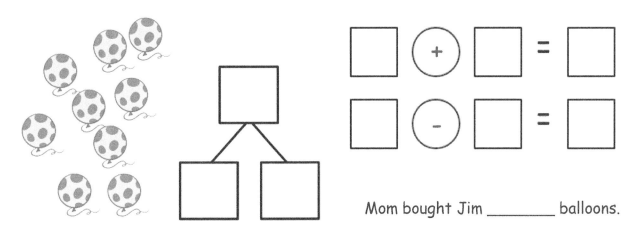

Mom bought Jim _____ balloons.

EUREKA MATH

Lesson 25: Solve add to with change unknown math stories with addition, and relate to subtraction. Model with materials, and write corresponding number sentences.

©2015 Great Minds. eureka-math.org
G1-M1-TE-BK1-1.3.1-01.2016

317

Draw a picture to solve the math story.

3. Missy buys some cupcakes and 2 cookies. Now, she has 6 desserts. How many cupcakes did she buy?

 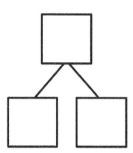 

Missy bought _____ cupcakes.

4. Jim invited 9 friends to his party. Three friends arrived late, but the rest came early. How many friends came early?

 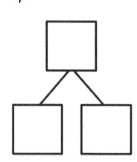 

_____ friends came early.

5. Mom paints her fingernails on both hands. First, she paints 2 red. Then, she paints the rest pink. How many fingernails are pink?

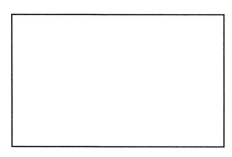 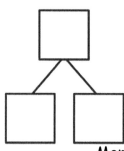 

Mom paints _____ fingernails pink.

Lesson 25: Solve *add to with change unknown* math stories with addition, and relate to subtraction. Model with materials, and write corresponding number sentences.

©2015 Great Minds. eureka-math.org
G1-M1-TE-BK1-1.3.1-01.2016

EUREKA
MATH™

Name _____ Date _____

 Race to the Top!

0	**2**	**4**	**6**	**8**	**10**

EUREKA
MATH™

Lesson 25: Solve *add to with change unknown* math stories with addition, and
relate to subtraction. Model with materials, and write corresponding
number sentences.

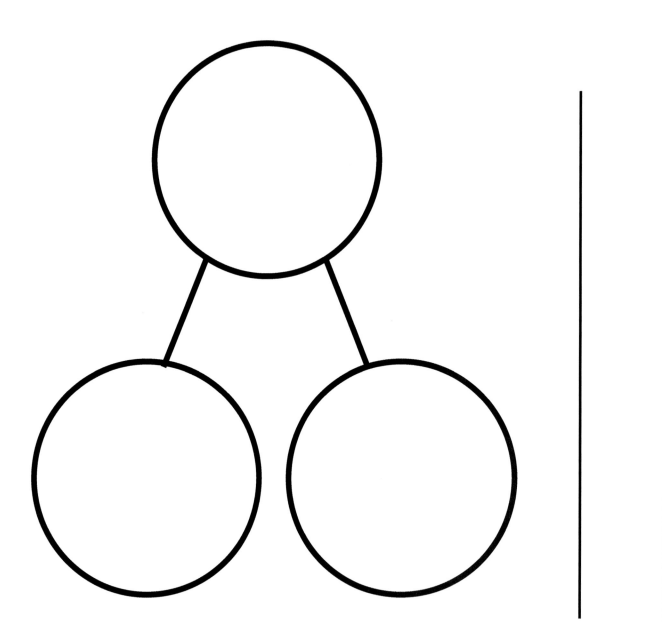

number bond and number sentences

Lesson 25: Solve *add to with change unknown* math stories with addition, and relate to subtraction. Model with materials, and write corresponding number sentences.

©2015 Great Minds. eureka-math.org
G1-M1-TE-BK1-1.3.1-01.2016

EUREKA
MATH

Lesson 26

Objective: Count on using the number path to find an unknown part.

Suggested Lesson Structure

■ Fluency Practice   (13 minutes)
▨ Application Problem   (7 minutes)
☐ Concept Development   (30 minutes)
▨ Student Debrief   (10 minutes)

Total Time   **(60 minutes)**

Fluency Practice (13 minutes)

- Number Path Hop **1.OA.5**   (3 minutes)
- Partners to 9 **1.OA.3, 1.OA.6**   (5 minutes)
- Number Bond Dash: 9 **1.OA.6**   (5 minutes)

Number Path Hop (3 minutes)

Materials: (S) 5-group cards (Lesson 5 Template 1), 1 counter

Note: This activity connects fluency work of addition and subtraction within 10 with the number path as a tool for modeling addition and subtraction.

Students make a number path by ordering their 5-group cards from 0 to 10. Instruct the students to place their counters on 0, and give a series of directions. "Hop forward 2. Where are you?" "Hop back 1 space. What number are you on?" "Hop from 1 to 5. How many hops did you make?" "What number do you add to 5 to make 9?"

Partners to 9 (5 minutes)

Materials: (T/S) 5-group cards (0–9) (Lesson 5 Template 1)

Note: Reviewing partners to 9 allows students to gain and maintain fluency with addition and subtraction facts within 10, a grade level objective. Students also apply the commutative property.

T: (Hold up the 5-group card with 5 dots.) How many dots do you see?
S: 5.
T: Hold up your 5-group card that shows how many more dots I need to make 9.
S: (Hold up the card with 4 dots.)

T: Say an addition sentence for 9, beginning with the number you see on my card.

S: 5 + 4 = 9.

T: Good. Now, say another addition sentence for 9. Begin with your card.

S: 4 + 5 = 9.

Continue playing, eliciting all partners to 9.

Number Bond Dash: 9 (5 minutes)

Materials: (T) Stopwatch or timer (S) Number bond dash 9 (Lesson 8 Fluency Template), marker to correct work

Note: This activity addresses the core fluency objective for Grade 1 of adding and subtracting within 10.

Follow the procedure for the Number Bond Dash in Lesson 5 Fluency Practice, remembering today is the second day with making 9. Students should recall their scores from Lesson 25 to see and celebrate improvement.

Application Problem (7 minutes)

There were 5 students in the cafeteria. Some more students came in late. Now, there are 7 students in the cafeteria. How many students came in late? Write a number bond to match the story. Write an addition sentence and a subtraction sentence to show two ways to solve the problem. Draw a rectangle around the unknown number that you found.

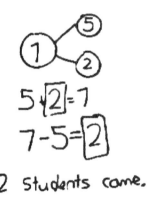

Note: This problem serves as a bridge from the previous *change unknown* lesson that allowed students to connect addition and subtraction, preparing students to do the same in a different context within today's lesson.

Concept Development (30 minutes)

Materials: (T) Giant number path (S) Personal white board, number path (Template)

Place a giant number path on the floor. Have students bring their personal white boards and sit in a semi-circle facing the number path.

T: (Write 6 − 4 = ___ on the board.) Fill in your number bond using this number sentence. One of the boxes should be left empty.

S: (Write 6 in the total box and 4 in the part box.)

T: Let's solve 6 − 4 by using this giant number path. What is the whole?

S: 6.

T: (Select and direct a student to stand above 6.) If we are using the number path to show how to take 4 away from 6, should we count on or count back on the number path? By how many?

©2015 Great Minds. eureka-math.org
G1-M1-TE-BK1-1.3.1-01.2016

S: We count down by 4.

T: As Paul hops down, let's keep track of our counts until we reach 4.

S: (Paul hops 1 square at a time as the rest of the class counts.) 1, 2, 3, 4. (He ends up on 2.)

T: What is 6 – 4?

S: 2.

S/T: (Write 2 in the number sentence. Complete the number bond.)

T: Is there another way to solve 6 – 4? Turn and talk to your partner.

S: We can also count on from 4 to 6. → We can use an addition sentence. → We can think,
       "4 + ___ = 6."

T: (Write 4 + ___ = 6.) We can *count on* using the number
       path! How many hops are needed to get to 6? Let's
       count on and keep track of the hops on our fingers.

T/S: Foouuur, 5, 6. (Put up a finger for each hop.)

T: How many does 4 need to get to 6?

S: 2.

T: What is the number sentence to show what we just
       did?

S: 4 + 2 = 6.

T: (Fill in the blank with 2.) Again, 2 was the number we
       were looking for. It's the same answer as the answer
       from the subtraction sentence.

NOTES ON
MULTIPLE MEANS
OF REPRESENTATION:

Present math concretely with familiar
objects. Students may prefer using
their fingers while others might prefer
using something to count, such as
bears or disks. Allow students to use
the manipulative that helps them solve
problems in the most effective way.

T: Which was easier, counting back or counting on?

S: Counting on was easier.

T: (Write 8 – 5 = ___ on the board.) When you see a subtraction problem, you can always add instead.
       How can I turn this into an addition sentence?

S: 5 + ___ = 8. (Read as "five plus an unknown part equals eight.")

T: Write the number sentence on your board.

T: On your number path, circle the 5. That's the part we already know. Let's find the unknown part by
       hopping to each number until we get to 8. Watch me as you help me count on.

T/S: (Circle 5 and draw to show hopping to each
       consecutive number.) Fiiiive, 6, 7, 8.

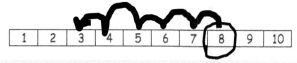

T: How many did 5 need to get to 8?

S: 3.

T: Fill in the unknown number, and put a circle around it to show that it was what we were solving for.

T: If 5 + 3 = 8, then 8 – 5 must be…?

S: 3.

T: Let's check our work by using the number path to solve 8 – 5. Erase the marks on your number path.
       Start at 8. Which way should we hop to show taking away 5? How many times?

S: Hop backward 5 times.

Lesson 26:   Count on using the number path to find an unknown part.

323

©2015 Great Minds. eureka-math.org
G1-M1-TE-BK1-1.3.1-01.2016

T: Let's count as we draw our hopping marks.

T/S: 1, 2, 3, 4, 5.

T: What number did you land on?

S: 3.

T: Write the number sentence, and put a circle around what we were solving for.

S: (Write 8 – 5 = 3, and circle 3.)

Repeat this process. Consider using the suggested sequence 9 – 2, 7 – 5, and 7 – 3. Some students may begin to see when counting on is more efficient and when counting back is more efficient. It is okay if they do not see this yet, as they will do more work with selecting an efficient strategy in Lesson 27.

Problem Set (10 minutes)

Students should do their personal best to complete the Problem Set within the allotted 10 minutes. For some classes, it may be appropriate to modify the assignment by specifying which problems they work on first. Some problems do not specify a method for solving. Students solve these problems using the RDW approach used for Application Problems.

On this Problem Set, all students should begin with Problems 16, possibly leaving Problems 7, 8, and 9 to the end if they still have time.

Student Debrief (10 minutes)

Lesson Objective: Count on using the number path to find an unknown part.

The Student Debrief is intended to invite reflection and active processing of the total lesson experience.

Invite students to review their solutions for the Problem Set. They should check work by comparing answers with a partner before going over answers as a class. Look for misconceptions or misunderstandings that can be addressed in the Debrief. Guide students in a conversation to debrief the Problem Set and process the lesson.

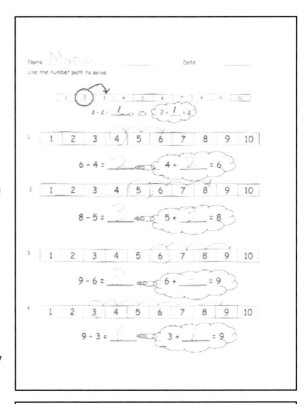

EUREKA MATH

Any combination of the questions below may be used to lead the discussion.

- Look at Problem 3 and Problem 4. How are these problems related? Which strategy would be easier to solve Problem 3? Which strategy would be wiser to use to solve Problem 4?

- Look at Problem 5 and Problem 6. What do you notice about these problems? What did you do differently or similarly to solve these problems?

- Look at your Application Problem and Problem Set Problem 7. Describe the connections between the two.

Exit Ticket (3 minutes)

After the Student Debrief, instruct students to complete the Exit Ticket. A review of their work will help with assessing students' understanding of the concepts that were presented in today's lesson and planning more effectively for future lessons. The questions may be read aloud to the students.

Lesson 26:   Count on using the number path to find an unknown part.

©2015 Great Minds. eureka-math.org
G1-M1-TE-BK1-1.3.1-01.2016

325

Name _____   Date _____

Use the number path to solve.

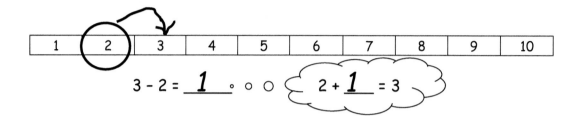

| 1 | 2 | 3 | 4 | 5 | 6 | 7 | 8 | 9 | 10 |

3 – 2 = __*1*__ ∘ ○ ○ ⟨ 2 + __*1*__ = 3 ⟩

1.

| 1 | 2 | 3 | 4 | 5 | 6 | 7 | 8 | 9 | 10 |

6 – 4 = _____ ∘○○ ⟨ 4 + _____ = 6 ⟩

2.

| 1 | 2 | 3 | 4 | 5 | 6 | 7 | 8 | 9 | 10 |

8 – 5 = _____ ∘○○ ⟨ 5 + _____ = 8 ⟩

3.

| 1 | 2 | 3 | 4 | 5 | 6 | 7 | 8 | 9 | 10 |

9 – 6 = _____ ∘○○ ⟨ 6 + _____ = 9 ⟩

4.

| 1 | 2 | 3 | 4 | 5 | 6 | 7 | 8 | 9 | 10 |

9 – 3 = _____ ∘○○ ⟨ 3 + _____ = 9 ⟩

Lesson 26:   Count on using the number path to find an unknown part.

EUREKA
MATH™

Use the number path to help you solve.

| 1 | 2 | 3 | 4 | 5 | 6 | 7 | 8 | 9 | 10 |

5. $5 - 4 =$ _____ $4 +$ _____ $= 5$

6. $5 - 1 =$ _____ $1 +$ _____ $= 5$

7. $7 - 5 =$ _____ $5 +$ _____ $= 7$

8. $10 - 6 =$ _____ $6 +$ _____ $= 10$

9. $9 - 3 =$ _____ $3 +$ _____ $= 9$

EUREKA MATH™

Lesson 26:   Count on using the number path to find an unknown part.

327

©2015 Great Minds. eureka-math.org
G1-M1-TE-BK1-1.3.1-01.2016

Name _____   Date _____

Use the number path to solve. Write the addition sentence you used to help you solve.

| 1 | 2 | 3 | 4 | 5 | 6 | 7 | 8 | 9 | 10 |

a. 7 – 5 = _____   _____

b. 9 – 2 = _____   _____

c. _____ = 10 – 3   _____

Lesson 26:   Count on using the number path to find an unknown part.

EUREKA
MATH™

©2015 Great Minds. eureka-math.org
G1-M1-TE-BK1-1.3.1-01.2016

Name _____ Date _____

Use the number path to solve.

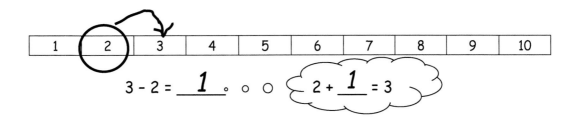

$$3 - 2 = \underline{\textit{1}} \quad \circ \quad \circ \quad \circ \quad 2 + \underline{\textit{1}} = 3$$

1.

| 1 | 2 | 3 | 4 | 5 | 6 | 7 | 8 | 9 | 10 |

$$5 - 3 = \underline{\hspace{1cm}} \quad \circ \circ \circ \quad 3 + \underline{\hspace{1cm}} = 5$$

2.

| 1 | 2 | 3 | 4 | 5 | 6 | 7 | 8 | 9 | 10 |

a. $8 - 6 = \underline{\hspace{1cm}}$ $6 + \underline{\hspace{1cm}} = 8$

b. $7 - 4 = \underline{\hspace{1cm}}$ $4 + \underline{\hspace{1cm}} = 7$

c. $8 - 2 = \underline{\hspace{1cm}}$ _____

d. $9 - 6 = \underline{\hspace{1cm}}$ _____

EUREKA MATH™

Lesson 26:   Count on using the number path to find an unknown part.

329

©2015 Great Minds. eureka-math.org
G1-M1-TE-BK1-1.3.1-01.2016

Use the number path to solve. Match the addition sentence that can help you.

| 1 | 2 | 3 | 4 | 5 | 6 | 7 | 8 | 9 | 10 |

3. a. 6 – 4 = _____

b. 9 – 5 = _____

c. 10 – 6 = _____

d. 10 – 7 = _____

6 + 4 = 10

10 = 7 + 3

4 + 5 = 9

6 = 4 + 2

4. Write an addition and subtraction number sentence for the number bond. You may use the number path to solve.

| 1 | 2 | 3 | 4 | 5 | 6 | 7 | 8 | 9 | 10 |

a. 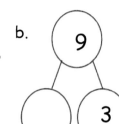 8 / 3 _____

_____

b. 9 / 3 _____

_____

Lesson 26:   Count on using the number path to find an unknown part.

EUREKA
MATH

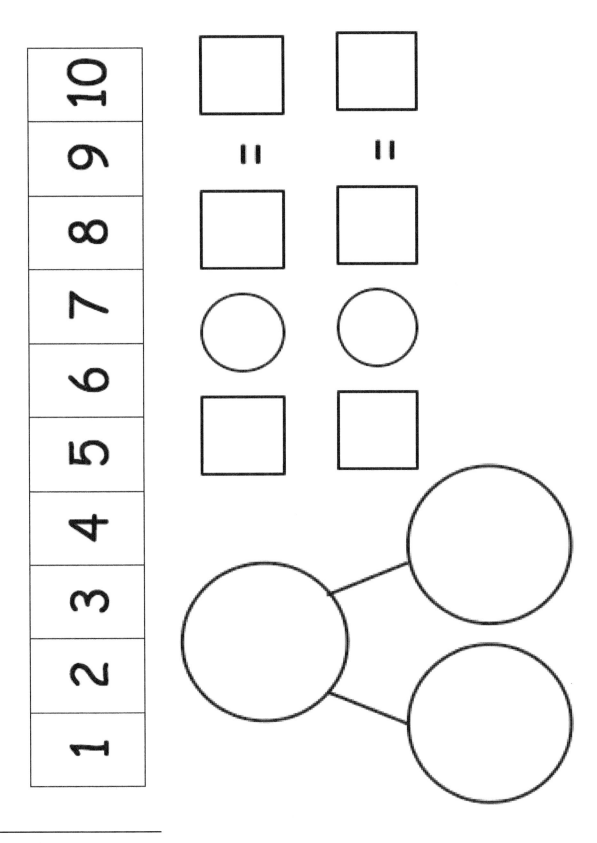

number path

Lesson 26:   Count on using the number path to find an unknown part.

331

©2015 Great Minds. eureka-math.org
G1-M1-TE-BK1-1.3.1-01.2016

Lesson 27

Objective: Count on using the number path to find an unknown part.

Suggested Lesson Structure

■ Fluency Practice   (10 minutes)
▨ Application Problem   (8 minutes)
▢ Concept Development   (30 minutes)
■ Student Debrief   (12 minutes)

   Total Time   **(60 minutes)**

Fluency Practice (10 minutes)

- Happy Counting by Twos **1.OA.5**   (2 minutes)
- Number Bond Roll **1.OA.6**   (5 minutes)
- Number Sentence Swap **1.OA.4**   (3 minutes)

Happy Counting by Twos (2 minutes)

Note: Reviewing counting on allows students to maintain fluency with adding 2.

Repeat the Happy Counting activity from Lesson 3, counting by twos from 10 to 20 and back.

Number Bond Roll (5 minutes)

Materials: (S) Die (with 6 replaced by 0), personal white board

Note: Reviewing number bonds allows students to build and maintain fluency with addition and subtraction facts within 10.

Match partners of equal ability. Each student rolls 1 die. Students use the numbers on their own die and their partner's die as the parts of a number bond. They each write a number bond, addition sentence, and subtraction sentence on their personal white boards. Once both partners have made their number bonds and number sentences, they check each other's work. For example, if Partner A rolls a 2 and Partner B rolls a 3, they each write the number bond showing 2 and 3 making 5 and write number sentences such as $2 + 3 = 5$ and $5 - 3 = 2$.

©2015 Great Minds. eureka-math.org
G1-M1-TE-BK1-1.3.1-01.2016

Number Sentence Swap (3 minutes)

Note: This activity supports the connection between subtraction and addition. The initial subtraction sentence, with the unknown number depicted as an empty box, may be written on the board as a visual support if needed.

Say a subtraction sentence aloud, saying "the mystery number" for the unknown answer (e.g., "5 − 3 = the mystery number"). Call on a student to rephrase the sentence as an addition sentence (e.g., "3 + the mystery number = 5"). Ask students to count on with you to solve the problem, for example, "3 (touch head), 4 (raise thumb), 5 (raise index finger)." Ask students how many fingers they counted on. (2.)

A suggested sequence is 5 − 3, 4 − 2, 6 − 4, 6 − 5, 7 − 6, 7 − 5, and 7 − 3.

Application Problem (8 minutes)

Materials: (S) Personal white board, number path (Lesson 26 Template)

Marcus has 9 strawberries. Six of them are small; the rest are big. How many strawberries are big? Fill in the template. Circle the mystery, or unknown, number in the number sentences, and write a statement to answer the question.

Note: This problem is designed as a bridge from the previous lesson's focus on adding on the number path as a means of solving subtraction problems.

Concept Development (30 minutes)

Materials: (T) 2 number paths (projected or charted)
(S) Personal white board, number path (Lesson 26 Template)

Have students bring their personal white boards and sit in a semicircle facing a projected number path.

- T: (Write 9 − 8 = ☐ on the board, and read the equation aloud with students.) Fill in your number bond using this number sentence. One of the boxes should be left empty.
- S: (Write 9 in the total box and 8 in the part box.)
- T: What are some ways we can solve this? Talk with your partner.
- S: (Share with a partner.)
- T: (Circulate and listen. Then, ask a student or two to share with the class.)

NOTES ON
MULTIPLE MEANS
OF ENGAGEMENT:

Some students may feel more comfortable moving forward in small steps with frequent opportunities to practice what they are learning. Not all students will be able to determine if they should count on or count back right away. Support the way they are solving the problems, and encourage them to eventually be able to choose the method that is most efficient.

Lesson 27: Count on using the number path to find an unknown part.

333

©2015 Great Minds. eureka-math.org
G1-M1-TE-BK1-1.3.1-01.2016

S: We can add! → We can count on using the number path! → We can count back!

T: I heard someone say that we can count back. Let's use the number path to count back and solve 9 – 8 = □. Which way should we hop to show taking away 8? How many times?

S: Hop backward 8 times.

T: Let's start with our whole, and count as we draw our hopping marks.

T/S: 1, 2, 3, 4, 5, 6, 7, 8.

T: What is 9 – 8?

S: 1.

T: Yes. Write that in your number bond, solve your number sentence, and circle the unknown or answer number we were solving for.

S: (Write 1 in the other part box, solve, and circle 1.)

T: We counted back 8 from 9 until we reached 1. Wow, that took us a long time! Hmmm, is there a faster way to solve this? I heard someone say that we can add instead. So, if we think addition, what addition sentence could we write to help us solve 9 – 8 = □?

S: 8 + □ = 9.

T: Good. Please write that number sentence. (Pause.) Let's use our number paths to solve 9 – 8 = □ by thinking of 8 + □ = 9.

T/S: (Circle 8, and draw an arced arrow to 9 as everyone counts.) Eeiiiight, 9.

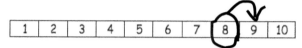

T: How many did we count on in order to solve?

S: 1.

T: Yes. Please solve your number sentence, and circle the unknown or answer number we were solving for.

MP.7

S: (Solve and circle 1.)

T: Look at these two strategies to solve the *same* problem, 9 – 8 = □. Talk with your partner. Did we get the same answer each time? Which way was more efficient, or faster?

T: (As students talk, circulate and listen. Then, ask a student or two to share and explain why.)

S: Counting *on* was more efficient, because we only had to count on 1 more. → Counting *back* took so much longer, and we still got 1 as our unknown, or answer number.

T: So, when you are solving subtraction number sentences, you can think and decide: "Would it be easier for me to count back or count on?"

NOTES ON
MULTIPLE MEANS
OF REPRESENTATION:

During this lesson it is important for students to articulate the way they chose to solve a problem so that other students can hear how they are thinking. This should help guide these students toward the most efficient method for solving subtraction problems.

334   Lesson 27:   Count on using the number path to find an unknown part.

EUREKA MATH

Continue this process, having students show the strategies on their own personal boards, just as in Lesson 26. Consider using the following suggested sequence: $7 - 6$, $9 - 2$, $8 - 3$, and $10 - 7$. Focus students on explaining why they would select a particular method, ensuring that they cite efficiency in some way.

Problem Set (10 minutes)

Students should do their personal best to complete the Problem Set within the allotted 10 minutes. For some classes, it may be appropriate to modify the assignment by specifying which problems they work on first. Some problems do not specify a method for solving. Students solve these problems using the RDW approach used for Application Problems.

Student Debrief (12 minutes)

Lesson Objective: Count on using the number path to find an unknown part.

The Student Debrief is intended to invite reflection and active processing of the total lesson experience.

Invite students to review their solutions for the Problem Set. They should check work by comparing answers with a partner before going over answers as a class. Look for misconceptions or misunderstandings that can be addressed in the Debrief. Guide students in a conversation to debrief the Problem Set and process the lesson.

Any combination of the questions below may be used to lead the discussion.

- What strategy did you use for Problem 10(a)? Why? Problem 10(b)? Problem 10(c)?

- What is different about Problem 10(f)? Is there one best way to solve it? (No. Counting on and counting back are the same. It depends on individual preference.)

- What did you notice about the times you chose to count on? When you counted back?

- What other strategies could you have used to solve these subtraction sentences?

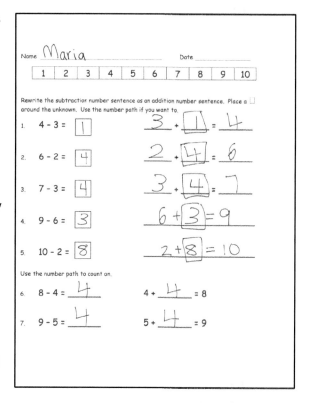

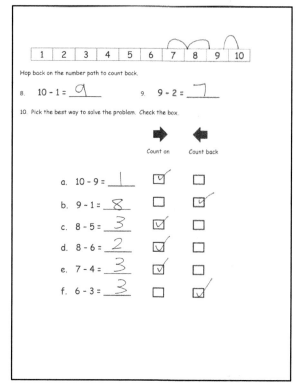

- Look at Problem 8 and Problem 9. Would you have preferred to count up or back? Why? Which is more efficient, and how do you know?
- What about if we had 117 – 115? Should we count on or back? What would our answer be?

Exit Ticket (3 minutes)

After the Student Debrief, instruct students to complete the Exit Ticket. A review of their work will help with assessing students' understanding of the concepts that were presented in today's lesson and planning more effectively for future lessons. The questions may be read aloud to the students.

©2015 Great Minds. eureka-math.org
G1-M1-TE-BK1-1.3.1-01.2016

Name _____   Date _____

1	2	3	4	5	6	7	8	9	10

Rewrite the subtraction number sentence as an addition number sentence.

Place a ☐ around the unknown. Use the number path if you want to.

1. 4 – 3 = ☐   _____ + _____ = _____

2. 6 – 2 = ☐   _____ + _____ = _____

3. 7 – 3 = ☐   _____ + _____ = _____

4. 9 – 6 = ☐   _____

5. 10 – 2 = ☐   _____

Use the number path to count on.

6. 8 – 4 = _____   4 + _____ = 8

7. 9 – 5 = _____   5 + _____ = 9

EUREKA MATH

Lesson 27:   Count on using the number path to find an unknown part.

337

©2015 Great Minds. eureka-math.org
G1-M1-TE-BK1-1.3.1-01.2016

| 1 | 2 | 3 | 4 | 5 | 6 | 7 | 8 | 9 | 10 |

Hop back on the number path to count back.

8. 10 – 1 = _____

9. 9 – 2 = _____

10. Pick the best way to solve the problem. Check the box.

Count on   Count back

a. 10 – 9 = _____   ☐   ☐

b. 9 – 1 = _____   ☐   ☐

c. 8 – 5 = _____   ☐   ☐

d. 8 – 6 = _____   ☐   ☐

e. 7 – 4 = _____   ☐   ☐

f. 6 – 3 = _____   ☐   ☐

EUREKA
MATH™

©2015 Great Minds. eureka-math.org
G1-M1-TE-BK1-1.3.1-01.2016

Name _____ Date _____

To solve 7 - 6, Ben thinks you should count back, and Pat thinks you should count on. Which is the best way to solve this expression? Make a simple math drawing to show why.

$$7 - 6 = \underline{\hspace{3cm}}$$

Name _____ Date _____

Use the number path to complete the number bond, and write an addition and a subtraction sentence to match.

1.

Number Path

| 1 | 2 | 3 | 4 | 5 | 6 | 7 | 8 | 9 | 10 |

a.
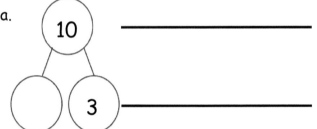

b.
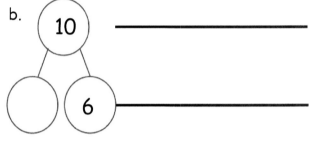

2. Solve the number sentences. Pick the best way to solve. Check the box.

 Count on   Count back

a. 9 – 7 = _____ ☐ ☐

b. 8 – 2 = _____ ☐ ☐

c. 7 – 5 = _____ ☐ ☐

Lesson 27:   Count on using the number path to find an unknown part.

©2015 Great Minds. eureka-math.org
G1-M1-TE-BK1-1.3.1-01.2016

EUREKA MATH

3. Solve the number sentence. Pick the best way to solve. Use the number path to show why.

Count on   Count back

a. 7 – 5 = _____   [ ]   [ ]

| 1 | 2 | 3 | 4 | 5 | 6 | 7 | 8 | 9 | 10 |

I counted _____ because it needed fewer hops.

b. 9 – 1 = _____   [ ]   [ ]

| 1 | 2 | 3 | 4 | 5 | 6 | 7 | 8 | 9 | 10 |

I counted _____ because it needed fewer hops.

c. 10 - 8 = ____   [ ]   [ ]

Make a math drawing or write a number sentence to show why this is best.

EUREKA
MATH

Lesson 27:   Count on using the number path to find an unknown part.

341

©2015 Great Minds. eureka-math.org
G1-M1-TE-BK1-1.3.1-01.2016

Mathematics Curriculum

1
GRADE

Topic H
Subtraction Word Problems

1.OA.1, 1.OA.4, 1.OA.5, 1.OA.8

Focus Standard:	1.OA.1	Use addition and subtraction within 20 to solve word problems involving situations of adding to, taking from, putting together, taking apart, and comparing, with unknowns in all positions, e.g., by using objects, drawings, and equations with a symbol for the unknown number to represent the problem.
	1.OA.4	Understand subtraction as an unknown-addend problem. *For example, subtract 10 – 8 by finding the number that makes 10 when added to 8.*
Instructional Days:	5	
Coherence **-Links from:**	GK–M4	Number Pairs, Addition and Subtraction to 10
-Links to:	G2–M4	Addition and Subtraction Within 200 with Word Problems to 100

With a smooth transition from Topic G, Topic H provides students with rich experiences connecting subtraction to their solid foundation of addition (**1.OA.4**), using various word problem types (**1.OA.1**). Lesson 28 begins with students solving action-based *take from with result unknown* problems, as they start with a set of objects, then take some away, and finally end with a smaller set of objects. Students then work with simple math drawings and equations to represent these *take from with result unknown* stories and connect the act of crossing off to the symbol for subtraction.

Then, Lesson 29 allows students to solve the relationship-based *take apart with result unknown* problems, which are both connected to *take from with result unknown* problems and are the counterpart to the familiar *put together with addend unknown* problems from earlier topics. In both Lessons 28 and 29, students make varied statements to explain the remaining amount, e.g., "There were 4 bears left," "Four bears stayed in the forest," "Then, there were 4 bears all together." This permits students to think and speak flexibly about the unknown, rather than associate specific key words with a particular operation. For example, *all together* does not always indicate addition.

Lesson 30 furthers the connection between addition and subtraction as teachers have students discuss ways to solve *add to with change unknown* word problems, as they use simple math drawings and equations to represent the problem and solution. With the introduction of a whole new problem type in Lesson 31, students use drawings to solve *take from with change unknown* problems such as, "Ben had 7 pencils. He gave away some. Now, he has 5. How many pencils did he give away?" The topic ends with another new relationship problem—*put together/take apart with addend unknown*. Throughout Topic G, students discuss and apply their understanding of addition as it relates to subtraction and vice versa.

EUREKA
MATH™

A Teaching Sequence Toward Mastery of Subtraction Word Problems

Objective 1: Solve *take from with result unknown* math stories with math drawings, true number sentences, and statements, using horizontal marks to cross off what is taken away.
(Lesson 28)

Objective 2: Solve *take apart with addend unknown* math stories with math drawings, equations, and statements, circling the known part to find the unknown.
(Lesson 29)

Objective 3: Solve *add to with change unknown* math stories with drawings, relating addition and subtraction.
(Lesson 30)

Objective 4: Solve *take from with change unknown* math stories with drawings.
(Lesson 31)

Objective 5: Solve put *together/take apart with addend unknown* math stories.
(Lesson 32)

©2015 Great Minds. eureka-math.org
G1-M1-TE-BK1-1.3.1-01.2016

Lesson 28

Objective: Solve *take from with result unknown* math stories with math drawings, true number sentences, and statements, using horizontal marks to cross off what is taken away.

Suggested Lesson Structure

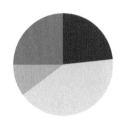

■ Fluency Practice   (14 minutes)
▧ Application Problem   (6 minutes)
▨ Concept Development   (25 minutes)
▨ Student Debrief   (15 minutes)

   Total Time   **(60 minutes)**

Fluency Practice (14 minutes)

- Beep Counting by Ones **1.NBT.1**   (2 minutes)
- Cold Call: 1 Less **1.OA.5, 1.OA.6**   (2 minutes)
- Sprint: 1 Less **1.OA.5, 1.OA.6**   (10 minutes)

Beep Counting by Ones (2 minutes)

Note: This activity focuses on practicing the counting sequence to 120 starting at any given number. Students remain attentive to small sets of consecutive numbers, considering the order of the numbers without relying on the typical predictability of rote counting.

Say a series of three numbers, but replace one of the numbers with the word *beep* (e.g., "5, 6, beep"). When signaled, students say the *beep* number. Scaffold number sequences from simple to complex. Include forward and backward number sentences.

NOTES ON MULTIPLE MEANS OF ACTION AND EXPRESSION:

Some students would benefit from having a visual model of the number sequence. Allow students to use personal white boards to record the sequence, or provide a visual representation.

Use the following suggested sequence: 5, 6, beep; 17, 18, beep; 28, 29, beep; 2, 1, beep; 42, 41, beep; 62, 61, beep; 8, beep, 10; 58, beep, 60; beep, 55, 56; beep, 71, 72; 88, 87, beep; 91, beep, 89; 99, beep, 101; and 109, beep, 111.

EUREKA MATH™

Cold Call: 1 Less (2 minutes)

Note: This activity continues to strengthen students' development of counting backward within the counting sequences up to 120.

Tell students you are going to say a number aloud, and instruct them to think about the number that is 1 less. They do not need to raise their hands, as you will cold call students to say an answer. Alternate between calling on individual students, the whole class, and groups of students (e.g., only girls, only boys, etc.). Begin with numbers within 10, and then expand to numbers within 40, then 80, and then 120.

Use the following suggested sequence: 2, 1, 8, 6, 9, 7, 10, 8, 18, 28, 38, 3, 13, 23, 33, etc.

Sprint: 1 Less (10 minutes)

Materials: (S) 1 Less Sprint

Note: This activity continues to strengthen students' development of counting backward within the counting sequences up to 32.

Application Problem (6 minutes)

Eight ducks are swimming in the pond. Four ducks fly away. How many ducks are still swimming in the pond? Write a number bond, number sentence, and statement. Draw a number path to prove your answer.

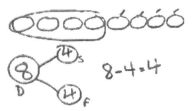

Note: This problem is a bridge from Lesson 27 and a lead-up to the Concept Development for the current lesson. Bringing students back to the number path from Lesson 27 provides a strong lead-in for using horizontal marks to show the part that is "taken away" in the current concept.

Concept Development (25 minutes)

Materials: (S) Personal white board

Invite students to sit in the circle area in a semicircle with their personal white boards.

- T: Welcome to another edition of Math Stories Theater! You will be watching math stories and having a hand at solving them.
- T: There were 6 children at the sleepover. (Call on 6 students to come to the front of the room and act out being at a sleepover.) Two children got picked up. (Draw an imaginary horizontal line in front of 2 students.)

NOTES ON
MULTIPLE MEANS
OF ACTION AND
EXPRESSION:

Using personal white boards for student responses is a great way to involve all learners. Some students might not feel comfortable participating orally, while others may not be able to respond orally. This way, both groups can show what they know on their personal white boards so that the teacher can check for understanding.

S: (Two students leave the group of 6 and sit down.)

T: How many children stayed?

S: 4.

T: Put that into a sentence.

S: Four children stayed.

T: Now, use simple math drawings to show how you know 4 children stayed. (Ask all actors to return to the circle.)

S: (Draw simple math drawings such as circles, and use their own strategies to show that 2 children left the sleepover.)

T: (Ask students to share their strategies.)

If a student shares the crossing off using horizontal marks strategy, have her share with the group, being sure to include key points from the script below. If no one uses horizontal marks, lead students into a dialogue similar to the one below.

T: What did we start with?

S: Six children at the sleepover.

OOOOOO

T: (Model drawing 6 circles in a linear configuration.) What is the whole in this story?

S: 6.

T: Yes. So, our drawing shows how we started with the *whole*. Then, what happened?

S: Two children had to leave.

T: When they were leaving I drew an imaginary line in front of them to show that they were leaving. Let's show that with our drawing. I'm going to cross 2 off with a line. (Model crossing off 2 of the circles and ask students to trace it in the air.) What does that line crossing out those 2 remind you of?

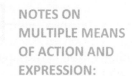

S: Taking away! → The subtraction symbol!

T: Good! Write a number bond and number sentence that tells the sleepover story. Don't forget to label your number bond.

T: (Circulate and listen. Then, ask a student or two to share with the class.)

S: For my number sentence, I wrote 6 – 2 = 4. For my number bond, I wrote 6 as the total children at the sleepover, and then one of the parts was 2 because those were the children who got picked up. The other part was 4 because those children stayed.

Have students erase their personal white boards. Continue to tell stories without actors, using the following suggested sequence and scenarios: 7 – 3 (frogs on a log), 8 – 6 (apples getting eaten), and 9 – 5 (flowers getting picked). Focus students on the referents, starting with the whole and crossing off to show the action of taking away.

NOTES ON MULTIPLE MEANS OF ACTION AND EXPRESSION:

Having students act out number stories is a great way to provide math they can see. This will help students with hearing impairments. It also provides visual and kinesthetic learners an opportunity to engage in the lesson using their preferred style of learning.

346   Lesson 28:   Solve *take from with result unknown* math stories with math drawings, true number sentences, and statements, using horizontal marks to cross off what is taken away.

©2015 Great Minds. eureka-math.org
G1-M1-TE-BK1-1.3.1-01.2016

Problem Set (10 minutes)

Distribute the Problem Set, and have students complete their work in partnerships or in small groups. When setting up partners, be sure that students who are unable to read the problems are paired with a student who can read the problems. This Problem Set may be best completed with the teacher reading each problem aloud.

Students should do their personal best to complete the Problem Set within the allotted 10 minutes. For some classes, it may be appropriate to modify the assignment by specifying which problems they work on first. Some problems do not specify a method for solving. Students solve these problems using the RDW approach used for Application Problems.

On this Problem Set, all students should begin with Problem 1 and possibly leave Problem 4 to the end if there is still time.

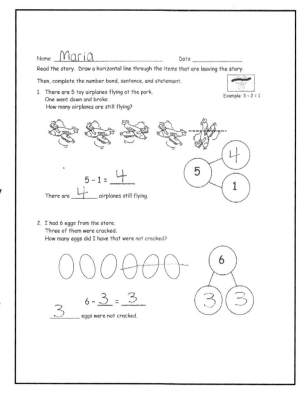

Student Debrief (15 minutes)

Lesson Objective: Solve *take from with result unknown* math stories with math drawings, true number sentences, and statements, using horizontal marks to cross off what is taken away.

The Student Debrief is intended to invite reflection and active processing of the total lesson experience.

Invite students to review their solutions for the Problem Set. They should check work by comparing answers with a partner before going over answers as a class. Look for misconceptions or misunderstandings that can be addressed in the Debrief. Guide students in a conversation to debrief the Problem Set and process the lesson.

Any combination of the questions below may be used to lead the discussion.

- Look at the drawings from your Application Problem and Problem 4 from your Problem Set. How are these two drawing strategies the same? How are they different? Does one seem more efficient than the other? Why?

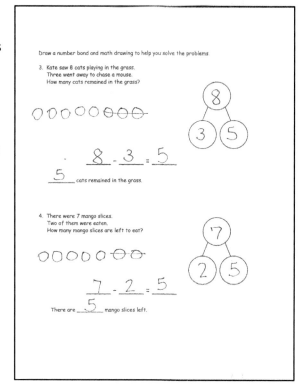

Lesson 28: Solve *take from with result unknown* math stories with math drawings, true number sentences, and statements, using horizontal marks to cross off what is taken away.

©2015 Great Minds. eureka-math.org
G1-M1-TE-BK1-1.3.1-01.2016

347

- What do our drawings in a row remind us of? (A number path. → 5-group cards.) Why would you draw our stories this way?

- Today, we all used drawings and number bonds to solve problems. Let's look at Problem 3 together.

  T: How many total cats did Kate see playing in the grass?

  S: 8 cats.

  T: How did you draw those 8 cats? (Invite students who have drawn in a linear configuration to share.)

  S: I drew 8 circles in a line.

  T: (Draw 8 circles in a line, and enclose them with a rectangle. Label the total.) How many cats went to chase a mouse?

  S: 3 cats.

  T: I see your number bonds show that. I'm going to make this into a picture number bond and show that 3 cats chased a mouse. (Draw a diagonal line to 3 circles enclosed with a rectangle. Label the part.)

  T: How many cats remained?

  S: 5 cats.

  T: Who can help me draw the other part of our picture number bond to show that 5 cats remained? (Call on one student.)

  S: (Draw another diagonal line to 5 circles enclosed with a rectangle.)

  T: These are the cats that…

  S: Remained! → Stayed!

  T: (Label the part. Ask the following questions to close the lesson.)

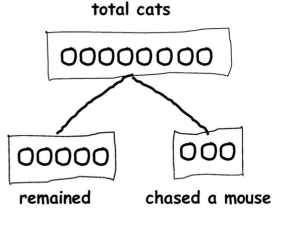

- How is this number bond different from your number bond? How is it the same?

- How is this number bond different from your math drawing? How is it the same?

- Can we always show a math story using a picture number bond? Does it only work for this story? (Try it out with Problem 4.)

Exit Ticket (3 minutes)

After the Student Debrief, instruct students to complete the Exit Ticket. A review of their work will help with assessing students' understanding of the concepts that were presented in today's lesson and planning more effectively for future lessons. The questions may be read aloud to the students.

EUREKA
MATH™

A

Name _____   Date _____

Number Correct:

*Write the number that is 1 less.

1.	5		16.	10	
2.	4		17.	8	
3.	3		18.	11	
4.	5		19.	10	
5.	3		20.	9	
6.	1		21.	1	
7.	4		22.	11	
8.	5		23.	21	
9.	7		24.	4	
10.	6		25.	14	
11.	7		26.	24	
12.	9		27.	10	
13.	8		28.	20	
14.	9		29.	21	
15.	10		30.	31	

Lesson 28: Solve *take from with result unknown* math stories with math drawings, true number sentences, and statements, using horizontal marks to cross off what is taken away.

©2015 Great Minds. eureka-math.org
G1-M1-TE-BK1-1.3.1-01.2016

349

B

Name _____   Date _____

Number Correct: ⛤

*Write the number that is 1 less.

1.	3		16.	10	
2.	2		17.	9	
3.	1		18.	11	
4.	6		19.	9	
5.	4		20.	13	
6.	2		21.	11	
7.	1		22.	1	
8.	3		23.	11	
9.	5		24.	21	
10.	7		25.	5	
11.	10		26.	15	
12.	9		27.	25	
13.	8		28.	20	
14.	6		29.	10	
15.	17		30.	21	

Lesson 28:   Solve *take from with result unknown* math stories with math drawings, true number sentences, and statements, using horizontal marks to cross off what is taken away.

©2015 Great Minds. eureka-math.org
G1-M1-TE-BK1-1.3.1-01.2016

EUREKA MATH™

Name _____   Date _____

Read the story. Draw a horizontal line through the items that are leaving the story.

Then, complete the number bond, sentence, and statement.

Example: 3 – 2 = 1

1. There are 5 toy airplanes flying at the park.
    One went down and broke.
    How many airplanes are still flying?

5 – 1 = _____

There are _____ airplanes still flying.

2. I had 6 eggs from the store.
    Three of them were cracked.
    How many eggs did I have that were not cracked?

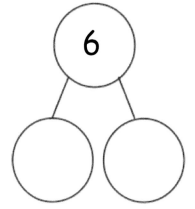

6 – ____ = _____

_____ eggs were not cracked.

EUREKA MATH™

Lesson 28:   Solve *take from with result unknown* math stories with math drawings,
true number sentences, and statements, using horizontal marks to
cross off what is taken away.

©2015 Great Minds. eureka-math.org
G1-M1-TE-BK1-1.3.1-01.2016

351

Draw a number bond and math drawing to help you solve the problems.

3. Kate saw 8 cats playing in the grass.
    Three went away to chase a mouse.
    How many cats remained in the grass?

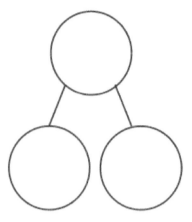

_____ - _____ = _____

_____ cats remained in the grass.

4. There were 7 mango slices.
    Two of them were eaten.
    How many mango slices are left to eat?

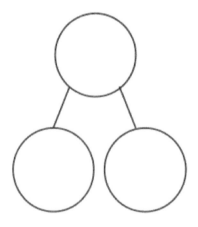

_____ - _____ = _____

There are _____ mango slices left.

Lesson 28:   Solve *take from with result unknown* math stories with math drawings,
                true number sentences, and statements, using horizontal marks to
                cross off what is taken away.

©2015 Great Minds. eureka-math.org
G1-M1-TE-BK1-1.3.1-01.2016

EUREKA
MATH™

Name _____   Date _____

Read the problem. Make a math drawing to solve.

There were 9 kites flying in the park. Three kites got caught in trees. How many kites were still flying?

____ − ____ = ____

____ kites were still flying.

Lesson 28: Solve *take from with result unknown* math stories with math drawings, true number sentences, and statements, using horizontal marks to cross off what is taken away.

©2015 Great Minds. eureka-math.org
G1-M1-TE-BK1-1.3.1-01.2016

353

Name _____   Date _____

Read the story. Make a math drawing to solve.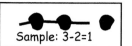

Sample: 3-2=1

1. There were 6 hot dogs on the grill. Two finish cooking and are removed. How many hot dogs remain on the grill?

   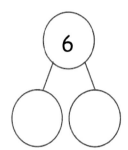

6 - ____ = ____

There are ____ hot dogs remaining on the grill.

2. Bob buys 8 new toy cars. He takes 3 out of the bag. How many cars are still in the bag?

   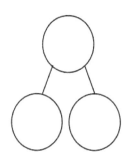

___ - ___ = ___

____ cars are still in the bag.

3. Kira sees 7 birds in the tree. Three birds fly away. How many birds are still in the tree?

   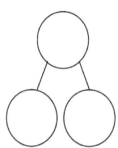

___ - ___ = ___

____ birds are still in the tree.

Lesson 28:   Solve *take from with result unknown* math stories with math drawings, true number sentences, and statements, using horizontal marks to cross off what is taken away.

©2015 Great Minds. eureka-math.org
G1-M1-TE-BK1-1.3.1-01.2016

EUREKA
MATH™

4. Brad has 9 friends over for a party. Six friends get picked up. How many friends are still at the party?

 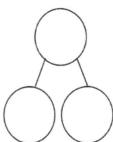

_____ - _____ = _____

_____ friends are still
at the party.

5. Jordan was playing with 10 cars. He gave 7 to Kate. How many cars is Jordan playing with now?

 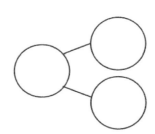

_____ - _____ = _____

Jordan is playing
with _____ cars now.

6. Tony takes 4 books from the bookshelf. There were 10 books on the shelf to start. How many books are on the shelf now?

 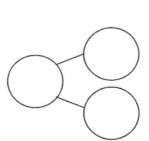

_____ - _____ = _____

_____ books are
on the shelf now.

EUREKA MATH™

Lesson 28: Solve *take from with result unknown* math stories with math drawings, true number sentences, and statements, using horizontal marks to cross off what is taken away.

©2015 Great Minds. eureka-math.org
G1-M1-TE-BK1-1.3.1-01.2016

355

Lesson 29

Objective: Solve *take apart with addend unknown* math stories with math drawings, equations, and statements, circling the known part to find the unknown.

Suggested Lesson Structure

■ Fluency Practice   (12 minutes)
▨ Application Problem   (8 minutes)
☐ Concept Development   (30 minutes)
■ Student Debrief   (10 minutes)
   Total Time   **(60 minutes)**

Fluency Practice (12 minutes)

- Stand on Even Numbers **1.OA.5**   (3 minutes)
- Cold Call: 2 Less **1.OA.5, 1.OA.6**   (2 minutes)
- Subtraction with Cards **1.OA.6**   (7 minutes)

Stand on Even Numbers (3 minutes)

Note: Practicing counting forward by twos helps promote automaticity with adding 2 and counting with automaticity up to 40.

Students sit in a circle and count by ones, each student saying one number to count up. When a student says an even number, she stands: 1, 2 (student stands), 3, 4 (student stands)… Continue counting until all students are standing. The last one sitting is the winner. Play again starting at a different point in the circle. This leads nicely into Cold Call, wherein all students start out standing.

Cold Call: 2 Less (2 minutes)

Note: This activity supports students' ability to relate counting back 2 to subtracting 2.

Tell students you are going to say a number aloud, and instruct them to think about the number that is 2 less. Let them know you will cold call students to say the answer as quickly as possible. Alternate between calling on individual students, the whole class, and groups of students (e.g., only girls, only boys, etc.). Begin with numbers within 10, and then expand to numbers within 20. Students stand with hands behind their backs to help them resist raising their hand when they hear the teacher's call.

A suggested sequence type is 3, 2, 8, 6, 9, 7, 10, 8, 18, 8, ten 8, 3, 13, etc.

Lesson 29:   Solve *take apart with addend unknown* math stories with math
                        drawings, equations, and statements, circling the known part to find
                        the unknown.
                ©2015 Great Minds. eureka-math.org
                G1-M1-TE-BK1-1.3.1-01.2016

EUREKA
MATH™

Subtraction With Cards (7 minutes)

Materials: (S) 1 set numeral side only 5-group cards (Lesson 5, Template 1) per pair, counters (if needed)

Note: This activity addresses the core fluency objective for Grade 1 of adding and subtracting within 10.

Students place cards face down between them. Each partner flips over two cards and subtracts the smaller number from the larger number. The partner with the smallest difference keeps the cards played by both players that round. The player with the most cards at the end of the game wins.

Application Problem (8 minutes)

Lucas has 9 pencils for school. He lends 4 of them to his friends. How many pencils does Lucas have left? Box the solution in your number sentence, and include a statement to answer the question. Be sure to draw your simple shapes in a straight line.

Note: This problem applies the objective from Lesson 28 and moves from crossing off a part that is taken away to circling a known part to identify an unknown part embedded within the total. In the Student Debrief, students will be able to compare and contrast the two strategies.

$$9 - 4 = \boxed{5}$$

00000~~0000~~

He has 5 pencils.

Concept Development (30 minutes)

Materials: (S) Personal white board

Invite students to sit in the circle area in a semi-circle with their personal white boards.

- T: Welcome to another edition of Math Stories Theater! Six children are at a sleepover. (Call 6 children to the front, lining them up in a straight row.)
- T: Four children are wearing black shoes. The rest are wearing white shoes.
- T: How many children are wearing white shoes at the sleepover?
- T: Write a subtraction sentence to answer the question.
- S: (Write 6 – 4 = 2.)
- T: By lining up our actors in a straight row, we can easily see the sets of students. Let's try another one.
- T: It's bedtime. Three children are in their sleeping bags. The rest are underneath their blankets. How many children are using blankets? Turn and decide with a partner.

NOTES ON
MULTIPLE MEANS
OF REPRESENTATION:

Frequent checks for understanding benefit English language learners and other students who may shy away from asking questions. Ask questions for comprehension and encourage students to retell the story to ensure the vocabulary and concept is being understood.

S: (Discuss with partner.)

S: Three children are using blankets.

T: Let's use the actors to see. These 3 have sleeping bags. (Gesture to students.) That means these children have blankets. Three children are using blankets.

T: Let's draw a simple math drawing to match this situation. (On a personal board, draw 6 circles in a row.)

T: These circles represent our 6 children in the story. We know that 3 of them are using sleeping bags. I'm going to circle the first 3 of these (circle the first 3 shapes), and then we should be able to see how many children are left using blankets. How many circles are left?

S: 3 circles.

T: Draw a simple math drawing like mine to match the story. Write the subtraction sentence that goes with it.

S: (Create a similar math drawing and write 6 – 3 = 3.)

Repeat the process with more *take apart* math stories. Listed below is a suggested sequence of story lines:

- 8 cupcakes in all: 6 with chocolate icing, and the rest with vanilla
- 7 sneakers in all: 3 with Velcro, and the rest with shoe laces
- 10 coats: 7 with buttons, and the rest with zippers
- 9 balls: 3 basketballs, and the rest are soccer balls

Each time, ask the students to draw a simple math story to check their solution to the story problem before having the actors portray the two parts. Focus on circling the part that is known to help solve the unknown part.

Problem Set (10 minutes)

Students should do their personal best to complete the Problem Set within the allotted 10 minutes. For some classes, it may be appropriate to modify the assignment by specifying which problems they work on first. Some problems do not specify a method for solving. Students solve these problems using the RDW approach used for Application Problems.

For this Problem Set, it is suggested that all students begin with Problem 1, possibly leaving Problem 4 to the end if there is still time.

> **NOTES ON MULTIPLE MEANS OF ENGAGEMENT:**
>
> Adjust the lesson structure to suit the specific needs of the class. Some students may need to continue with concrete representations throughout the lesson. Other students may be ready for more challenging numbers or the opportunity to develop their own math stories.

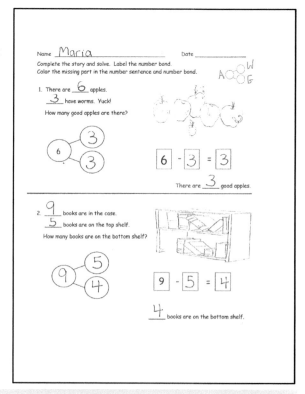

Lesson 29: Solve *take apart with addend unknown* math stories with math drawings, equations, and statements, circling the known part to find the unknown.

©2015 Great Minds. eureka-math.org
G1-M1-TE-BK1-1.3.1-01.2016

EUREKA MATH

Student Debrief (10 minutes)

Lesson Objective: Solve *take apart with addend unknown* math stories with math drawings, equations, and statements, circling the known part to find the unknown.

The Student Debrief is intended to invite reflection and active processing of the total lesson experience.

Invite students to review their solutions for the Problem Set. They should check work by comparing answers with a partner before going over answers as a class. Look for misconceptions or misunderstandings that can be addressed in the Debrief. Guide students in a conversation to debrief the Problem Set and process the lesson.

Any combination of the questions below may be used to lead the discussion.

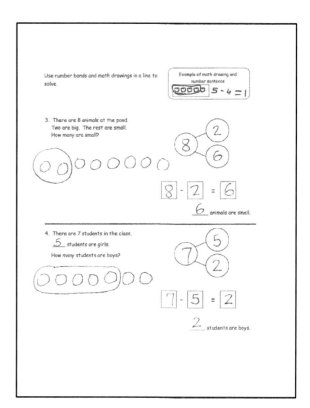

- In what way does making your drawing in a straight line help you solve the math problems? Use Problem 3 to help you explain your thinking.

- Explain your choices for Problem 4 to a partner. Did you and your partner complete Problem 4 in the same way or in different ways? Can you both be right even if you have different numbers for the parts? Why?

- With your partner, come up with different ways to make Problem 4 true.

- How did the Application Problem connect to today's lesson? How is the strategy of crossing out in our math drawing similar to the strategy we used today? Why might we choose one strategy instead of another when solving story problems?

- Help students make a distinction between the *take apart* and *take from* stories, the two problem types using subtraction they have encountered thus far in the module.

  T: When we used subtraction today, we didn't cross off any parts of our drawings. What does it mean when we cross things off in our drawings? (Give an example.)

  S: Something is going away.

  T: Why didn't we cross things off today? (Give an example.)

  S: Because nothing went away. It was just that one part was different from the other. We were looking for the other part.

Lesson 29:   Solve *take apart with addend unknown* math stories with math drawings, equations, and statements, circling the known part to find the unknown.

©2015 Great Minds. eureka-math.org
G1-M1-TE-BK1-1.3.1-01.2016

359

- Another strategy for problems like the ones we had today is to draw the parts into a picture number bond. This number bond math drawing represents one of the problems in the Problem Set. (Draw the picture to the right on the board.) Which problem do you think this drawing represents? (Problem 2.) How can you tell? Describe each part. (Label as each part is described. The top row represents all of the books. The bottom row has 2 parts, with 1 part representing books on the top shelf and the other part representing the books on the bottom shelf.)

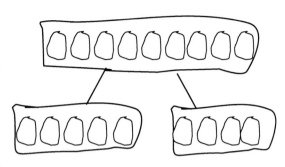

Exit Ticket (3 minutes)

After the Student Debrief, instruct students to complete the Exit Ticket. A review of their work will help with assessing students' understanding of the concepts that were presented in today's lesson and planning more effectively for future lessons. The questions may be read aloud to the students.

360   Lesson 29:   Solve *take apart with addend unknown* math stories with math
                              drawings, equations, and statements, circling the known part to find
                              the unknown.
                ©2015 Great Minds. eureka-math.org
                G1-M1-TE-BK1-1.3.1-01.2016

EUREKA
MATH

Name _____   Date _____

Complete the story and solve. Label the number bond.
Color the missing part in the number sentence and number bond.

1. There are _____ apples.

   _____ have worms. Yuck!

   How many good apples are there?

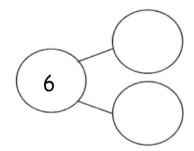

$$\boxed{6} - \boxed{} = \boxed{}$$

There are _____ good apples.

2. _____ books are in the case.

   _____ books are on the top shelf.

   How many books are on the bottom shelf?

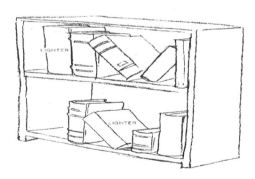

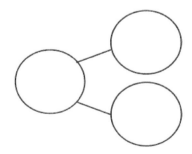

$$\boxed{9} - \boxed{} = \boxed{}$$

_____ books are on the bottom shelf.

EUREKA MATH™   **Lesson 29:**   Solve *take apart with addend unknown* math stories with math drawings, equations, and statements, circling the known part to find the unknown.   361

©2015 Great Minds. eureka-math.org
G1-M1-TE-BK1-1.3.1-01.2016

Use number bonds and math drawings in a line to solve.

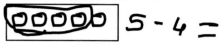
Example of math drawing and number sentence
$5 - 4 = 1$

3. There are 8 animals at the pond.
    Two are big. The rest are small.
    How many are small?

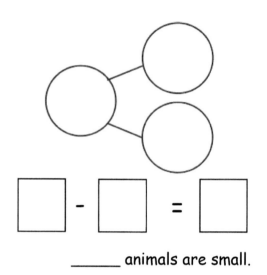

$$\boxed{} - \boxed{} = \boxed{}$$

_____ animals are small.

4. There are 7 students in the class.
    _____ students are girls.
    How many students are boys?

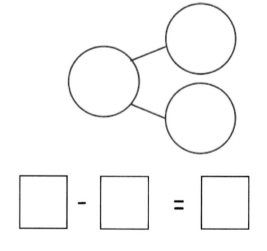

$$\boxed{} - \boxed{} = \boxed{}$$

_____ students are boys.

Lesson 29:   Solve *take apart with addend unknown* math stories with math
drawings, equations, and statements, circling the known part to find
the unknown.

EUREKA
MATH™

Name _____ Date _____

Read the story. Make a math drawing to solve.

There are 9 baseball players on the team. Seven are on the bench. How many are not on the bench?

_____ - _____ = _____

_____ players are not on the bench.

Lesson 29:   Solve *take apart with addend unknown* math stories with math
drawings, equations, and statements, circling the known part to find
the unknown.
©2015 Great Minds. eureka-math.org
G1-M1-TE-BK1-1.3.1-01.2016

363

Name _____   Date _____

Read the math stories. Make math drawings to solve. ⬚⬚⬚⬚⬚ $5 - 4 = 1$

1. Tom has a box of 7 crayons. Five crayons are red. How many crayons are not red?

    ____ - ____ = ____

    _____ crayons are not red.

2. Mary picks 8 flowers. Two are daisies. The rest are tulips. How many tulips does she pick?

    ____ - ____ = ____

    Mary picks _____ tulips.

3. There are 9 pieces of fruit in the bowl. Four are apples. The rest are oranges. How many pieces of fruit are oranges?

    ____ - ____ = ____

    The bowl has _____ oranges.

Solve *take apart with addend unknown* math stories with math drawings, equations, and statements, circling the known part to find the unknown.
©2015 Great Minds. eureka-math.org
G1-M1-TE-BK1-1.3.1-01.2016

EUREKA
MATH™

4. Mom and Ben make 10 cookies. Six are stars. The rest are round. How many cookies are round?

 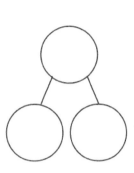

_____ - _____ = _____

There are _____ round cookies.

5. The parking lot has 7 spaces. Two cars are parked in the lot. How many more cars can park in the lot?

 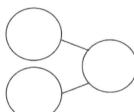

_____ - _____ = _____

_____ more cars can park in the lot.

6. Liz has 2 fingers with Band Aids. How many fingers are not hurt?

 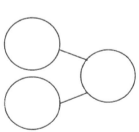

_____ - _____ = _____

Write a statement for your answer:

_____

EUREKA MATH™

Lesson 29:   Solve *take apart with addend unknown* math stories with math drawings, equations, and statements, circling the known part to find the unknown.

©2015 Great Minds. eureka-math.org
G1-M1-TE-BK1-1.3.1-01.2016

365

Lesson 30

Objective: Solve *add to with change unknown* math stories with drawings, relating addition and subtraction.

Suggested Lesson Structure

■ Fluency Practice   (12 minutes)
▨ Application Problem   (5 minutes)
▢ Concept Development   (33 minutes)
■ Student Debrief   (10 minutes)

    Total Time   **(60 minutes)**

Fluency Practice (12 minutes)

- Happy Counting by Tens **1.NBT.1, 1.NBT.5**   (2 minutes)
- Math Hands Flash: Partners to 10 **1.OA.4, 1.OA.6**   (5 minutes)
- Number Bond Dash: 10 **K.OA.3, 1.OA.6**   (5 minutes)

Happy Counting by Tens (2 minutes)

Note: Practice counting forward and back by tens helps promote automaticity with 10 more and 10 less addition and subtraction problems.

Repeat the Happy Counting activity from Lesson 3, counting by tens. First, count from 0 to 120 and back, and then from 9 to 119 and back.

Math Hands Flash: Partners of 10 (5 minutes)

Note: This activity provides an opportunity for students to maintain their fluency with partners of 10 and strengthen their visualization of 5-groups by using their hands to see the math. The activity also continues to support students in seeing the connection between addition and subtraction.

Guide students to relate addition and subtraction problems while building fluency with partners of 10.

    T: (Hold up 9 fingers.) Show me how many fingers I need to make 10.
    S: (Hold up 1 finger.)
    T: 9 plus what number equals 10?
    S: 1.
    T: Good! 9 + 1 = 10, so 10 − 9 = ? Look at your hands.
    S: 1.

Continue playing, eliciting all partners of 10. If students are highly successful, switch to other totals within 10, such as 9, 8, or 7.

Number Bond Dash: 10 (5 minutes)

Materials: (T) Stopwatch or timer (S) Number Bond Dash 10 (Lesson 9 Fluency Template), marker to correct
work

Note: By using the same system repeatedly, students can focus on the mathematics alone. This activity
addresses the core fluency for Grade 1 of adding and subtracting within 10.

Follow the procedure for the Number Bond Dash in Lesson 5 Fluency Practice. Tell students to remember
how many problems they get correct so they can try to improve their scores tomorrow.

Application Problem (5 minutes)

Freddie has 10 action figures in his pocket. Five of them are good guys.
How many of his action figures are bad guys? Box the solution in your
number sentence, and include a statement to answer the question. Make a
math drawing. Circle the part that is good guys to show you have the
correct number of bad guys.

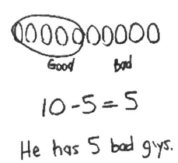

Note: This problem applies learning from the previous lesson on solving
take apart story problems by circling the known part to find the unknown
part. During the Student Debrief, students will connect this with their new
learning as they create a picture number bond to go with the problem.

Concept Development (33 minutes)

Materials: (T) Books of different sizes (S) Personal white board, number path (Lesson 26 Template), yellow
colored pencil or highlighter

Display 5 books (either on the ledge of the board or on a shelf).
Invite students to sit in the meeting area in a semicircle with
their personal white boards.

- T: How many books do I have on this shelf? (Gesture to
  the books.)
- S: 5 books.
- T: A student came and put some more books on the
  shelf. Close your eyes. (Add 2 more books.) Open
  your eyes. How many books are there now?
- S: 7 books.
- T: Let's make a number bond to figure out how many more books the student brought. (Ask students
  to identify what they already know from the story and decide if it is a part or the total as they fill in
  the boxes. Have students identify the referents for each number and label the boxes accordingly.)

**NOTES ON
MULTIPLE MEANS
OF ACTION AND
EXPRESSION:**

Provide sentence frames to support
verbal responses for English language
learners and other students who may
require language support.

T: Turn and talk to your partner about what you can do to solve how many more books the student put on the shelf. Write the number sentence, but leave the mystery number blank.

S: (Discuss and write 5 + ☐ = 7 or 7 − 5 = ☐ .)

T: (Circulate and listen. Ask a student who used addition to share.)

S: (Show the number sentence.) I counted on. Fiiive, 6, 7. I added 2 more. → I said 5 plus what equals 7 and just knew it was 2.

T: Great strategies! (Choose a student who used subtraction to share.)

S: I knew there were 7 books total, so I took away 5 books that we already had and got 2 books.

T: Nice work! Did we all get the same answer, even though some used an addition sentence and others used a subtraction sentence?

S: Yes!

Have students fill in the missing part of the number bond and label it.

T: Let's draw a picture number bond to show the story.

T: Draw circles in a row to represent the total of 7 books. Put a box around it, just like the number has a box around it in the number bond. (Model and emphasize the importance of making circles the same size. Each circle represents 1 book, not the size of each book.)

S: (Draw.)

T: Draw circles in a row to represent the number of books we began with. Put a box around it. (Model and draw a diagonal line to connect the part and total box.)

S: (Draw.)

T: Draw a box to show the part that will contain the number of books the student brought. (Model and draw another diagonal line.) Fill in the box with circles that represent how many more books were put on the shelf.

S: (Draw 2 more circles.)

T: Write the labels to show what each box and its circles stand for. (Guide the students if necessary.)

S: (Write labels.)

Repeat the process by telling more *add to with change unknown* stories. Use the following suggested sequence: 4 + ☐ = 7, 6 + ☐ = 8, and 6 + ☐ = 9. At times, rotate the picture number bond so that the parts are above the total, as shown on the Problem Set. This will help students focus on recognizing which is the total and which sections are the parts based on the lines, or arms, of the bond.

T: How did you use your math drawing to show how you can use addition to solve the problem?

S: I started with the 6 books and used my fingers to count on 3 (or add 3) to get to the total.

T: How did you use your math drawing to show how you can use subtraction to solve the problem?

S: I started with the total, which is 9, separated the 6, and saw that 3 were left.

Lesson 30:   Solve *add to with change unknown* math stories with drawings, relating addition and subtraction.

©2015 Great Minds. eureka-math.org
G1-M1-TE-BK1-1.3.1-01.2016

Problem Set (10 minutes)

Students should do their personal best to complete the Problem Set within the allotted 10 minutes. For some classes, it may be appropriate to modify the assignment by specifying which problems they work on first. Some problems do not specify a method for solving. Students solve these problems using the RDW approach used for Application Problems.

In this Problem Set, students should begin with Problem 1, possibly leaving Problem 4 to the end if there is still time.

Student Debrief (10 minutes)

Lesson Objective: Solve *add to with change unknown* math stories with drawings, relating addition and subtraction.

The Student Debrief is intended to invite reflection and active processing of the total lesson experience.

Invite students to review their solutions for the Problem Set. They should check work by comparing answers with a partner before going over answers as a class. Look for misconceptions or misunderstandings that can be addressed in the Debrief. Guide students in a conversation to debrief the Problem Set and process the lesson.

Any combination of the questions below may be used to lead the discussion.

- How did the addition sentences help you solve today's problems? How did subtraction sentences help you solve today's problems?

- Which problem do you think would be solved most efficiently using subtraction? Why?

- What new math strategy did we use today to communicate precisely? Explain how it is helpful.

- How is drawing a picture number bond similar to and different from your past math drawings?

- How did the Application Problem connect to today's lesson? Draw a picture number bond to match the story.

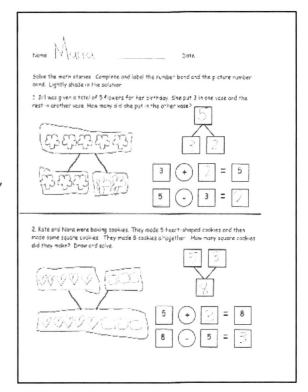

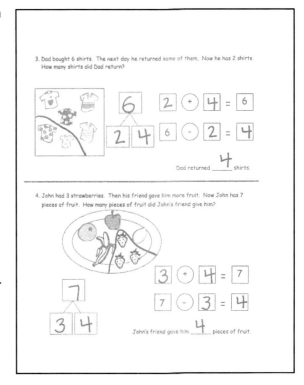

Lesson 30:   Solve *add to with change unknown* math stories with drawings,
               relating addition and subtraction.

369

▪   Let's compare our problems using subtraction again.

  T: When we used subtraction yesterday, we didn't cross off any parts of our drawings. What does it mean when we cross things off in our drawings? (Give an example.)

  S: Something is going away.

  T: Why didn't we cross things off today? (Give an example.)

  S: Something was being added, but we didn't know what. → We added on the mystery number. → We just subtracted because it was a missing part, but it didn't sound like subtraction. → I didn't even write a subtraction sentence at first! → I didn't need to, because I saw the number bond in my mind. A part was missing.

Exit Ticket (3 minutes)

After the Student Debrief, instruct students to complete the Exit Ticket. A review of their work will help with assessing students' understanding of the concepts that were presented in today's lesson and planning more effectively for future lessons. The questions may be read aloud to the students.

Lesson 30:   Solve *add to with change unknown* math stories with drawings, relating addition and subtraction.

©2015 Great Minds. eureka-math.org
G1-M1-TE-BK1-1.3.1-01.2016

Name _____   Date _____

Solve the math stories. Complete and label the number bond and the picture number bond. Lightly shade in the solution.

1. Jill was given a total of 5 flowers for her birthday. She put 3 in one vase and the rest in another vase. How many flowers did she put in the other vase?

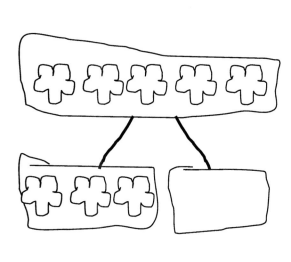 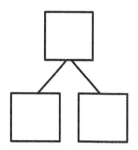

2. Kate and Nana were baking cookies. They made 5 heart-shaped cookies and then made some square cookies. They made 8 cookies altogether. How many square cookies did they make? Draw and solve.

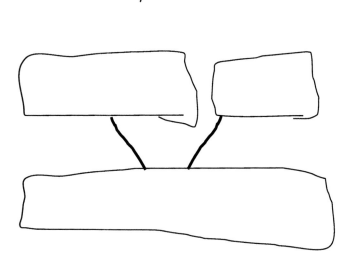 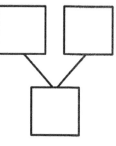

Lesson 30:   Solve *add to with change unknown* math stories with drawings, relating addition and subtraction.

371

Solve. Complete and label the number bond and the picture number bond. Circle the unknown number.

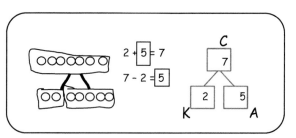

3. Bill has 2 trucks. His friend James came over with some more.
   Together, they have 6 trucks.
   How many trucks did James bring over?

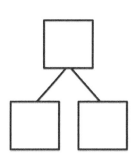

_____ + _____ = 6

6 - _____ = _____

James brought over _____ trucks.

4. Jane caught 5 fish before she stopped to eat lunch.
   After lunch, she caught some more.
   At the end of the day, she had 9 fish.
   How many fish did she catch after lunch?

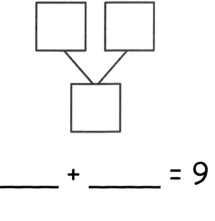

_____ + _____ = 9

9 - _____ = _____

Jane caught _____ fish after lunch.

Lesson 30:   Solve *add to with change unknown* math stories with drawings, relating addition and subtraction.

©2015 Great Minds. eureka-math.org
G1-M1-TE-BK1-1.3.1-01.2016

EUREKA MATH™

Name _____   Date _____

Draw and label a picture number bond to solve.

Toby collects shells. On Monday, he finds 6 shells. On Tuesday, he finds some more.
Toby finds a total of 9 shells. How many shells does Toby find on Tuesday?

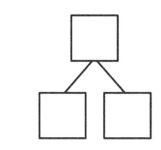

_____ + _____ = _____

_____ - _____ = _____

Toby finds _____ shells on Tuesday.

Lesson 30:   Solve *add to with change unknown* math stories with drawings,
relating addition and subtraction.

373

Name _____ Date _____

Solve the math stories. Draw and label a picture number bond to solve. Circle the unknown number.

1. Grace has a total of 7 dolls. She puts 2 in the toy box and takes the rest to her friend's house. How many dolls does she take to her friend's house?

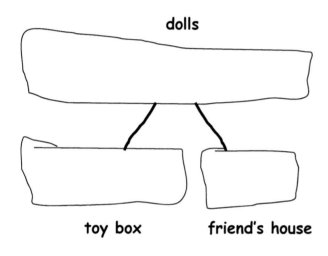

dolls

toy box   friend's house

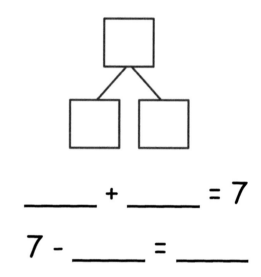

_____ + _____ = 7

7 - _____ = _____

Grace takes _____ dolls to her friend's house.

2. Jack can invite 8 friends to his birthday party. He makes 3 invitations. How many invitations does he still need to make?

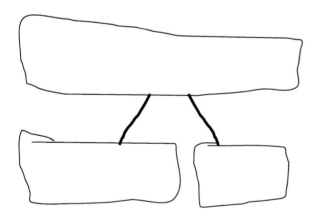

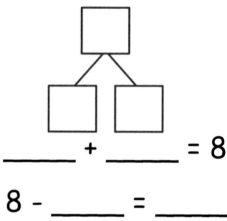

_____ + _____ = 8

8 - _____ = _____

Jack still needs to make _____ invitations.

Lesson 30:   Solve *add to with change unknown* math stories with drawings, relating addition and subtraction.

EUREKA MATH

3. There are 9 dogs at the park. Five dogs play with balls. The rest are eating bones. How many dogs are eating bones?

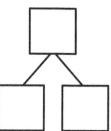

_____ + _____ = 9

_____ dogs are eating bones.

_____ - _____ = _____

4. There are 10 students in Jim's class. Seven bought lunch at school. The rest brought lunch from home. How many students brought lunch from home?

_____ + _____ = _____

_____ - _____ = _____

_____ students brought lunch from home.

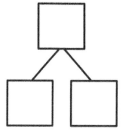

EUREKA MATH™

Lesson 30: Solve *add to with change unknown* math stories with drawings, relating addition and subtraction.

375

©2015 Great Minds. eureka-math.org
G1-M1-TE-BK1-1.3.1-01.2016

Lesson 31

Objective: Solve *take from with change unknown* math stories with drawings.

Suggested Lesson Structure

■ Fluency Practice   (13 minutes)
▨ Application Problem   (5 minutes)
▢ Concept Development   (32 minutes)
■ Student Debrief   (10 minutes)
   Total Time   **(60 minutes)**

Fluency Practice (13 minutes)

- Beep Counting by Tens **1.NBT.5**   (3 minutes)
- Penny Drop: Count On from 10 **1.OA.6**   (5 minutes)
- Number Bond Dash: 10 **1.OA.6**   (5 minutes)

Beep Counting by Tens (3 minutes)

Note: This fluency activity helps students recognize patterns while building fluency with adding and subtracting 10.

Say a series of three numbers but replace one of the numbers with the word *beep*. When signaled, students say the *beep* number. (See Lesson 28.)

Suggested sequence types are basic multiples of 10 (10, 20, beep; 80, 90, beep; etc.) and 10 more with some ones (25, 35, beep; 48, 58, beep; etc.). If students are ready, try counting backward or placing the beep first or second in the sequence.

Penny Drop: Count on from 10 (5 minutes)

Materials: (T) 15 pennies, 1 can

Note: This activity reviews the Kindergarten standards of identifying 10 ones and some additional ones. This concept is foundational for Module 2, where students use the make ten strategy to add within 20.

Tell students that 10 pennies are in the can. Have students close their eyes and listen. Drop 1 to 5 pennies in the can, one at a time. Ask students to open their eyes and tell you how many pennies are in the can now.

**NOTES ON
MULTIPLE MEANS
OF ACTION AND
EXPRESSION:**

Scaffold tasks by carefully selecting numbers that are most appropriate for learners. Some students would benefit from a longer sequence to make the pattern more apparent. Challenge higher-level students by changing the placement of the beeps or using more challenging number sequences.

Lesson 31:   *Solve take from with change unknown math stories with drawings.*   EUREKA MATH™

©2015 Great Minds. eureka-math.org
G1-M1-TE-BK1-1.3.1-01.2016

Number Bond Dash: 10 (5 minutes)

Materials: (T) Stopwatch or timer (S) Number Bond Dash 10 (Lesson 9 Fluency Template), marker to correct work

Note: Reviewing number bonds allows students to build and maintain fluency with addition and subtraction facts within 10.

Follow the procedure for the Number Bond Dash from Lesson 5 Fluency Practice. Remember that today is the second day with the Number Bond Dash 10. Students should recall their scores from the previous lesson to celebrate improvement.

Application Problem (5 minutes)

Shanika saw 5 pigeons on the roof. Some more pigeons flew onto the roof. She then counted 8 pigeons. How many pigeons flew over?

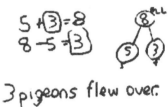

Write a number bond and both addition and subtraction number sentences to match the story. Box the solution in your number sentences, and include a statement to answer the question.

Note: This problem applies learning from Lesson 30, where students use strategies to solve *add to with change unknown* problems. By writing both addition and subtraction number sentences, students continue to strengthen their understanding of the relationship between the operations.

Concept Development (32 minutes)

Materials: (T) Books of different sizes (S) Personal white board, yellow colored pencil

T: I borrowed 7 books from the library. On my way home, I lent some of the books to a friend. Will my backpack have more or *fewer* books than 7? How do you know?

S: Fewer books because you took away some books to give to your friend.

T: You're right! There are 5 books still in the backpack. How many books did I lend?

T: Let's make a number bond to find out. On your board, make and fill in the number bond. What does 7 stand for?

S: The books you borrowed from the library.

T: Is that a part or the total number of books in the story?

S: The total.

T/S: (Fill in 7 on the number bond and label *B* for borrowed books.)

T: What else do you know?

S: You have 5 books left.

T: Are these 5 books part of the total number of books?

S: Yes.

T/S: (Fill in 5 and label *L* for leftover books.)

T: What about this part box? What does it stand for?

S: That's the mystery number. It stands for how many books you gave to your friend.

T: Let's write a number sentence. How did the story begin?

S: You borrowed 7 books.

T: (Write 7.) What happened next? How can we continue our number sentence?

S: You gave away some books, so use *minus*. → Write *7 minus box,* because we don't know how many books you gave away.

T: (Write 7 – ___.) What happened last? How can we continue our number sentence?

S: You ended up with 5 books. Seven minus something is 5.

T: (Writes 7 – ___ = 5.)

T: Let's make a math drawing to show what we know so far.

S: (Draw 7 circles.)

T: Group the circles that show how many books I still have.

S: (Group 5 circles together.)

T: What are these books that we didn't group? (Gesture to the 2 remaining books.)

S: The books you gave to your friend.

T: How can we show that I gave away these books?

MP.6

S: Say, goodbye 2. Make the line look like one big subtraction sign.

T: Write a number sentence to show what you just did.

S: (Write 7 – 2 = 5.)

T: How many books did I give away?

S: You gave away 2 books.

T: Circle the part of the number sentence that shows this answer.

S: (Circle 2.)

Continue to tell *take from with change unknown* stories using the following suggested sequence and scenarios:

- Hansel and Gretel have a bag with 8 pieces of bread. They drop some on their path and have 3 pieces remaining.

- Nine children are playing hide and seek. Some went away to hide. Four children can still be seen.

- We caught 9 fireflies. Some flew away. Six fireflies are left in the jar.

©2015 Great Minds. eureka-math.org
G1-M1-TE-BK1-1.3.1-01.2016

Problem Set (10 minutes)

Students should do their personal best to complete the Problem Set within the allotted 10 minutes. For some classes, it may be appropriate to modify the assignment by specifying which problems they work on first. Some problems do not specify a method for solving. Students solve these problems using the RDW approach used for Application Problems.

On this Problem Set, students should begin with Problems 1–3, possibly leaving Problem 4 to the end if there is still time.

Student Debrief (10 minutes)

Lesson Objective: Solve *take from with change unknown* math stories with drawings.

The Student Debrief is intended to invite reflection and active processing of the total lesson experience.

Invite students to review their solutions for the Problem Set. They should check work by comparing answers with a partner before going over answers as a class. Look for misconceptions or misunderstandings that can be addressed in the Debrief. Guide students in a conversation to debrief the Problem Set and process the lesson.

Any combination of the questions below may be used to lead the discussion.

- What pattern did you notice about all of our story problems today?

- What new math strategy did we use to solve our story problems today?

- One at a time, share some student drawings that have particular strengths (e.g., use of simple circles or squares, picture number bonds, straight rows or similarly sized shapes, clear labels). What do you notice about this math drawing? What qualities make it useful for solving math problems?

- Today, we did not include addition sentences on our Problem Set. How does the number bond help you continue to use addition to help you think about subtraction?

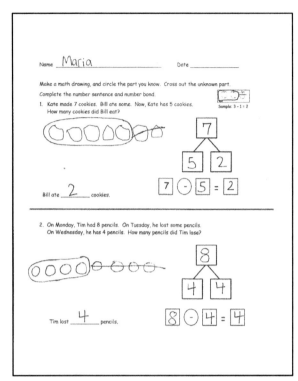

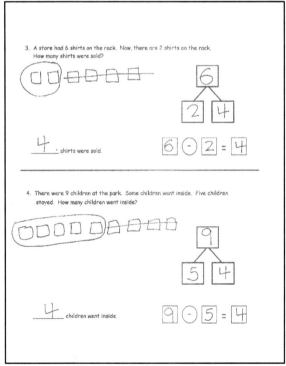

- Explain to your partner how you can use addition to solve Problem 1. Explain how you can use counting on to solve addition and subtraction. How can you use counting on or counting back to help you solve subtraction problems?

- Is counting on or counting back for Problem 1 more efficient? Explain your thinking.

- Look at your Application Problem. How could making a quick math drawing help you solve it?

Exit Ticket (3 minutes)

After the Student Debrief, instruct students to complete the Exit Ticket. A review of their work will help with assessing students' understanding of the concepts that were presented in today's lesson and planning more effectively for future lessons. The questions may be read aloud to the students.

©2015 Great Minds. eureka-math.org
G1-M1-TE-BK1-1.3.1-01.2016

Name _____   Date _____

Make a math drawing, and circle the part you know. Cross out the unknown part.

Complete the number sentence and number bond.

Sample: 3 – 1 = 2

1. Kate made 7 cookies. Bill ate some. Now, Kate has 5 cookies.
   How many cookies did Bill eat?

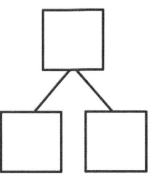

$$7 \bigcirc - \square = \square$$

Bill ate _____ cookies.

2. On Monday, Tim had 8 pencils. On Tuesday, he lost some pencils.
   On Wednesday, he has 4 pencils. How many pencils did Tim lose?

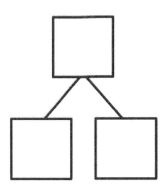

Tim lost _____ pencils.

$$\square \bigcirc - \square = \square$$

3. A store had 6 shirts on the rack. Now, there are 2 shirts on the rack.
   How many shirts were sold?

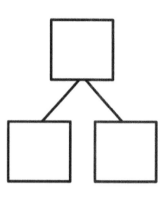

_____ shirts were sold.

___

4. There were 9 children at the park. Some children went inside. Five children stayed.
   How many children went inside?

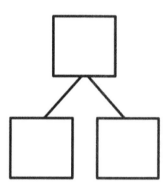

_____ children went inside.

Lesson 31:   Solve *take from with change unknown* math stories with drawings.   EUREKA
                                                                                                 MATH™

©2015 Great Minds. eureka-math.org
G1-M1-TE-BK1-1.3.1-01.2016

Name _____   Date _____

Make a math drawing, and circle the part you know. Cross out the unknown part.
Complete the number sentence and number bond.

Deb blows up 9 balloons. Some balloons popped. Three balloons are left.
How many balloons popped?

_____ balloons popped.

EUREKA
MATH™

Lesson 31:   Solve *take from with change unknown* math stories with drawings.

383

©2015 Great Minds. eureka-math.org
G1-M1-TE-BK1-1.3.1-01.2016

Name _____ Date _____

Make a math drawing, and circle the part you know.
Cross out the unknown part.
Complete the number sentence and number bond.

Sample 3 - 1 = 2

1. Missy gets 6 presents for her birthday. She unwraps some. Four are still wrapped. How many presents did she unwrap?

Missy unwrapped _____ presents.

6

$6 \bigcirc - \square = \square$

2. Ann has a box of 8 markers. Some fall on the floor. Six are still in the box. How many markers fell on the floor?

_____ markers fell on the floor.

$\square \bigcirc - \square = \square$

3. Nick makes 7 cupcakes for his friends. Some cupcakes were eaten. Now, there are 5 left. How many cupcakes were eaten?

_____ cupcakes were eaten.

$\square \bigcirc - \square = \square$

EUREKA MATH

©2015 Great Minds. eureka-math.org
G1-M1-TE-BK1-1.3.1-01.2016

4. A dog has 8 bones. He hides some. He still has 5 bones. How many bones are hidden?

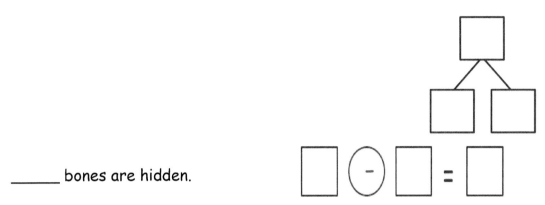

_____ bones are hidden.

5. The cafeteria table can seat 10 students. Some of the seats are taken. Seven seats are empty. How many seats are taken?

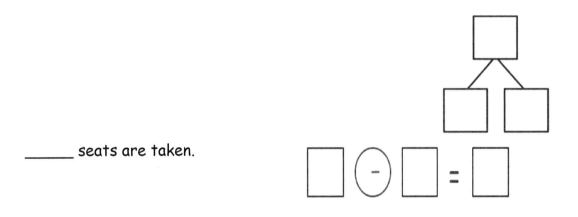

_____ seats are taken.

6. Ron has 10 sticks of gum. He gives one stick to each of his friends. Now, he has 3 sticks of gum left. How many friends did Ron share with?

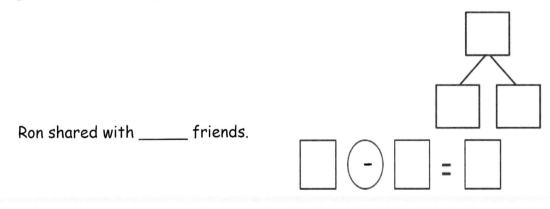

Ron shared with _____ friends.

EUREKA MATH™

Lesson 31:   Solve _take from with change unknown_ math stories with drawings.

385

©2015 Great Minds. eureka-math.org
G1-M1-TE-BK1-1.3.1-01.2016

Lesson 32

Objective: Solve *put together/take apart with addend unknown* math stories.

Suggested Lesson Structure

■ Fluency Practice   (15 minutes)
▨ Application Problem   (5 minutes)
▢ Concept Development   (30 minutes)
■ Student Debrief   (10 minutes)

Total Time   **(60 minutes)**

Fluency Practice (15 minutes)

- Happy Counting the Say Ten Way **1.OA.5**   (3 minutes)
- 5-Group Match: Partners to 10 **1.OA.6**   (10 minutes)
- Number Sentence Swap **1.OA.4**   (2 minutes)

Happy Counting the Say Ten Way (3 minutes)

Note: This activity helps students maintain their ability to count by tens, which is foundational to later Grade 1 work with adding and subtracting tens. Remember, the Rekenrek can be used on the first count to help students visualize the numbers as they count forward and backward.

Have students count up and down between 20 and 120 the Say Ten way, depending on their skill level (see Lesson 3). If they are very proficient up to 40, start at 40 and quickly go up to 80. If they are proficient between 40 and 80, Happy Count between 80 and 120. Alternate at times between regular and Say Ten counting, too.

5-Group Match: Partners to 10 (10 minutes)

Materials: (S) 5-group cards (0–10) with 1 extra 5 card per pair (Lesson 5 Template 1)

Note: Strong fluency with partners to 10 will be critical in Module 2 so that students can avoid using up too many of their attention resources on lower-level skills when they are addressing higher-level problems.

Assign students partners. Partner 1 closes his eyes. Partner 2 quickly lays out the 5-group cards, numeral side up. Partner 1 opens his eyes and tries to match all partners to ten as quickly as possible. Each player tries twice in a row to see if they can increase their speed.

EUREKA MATH

Number Sentence Swap (2 minutes)

Note: This activity supports students in developing a strong foundation in the relationship between addition and subtraction.

Give a subtraction sentence aloud, saying "the mystery number" for the unknown answer (e.g., "5 – 3 = the mystery number"). Call on a student to rephrase the sentence as an addition sentence (e.g., "3 + blank = 5"). Ask students to count on to solve the problem, for example, "threeeeee (touch head or hold up fist), 4 (raise thumb), 5 (raise index finger)." Ask students how many fingers they counted on. (2.)

Application Problem (5 minutes)

There are 8 juice boxes in the cubbies. Some children drink their juice. Now, there are only 5 juice boxes. How many juice boxes were taken from the cubbies?

Make a number bond. Write a subtraction sentence and a statement to match the story. Make a box around the solution in your number sentence. Make a math drawing to show how you know.

3 boxes were taken.

Note: This problem applies learning from Lesson 31, where students use strategies to solve *take from with change unknown* problems. The continued use of the number bond supports students' growing understanding of the relationship between addition and subtraction as they solve various problem types.

Concept Development (30 minutes)

Materials: (T) 10 white linking cubes (S) Personal white board

Invite students to come to the meeting area with their personal white boards and sit in a semicircle.

- T: There are 8 apples. (In a line, lay out 8 individual white linking cubes.) Put on your magic glasses that will show different colors. (Pretend to put on glasses.)
- S: (Pretend to put on glasses.)
- T: Ooooh, I see two parts. There are five red apples, here on this side. (Gesture.) That's one part. Thumbs up if you can see the red apples.
- S: (Show thumbs up.)
- T: The other part of the apples is green. Can you see the two parts?
- S: Yes!

Lesson 32:   Solve *put together/take apart with addend unknown* math stories.

387

©2015 Great Minds. eureka-math.org
G1-M1-TE-BK1-1.3.1-01.2016

T: Make a number bond to find out how many apples are green. Be sure to label each box, even the mystery box.

S: (Make a number bond with labels.)

T: Make a math drawing to show how you can solve the mystery number. Remember to line up your pictures in a straight row.

S: (Drawings may vary.)

T: Write the number sentence to solve. Be sure to circle the solution.

S: (Number sentences may vary.)

T: (Circulate and observe. Choose two students to share different strategies and number sentences. Possibilities include counting up, counting back, and writing addition or subtraction sentences.)

T: James wrote 5 + ___ = 8, and Lily wrote 8 − 5 = ___. Even though they used different number sentences and drawings, did they get the same answer?

S: Yes!

T: Hmmm, which was a faster or more efficient way to solve? Counting up or counting back? Turn and talk to your partner and explain why.

S: Counting up! You only need to count on 3 times to get to 8. Taking away 5 takes longer.

T: (While guiding students to notice that counting on 3 is more efficient, accept all explanations. Some students may know their −5 facts and find 8 − 5 a better strategy.)

NOTES ON MULTIPLE MEANS OF REPRESENTATION:

Never underestimate the use of manipulatives when students are learning a new skill. Students should use 5-group cards, number path, or other manipulatives such as counting bears when they need extra support. Allow students to use the extra support as long as they need it.

Repeat the process with math stories using the following suggested sequence: 7 + ___ = 9, 3 + ___ = 7, 4 + ___ = 8, and 6 + ___ = 9. After each story, ask students to identify which number sentence, addition or subtraction, they used to solve. Guide students to make a generalization about when it would be a better shortcut to use counting on or counting back, along with just knowing the decompositions.

T: Look at this number bond. (Write 8 as the total and 6 as a part.)

T: Think of a math story with a missing part where nothing goes away that could go with this number bond. Tell it to your partner.

T: Make a math drawing, write an addition and subtraction number sentence, and solve. Circle each of your solutions.

S: (Solve.)

Repeat the process by asking students to create their own number bond with 9 as the total.

Lesson 32:   Solve *put together/take apart with addend unknown* math stories.

©2015 Great Minds. eureka-math.org
G1-M1-TE-BK1-1.3.1-01.2016

Problem Set (10 minutes)

Students should do their personal best to complete the Problem Set within the allotted 10 minutes. For some classes, it may be appropriate to modify the assignment by specifying which problems they work on first. Some problems do not specify a method for solving. Students solve these problems using the RDW approach used for Application Problems.

Student Debrief (10 minutes)

Lesson Objective: Solve *put together/take apart with addend unknown* math stories.

The Student Debrief is intended to invite reflection and active processing of the total lesson experience.

Invite students to review their solutions for the Problem Set. They should check work by comparing answers with a partner before going over answers as a class. Look for misconceptions or misunderstandings that can be addressed in the Debrief. Guide students in a conversation to debrief the Problem Set and process the lesson.

Any combination of the questions below may be used to lead the discussion.

- Choose one of your stories for Problem 3 or Problem 4. Tell it to your partner and have him solve and explain what he did.
- How can solving Problem 2 help you solve Problem 3?
- When you use different strategies, do you always find the unknown number in the same place in your number sentence? Give an example to explain your thinking.
- Was it easier for you to use an addition sentence or a subtraction sentence to solve today's math stories? Why do you think that is?
- When is it wiser for you to use an addition sentence to solve the problem? Give an example from the Problem Set. What about using a subtraction sentence?

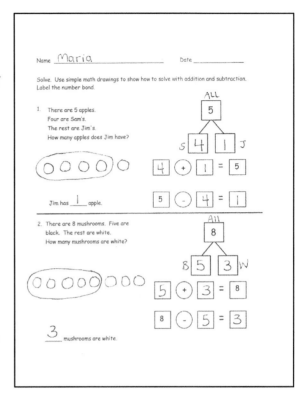

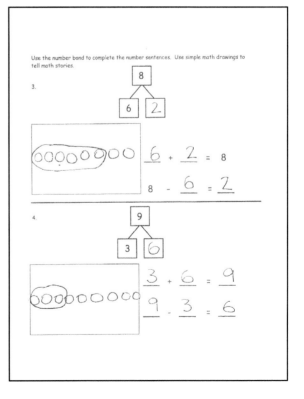

- Remember when we were thinking about if it was better to count on or count back? I'm thinking of a subtraction sentence where counting on or counting back would take the same amount of time. What number sentence could I be thinking of? (10 – 5 = 5, 8 – 4 = 4, etc.)
- How did the Application Problem connect to today's lesson?

Exit Ticket (3 minutes)

After the Student Debrief, instruct students to complete the Exit Ticket. A review of their work will help with assessing students' understanding of the concepts that were presented in today's lesson and planning more effectively for future lessons. The questions may be read aloud to the students.

©2015 Great Minds. eureka-math.org
G1-M1-TE-BK1-1.3.1-01.2016

Name _____   Date _____

Solve. Use simple math drawings to show how to solve with addition and subtraction.
Label the number bond.

1.

There are 5 apples.
Four are Sam's.
The rest are Jim's.
How many apples does Jim have?

Jim has _____ apple.

2.

There are 8 mushrooms. Five are black. The rest are white.
How many mushrooms are white?

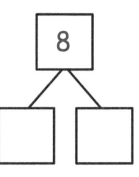

_____ mushrooms are white.

Lesson 32:　　Solve *put together/take apart with addend unknown* math stories.

©2015 Great Minds. eureka-math.org
G1-M1-TE-BK1-1.3.1-01.2016

Use the number bond to complete the number sentences. Use simple math drawings to tell math stories.

3.

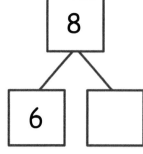

___ + ___ = 8

8 - ___ = ___

4.

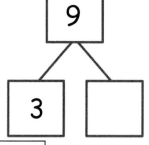

391

___ + ___ = ___

___ - ___ = ___

son 32:   Solve *put together/take apart with addend unknown* math stories.

EUREKA
MATH

Name _____   Date _____

Read the math story. Make a math drawing and solve.

Glenn has 9 pens. Five are black. The rest are blue. How many pens are blue?

_____ pens are blue.

_____ - _____ = _____   _____ + _____ = _____

Lesson 32:   Solve *put together/take apart with addend unknown* math stories.

393

©2015 Great Minds. eureka-math.org
G1-M1-TE-BK1-1.3.1-01.2016

Name _____   Date _____

Match the math stories to the number sentences that tell the story. Make a math drawing to solve.

1. a.

| There are 10 flowers in a vase.
6 are red.
The rest are yellow.
How many flowers are yellow? | $\square \; (+) \; \square = 9$

$9 \; (-) \; \square = \square$ |

b.

| There are 9 apples in a basket.
6 are red.
The rest are green.
How many apples are green? | $3 \; (+) \; \square = 10$

$10 \; (-) \; \square = \square$ |

c.

| Kate has her fingernails painted.
3 have designs.
The rest are plain.
How many fingernails are plain? | $6 \; (+) \; \square = 10$

$10 \; (-) \; 6 = \square$ |

Lesson 32:   Solve *put together/take apart with addend unknown* math stories.

EUREKA MATH

Use the number bond to tell an addition and subtraction math story with pictures. Write an addition and subtraction number sentence.

2.

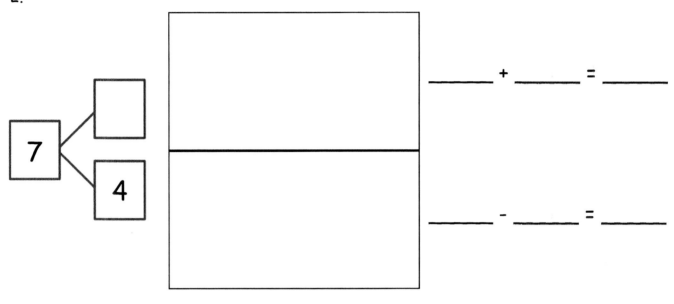

_____ + _____ = _____

_____ - _____ = _____

3.

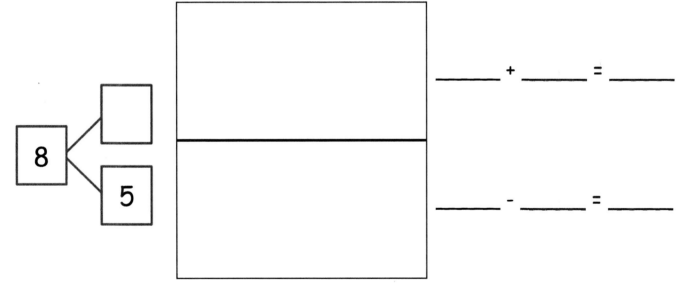

_____ + _____ = _____

_____ - _____ = _____

Lesson 32:   Solve *put together/take apart with addend unknown* math stories.

395

©2015 Great Minds. eureka-math.org
G1-M1-TE-BK1-1.3.1-01.2016

Mathematics Curriculum

1
GRADE

Topic I

Decomposition Strategies for Subtraction

1.OA.5, 1.OA.6, 1.OA.4

Focus Standard:	1.OA.5	Relate counting to addition and subtraction (e.g., by counting on 2 to add 2).
	1.OA.6	Add and subtract within 20, demonstrating fluency for addition and subtraction within 10. Use strategies such as counting on; making ten (e.g., 8 + 6 = 8 + 2 + 4 = 10 + 4 = 14); decomposing a number leading to a ten (e.g., 13 − 4 = 13 − 3 − 1 = 10 − 1 = 9); using the relationship between addition and subtraction (e.g., knowing that 8 + 4 = 12, one knows 12 − 8 = 4); and creating equivalent but easier or known sums (e.g., adding 6 + 7 by creating the known equivalent 6 + 6 + 1 = 12 + 1 = 13).
Instructional Days:	5	
Coherence -Links from:	GK–M4	Number Pairs, Addition and Subtraction to 10
-Links to:	G2–M4	Addition and Subtraction Within 200 with Word Problems to 100

Similar to Topic E's addition methods, Topic I allows students to learn methods for subtraction that involve subtracting 0 and 1, subtracting the whole number, subtracting one less than the whole number, and using familiar decompositions (5-groups and partners of 10) to conceptualize subtraction as finding a missing part (**1.OA.6**).

In Lesson 33, students use pictures and simple math drawings to show 0 less and 1 less and construct number sentences (**1.OA.5**). The discussion in Lesson 34 around what happens each time students take away 0 or 1 with numbers within 10 leads them to an understanding that this same reality remains true with all numbers. Similarly, students explore what happens in both $n - n$ and $n - (n - 1)$ situations. They notice, "When I take 5 away from 5, I'm left with zero every time." and "5 − 4 is 1, just like 6 − 5 is 1." Students generalize their understanding: "Any number minus a number that's one less will leave us with just 1."

In Lesson 35, students relate their knowledge of both doubles and fives to the context of subtraction, where they extract those known facts from given expressions. For instance, when faced with 8 − 5, students access the decomposition of 8 ("I know that 5 and 3 makes 8.") and apply that understanding to help them solve subtraction problems ("So, 8 − 5 must be 3.").

EUREKA
MATH™

Lessons 36 and 37 continue on this explicit decomposition and subtraction connection as students use their knowledge of partners of 10 and partners of 9 to help them solve subtraction stories and equations efficiently. Topic I is full of students using strategies and discussing those strategies and patterns in order to gain fluency and facility with subtraction within 10, and ultimately beyond.

A Teaching Sequence Toward Mastery of Decomposition Strategies for Subtraction
Objective 1: Model 0 less and 1 less pictorially and as subtraction number sentences. (Lesson 33)
Objective 2: Model $n - n$ and $n - (n - 1)$ pictorially and as subtraction sentences. (Lesson 34)
Objective 3: Relate subtraction facts involving fives and doubles to corresponding decompositions. (Lesson 35)
Objective 4: Relate subtraction from 10 to corresponding decompositions. (Lesson 36)
Objective 5: Relate subtraction from 9 to corresponding decompositions. (Lesson 37)

Lesson 33

Objective: Model 0 less and 1 less pictorially and as subtraction number sentences.

Suggested Lesson Structure

■ Fluency Practice   (15 minutes)
▨ Application Problem   (5 minutes)
▨ Concept Development   (30 minutes)
■ Student Debrief   (10 minutes)

   Total Time   **(60 minutes)**

Fluency Practice (15 minutes)

- Rekenrek Counting Within 20 **K.NBT.1**   (3 minutes)
- Sprint: Addition **1.OA.6**   (10 minutes)
- 0 Less, 1 Less **1.OA.5, 1.OA.6**   (2 minutes)

Rekenrek Counting Within 20 (3 minutes)

Materials: (T) Rekenrek

Note: Reviewing the Kindergarten standard **K.NBT.1** will prepare students for work with teen numbers in Module 2.

   T: (Move the top 10 beads on the Rekenrek to the right). How many red beads do you see?
   S: 5.
   T: How many white beads do you see?
   S: 5.
   T: 5 and 5 make…?
   S: 10.
   T: Count the Say Ten way as I move the beads. (Move one bead at a time up to 2 tens and back down to 10.)
   S: Ten 1, ten 2, …ten 9, 2 tens, ten 9, ten 8, …ten.

Work up and down from ten 1 to 2 tens, from ten 2 to ten 9, from ten 3 to ten 8, ten 4 to ten 7, and ten 5 to ten 6 and back out again.

Lesson 33:   Model 0 less and 1 less pictorially and as subtraction number
                sentences.

EUREKA
MATH™

Sprint: Addition (10 minutes)

Materials: (S) Addition Sprint

Note: This activity addresses the core fluency objective for Grade 1 of adding and subtracting within 10.

0 Less, 1 Less (2 minutes)

Ask questions to review subtraction language. Instruct students to answer on your signal.

Note: This activity addresses the core fluency objective for Grade 1 of adding and subtracting within 10.

Suggested questions: What's 1 less than 8? What comes before 6? 6 minus 0 equals…? 0 less than 9 is…? 9 is 1 less than…? 9 equals 10 minus…?

Application Problem (5 minutes)

Nine children are playing outside. One child is on the swings and the rest are playing tag. How many children are playing tag? Write a number bond and number sentence. Make a math drawing to show how you know.

Note: This problem provides an application of the Lesson 32 objective, solving unknown addends, as well as continuing to explore *1 less,* a segment of this lesson's objective.

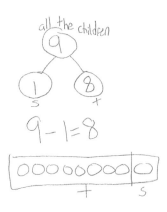

Concept Development (30 minutes)

Materials: (T) Number bracelet of 10, white board or easel (S) Number bracelet of 10 beads made with 5 red and 5 white beads (see Lesson 8), personal white board

Have students bring materials to meeting area and sit in a semi-circle.

> T: How many beads are on your number bracelet? (Hold up the bracelet.)
>
> S: 10 beads! (Hold up the bracelet.)
>
> T: Take 1 bead away.
>
> T/S: (Push 1 white bead away from the set, as shown.)

> T: How many beads do we have now?
>
> S: (Count the beads as needed.) 9 beads!
>
> T: Write a number sentence to show what we did.

Lesson 33:   Model 0 less and 1 less pictorially and as subtraction number
            sentences.

399

©2015 Great Minds. eureka-math.org
G1-M1-TE-BK1-1.3.1-01.2016

T/S: (Write 10 − 1 = 9.)

T: Push that bead all the way up until it is hiding in your hand.

T/S: (Push the bead into the palm, as shown.)

T: We have 9 beads.

Repeat the process of taking 1 bead away and writing the new number sentence for the following suggested sequence: 9 − 1, 8 − 1, and 7 − 1.

T: Push your beads back, and open your pipe cleaner so that your beads are in a straight line.

T/S: (Adjust the beads and pipe cleaner as shown.)

T: Push a set of 3 white beads away to the end of the pipe cleaner. (Be sure students push 3 beads as a set, rather than one at a time, to encourage decomposition rather than 1 to 1 counting.)

T: Tell me a number sentence to describe what we did.

S: 10 − 3 = 7.

T: Use your beads to show me 7 − 1. Write the number sentence on your board.

S: (Show 6 beads together and 1 separated bead. Write 7 − 1 = 6 on personal boards.)

Repeat the process for 5 − 1.

T: We have 4 beads. This time, take 0 away.

S: (Look at their beads.)

T: How many beads do we have now?

S: 4 beads!

T: Hmmm. Let's try that with a larger number. Push all your beads back to the middle so we can start with 10.

T/S: (Push beads back to middle, showing all 10 beads.)

T: We have 10 beads. Take away 0 beads. How many beads do we have now?

S: 10 beads!

T: Write the number sentence to show what we did.

S/T: (Write 10 − 0 = 10.)

NOTES ON MULTIPLE MEANS OF ENGAGEMENT:

NOTES ON MULTIPLE MEANS OF ENGAGEMENT:

Cultivate excitement for students who are ready to work with larger numbers by presenting numbers to 100. These students would also benefit from developing their own story, song, or poem for larger numbers.

Repeat the process of taking 0 beads away and writing the new number sentence for the following suggested sequence: 9 − 0 and 6 − 0.

Lesson 33:   Model 0 less and 1 less pictorially and as subtraction number sentences.

©2015 Great Minds. eureka-math.org
G1-M1-TE-BK1-1.3.1-01.2016

Problem Set (10 minutes)

Students should do their personal best to complete the Problem Set within the allotted 10 minutes. For some classes, it may be appropriate to modify the assignment by specifying which problems they work on first. Some problems do not specify a method for solving. Students solve these problems using the RDW approach used for Application Problems.

Student Debrief (10 minutes)

Lesson Objective: Model 0 less and 1 less pictorially and as subtraction number sentences.

The Student Debrief is intended to invite reflection and active processing of the total lesson experience.

Invite students to review their solutions for the Problem Set. They should check work by comparing answers with a partner before going over answers as a class. Look for misconceptions or misunderstandings that can be addressed in the Debrief. Guide students in a conversation to debrief the Problem Set and process the lesson.

Any combination of the questions below may be used to lead the discussion.

- How can solving Problem 1 help you solve Problem 3?
- Explain to your partner any patterns you see in Problems 3 –10.
- Talk to your partner about how visualizing your 5-groups can help you solve Problem 17(g).
- **MP.8** Explain how solving 10 – 0 can help you solve 122 – 0. What happens every time you subtract 0?
- Explain how solving 9 – 1 can help you solve 73 – 1. What happens every time you subtract 1? How does subtracting 1 relate to counting?
- How did the Application Problem connect to today's lesson?

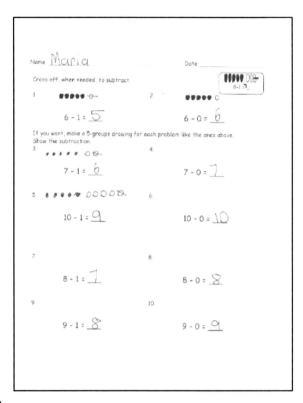

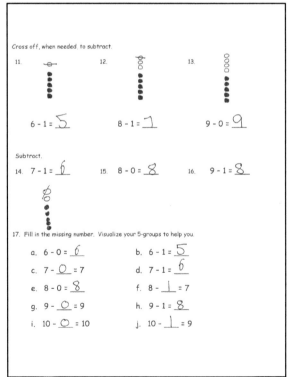

Lesson 33:   Model 0 less and 1 less pictorially and as subtraction number sentences.

©2015 Great Minds. eureka-math.org
G1-M1-TE-BK1-1.3.1-01.2016

401

Exit Ticket (3 minutes)

After the Student Debrief, instruct students to complete the Exit Ticket. A review of their work will help with assessing students' understanding of the concepts that were presented in today's lesson and planning more effectively for future lessons. The questions may be read aloud to the students.

©2015 Great Minds. eureka-math.org
G1-M1-TE-BK1-1.3.1-01.2016

A

Number Correct: _____

Addition

1.	3 + 1 =		23.	1 + 2 =	
2.	4 + 1 =		24.	3 + 6 =	
3.	5 + 1 =		25.	1 + 8 =	
4.	9 + 1 =		26.	2 + 3 =	
5.	6 + 1 =		27.	1 + 4 =	
6.	8 + 1 =		28.	2 + 4 =	
7.	2 + 1 =		29.	1 + 3 =	
8.	7 + 1 =		30.	1 + 5 =	
9.	1 + 7 =		31.	3 + 3 =	
10.	1 + 9 =		32.	4 + 3 =	
11.	1 + 6 =		33.	5 + 3 =	
12.	2 + 2 =		34.	6 + 3 =	
13.	3 + 2 =		35.	7 + 3 =	
14.	4 + 2 =		36.	3 + 7 =	
15.	8 + 2 =		37.	3 + 4 =	
16.	5 + 2 =		38.	3 + 5 =	
17.	6 + 2 =		39.	4 + 4 =	
18.	7 + 2 =		40.	5 + 4 =	
19.	2 + 7 =		41.	6 + 4 =	
20.	2 + 8 =		42.	4 + 6 =	
21.	2 + 5 =		43.	4 + 5 =	
22.	2 + 6 =		44.	5 + 5 =	

Lesson 33: Model 0 less and 1 less pictorially and as subtraction number sentences.

403

B

Number Correct: _____

Improvement: _____

Addition

1.	2 + 1 =	
2.	3 + 1 =	
3.	4 + 1 =	
4.	8 + 1 =	
5.	5 + 1 =	
6.	7 + 1 =	
7.	9 + 1 =	
8.	6 + 1 =	
9.	1 + 6 =	
10.	1 + 9 =	
11.	1 + 7 =	
12.	2 + 2 =	
13.	3 + 2 =	
14.	4 + 2 =	
15.	7 + 2 =	
16.	5 + 2 =	
17.	8 + 2 =	
18.	6 + 2 =	
19.	2 + 6 =	
20.	2 + 8 =	
21.	2 + 5 =	
22.	2 + 7 =	

23.	1 + 8 =	
24.	3 + 7 =	
25.	1 + 5 =	
26.	2 + 4 =	
27.	1 + 4 =	
28.	2 + 3 =	
29.	1 + 3 =	
30.	1 + 2 =	
31.	3 + 3 =	
32.	4 + 3 =	
33.	5 + 3 =	
34.	7 + 3 =	
35.	6 + 3 =	
36.	3 + 6 =	
37.	3 + 5 =	
38.	3 + 4 =	
39.	4 + 4 =	
40.	5 + 4 =	
41.	6 + 4 =	
42.	4 + 6 =	
43.	4 + 5 =	
44.	5 + 5 =	

Lesson 33: Model 0 less and 1 less pictorially and as subtraction number sentences.

EUREKA MATH

Name _____ Date _____

Cross off, when needed, to subtract.

8-1 = ⅂_

1.

$6 - 1 =$ ___

2. ⬤⬤⬤⬤⬤ ⬜

$6 - 0 =$ ___

If you want, make a 5-group drawing for each problem like the ones above.
Show the subtraction.

3.

$7 - 1 =$ ___

4.

$7 - 0 =$ ___

5.

$10 - 1 =$ ___

6.

$10 - 0 =$ ___

7.

$8 - 1 =$ ___

8.

$8 - 0 =$ ___

9.

$9 - 1 =$ ___

10.

$9 - 0 =$ ___

EUREKA MATH™

Lesson 33: Model 0 less and 1 less pictorially and as subtraction number sentences.

405

©2015 Great Minds. eureka-math.org
G1-M1-TE-BK1-1.3.1-01.2016

Cross off, when needed, to subtract.

11.

   6 – 1 = ___

12.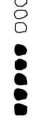

   8 – 1 = ___

13.

   9 – 0 = ___

Subtract.

14. 7 – 1 = ___   15. 8 – 0 = ___   16. 9 – 1 = ___

17. Fill in the missing number. Visualize your 5-groups to help you.

    a. 6 – 0 = ___   b. 6 – 1 = ___

    c. 7 – ___ = 7   d. 7 – 1 = ___

    e. 8 – 0 = ___   f. 8 – ___ = 7

    g. 9 – ___ = 9   h. 9 – 1 = ___

    i. 10 – ___ = 10   j. 10 – ___ = 9

Lesson 33:   Model 0 less and 1 less pictorially and as subtraction number sentences.

EUREKA
MATH™

Name _____   Date _____

Complete the number sentences. If you want, use 5-group drawings to show the subtraction.

1.

$9 - 1 = $ _____

2.

$8 = $ _____ $- 0$

3.

$8 = $ _____ $- 1$

4.

$10 = 10 - $ _____

EUREKA MATH

Lesson 33:   Model 0 less and 1 less pictorially and as subtraction number sentences.

407

©2015 Great Minds. eureka-math.org
G1-M1-TE-BK1-1.3.1-01.2016

Name _____   Date _____

Show the subtraction. If you want, use a 5-group drawing for each problem.

8-1 = 7

1.

2.

$$9 - 1 = \underline{\quad}$$

$$9 - 0 = \underline{\quad\quad}$$

3.

4.

$$6 - \underline{\quad} = 6$$

$$6 = 7 - \underline{\quad\quad}$$

Show the subtraction. If you want, use a 5-group drawing like the model for each problem.

5.

6.

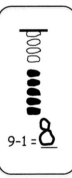
9-1 = 8

$$9 - \underline{\quad} = 9$$

$$8 = 8 - \underline{\quad\quad}$$

7.

8.

$$10 - \underline{\quad} = 9$$

$$7 - \underline{\quad} = 7$$

Lesson 33:   Model 0 less and 1 less pictorially and as subtraction number
              sentences.

**EUREKA
MATH**™

©2015 Great Minds. eureka-math.org
G1-M1-TE-BK1-1.3.1-01.2016

Write the subtraction number sentence to match the 5-group drawing.

9.

____ - ____ = ____

10. ●●●●● ◯ ◻

____ - ____ = ____

11.

____ - ____ = ____

12.

____ - ____ = ____

13.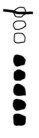

____ - ____ = ____

14. Fill in the missing number. Visualize your 5-groups to help you.

a. $7 - \underline{\hspace{1cm}} = 6$

b. $0 = 7 - \underline{\hspace{1cm}}$

c. $8 - \underline{\hspace{1cm}} = 7$

d. $6 - \underline{\hspace{1cm}} = 5$

e. $8 = 9 - \underline{\hspace{1cm}}$

f. $9 = 10 - \underline{\hspace{1cm}}$

g. $10 - \underline{\hspace{1cm}} = 10$

h. $9 - \underline{\hspace{1cm}} = 8$

Lesson 34

Objective: Model $n - n$ and $n - (n - 1)$ pictorially and as subtraction sentences.

Suggested Lesson Structure

■ Fluency Practice   (12 minutes)
▨ Application Problem   (5 minutes)
□ Concept Development   (33 minutes)
▪ Student Debrief   (10 minutes)
   Total Time   **(60 minutes)**

Fluency Practice (12 minutes)

- 1 Less, 2 Less **1.OA.6**   (2 minutes)
- Sprint: $n - 0$ and $n - 1$ **1.OA.6**   (10 minutes)

1 Less, 2 Less (2 minutes)

Note: This activity builds on the previous day's lesson and prepares students to solve today's Application Problem. It builds on the counting sequence within 120.

   T: I'll say a number. You say 1 less at the signal.

Use the following suggested sequence: 4, 14, 24, 9, 19, 20, 10, 20, 30, 25, 35, 45, 63, 73, 83, 81, 91, and 101. When ready, change to 2 less.

Sprint: $n - 0$ and $n - 1$ (10 minutes)

Materials: (S) $n - 0$ and $n - 1$ Sprint

Note: This activity addresses the core fluency objective for Grade 1 of adding and subtracting within 10.

Application Problem (5 minutes)

Eighty-three beads spill on the floor. A student picks up 1 bead. How many beads are still on the floor? Write a number bond, number sentence, and a statement to share your solution.

Extension: If a second child picks up 10 more beads, how many beads will remain on the floor? Use number bonds to show how you know.

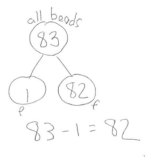

Lesson 34:   Model $n - n$ and $n - (n - 1)$ pictorially and as subtraction sentences.   EUREKA
MATH™

Note: This problem enables students to apply their learning from the previous lesson to a quantity they cannot visualize easily. Instead, students will use their understanding of *subtracting 1* along with their knowledge of the counting sequence within 120.

Concept Development (33 minutes)

Materials: (T) Number bracelet of 10, white board or easel (S) Number bracelet of 10 beads (5 red, 5 white) (see Lesson 8), personal white board

Have students bring materials to meeting area and sit in a semicircle.

T: Stretch out your bracelet into a long line of beads like we did in our last lesson.

T/S: (Adjust the pipe cleaner into a straight line.)

T: How many beads do we have in this set?

S: 10 beads!

T: Take 10 beads away.

T/S: (Push 10 beads to the other side of the pipe cleaner.)

T: How many beads do we have now?

S: Zero!

T: Write the number sentence to show what you did. Write the number bond also.

T/S: (Write 10 – 10 = 0 and number bond.)

T: Start with 8 beads now.

T/S: (Push 8 beads back to the main section of the pipe cleaner.)

Repeat the process using the following suggested sequence: 8 – 8, 7 – 7, and 6 – 6.

T: How are these problems similar to each other?

S: We are taking away the total amount.

T: When we have a number and then subtract that exact number, what part are we left with?

S: Zero!

T: Let's try something different. Start with 10 beads again.

T/S: (Reset pipe cleaner to show all 10 beads as a set.)

T: Take away 9 beads.

T/S: (Push 9 beads slightly farther down the pipe cleaner.)

T: How many beads do we have left?

S: 1 bead!

> **NOTES ON MULTIPLE MEANS OF REPRESENTATION:**
>
> Providing opportunities for all students to work at the concrete level facilitates student discovery of patterns and structures in their math work. Allow time for students to explore with the number bracelets throughout the week to help solidify 5-groups and to discourage counting all.

> **NOTES ON MULTIPLE MEANS OF ACTION AND EXPRESSION:**
>
> Provide students with a variety of ways to respond. Some students need concrete models to show their understanding, while others benefit from a partner share.

Lesson 34: Model *n* – *n* and *n* – (*n* – 1) pictorially and as subtraction sentences.

411

©2015 Great Minds. eureka-math.org
G1-M1-TE-BK1-1.3.1-01.2016

T: Write the number sentence to show what you did. Write the number bond also.

T/S: (Write 10 − 9 = 1.)

T: Start with 9 beads now.

Repeat the process using the following suggested sequence: 9 − 8, 8 − 7, and 7 − 6. Be sure to keep these number sentences on the board for discussion.

T: How are these problems similar to each other? Turn and talk to your partner. (Circulate and listen.)

S: (Discuss.)

T: How are these problems similar?

S: The answer is 1 every time!

T: Let's try a few more. This time, try to complete the number sentence and number bond without using the beads. Then, check your answer using your beads.

Repeat the process again using expressions that vary between subtracting all and subtracting all but one through the following suggested sequence: 6 − 6, 6 − 5, 8 − 8, 8 − 7, 9 − 9, and 9 − 8.

T: When you are working today, see if you can figure out how to tell quickly that the answer to a subtraction problem will be 1 or that the answer will be 0.

Problem Set (10 minutes)

Students should do their personal best to complete the Problem Set within the allotted 10 minutes. For some classes, it may be appropriate to modify the assignment by specifying which problems they work on first. Some problems do not specify a method for solving. Students solve these problems using the RDW approach used for Application Problems.

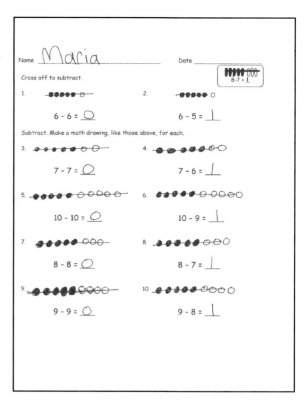

Student Debrief (10 minutes)

Lesson Objective: Model $n − n$ and $n − (n − 1)$ pictorially and as subtraction sentences.

The Student Debrief is intended to invite reflection and active processing of the total lesson experience.

Invite students to review their solutions for the Problem Set. They should check work by comparing answers with a partner before going over answers as a class. Look for misconceptions or misunderstandings that can be addressed in the Debrief.

Guide students in a conversation to debrief the Problem Set and process the lesson.

Lesson 34:   Model $n − n$ and $n − (n − 1)$ pictorially and as subtraction sentences.

©2015 Great Minds. eureka-math.org
G1-M1-TE-BK1-1.3.1-01.2016

Any combination of the questions below may be used to lead the discussion.

- What pattern did you notice between Problems 3 and 10?

- How were your drawings different in Problems 5 and 6?

- How did the Application Problem connect to today's lesson?

- How can solving 10 – 10 help you solve 1,272 – 1,272; 10,629 – 10,629; or 1,000,000 – 1,000,000?

- How can solving 9 – 8 help you solve 759 – 758… 2,478 – 2,477 and 1,000,001 – 1,000,000?

Exit Ticket (3 minutes)

After the Student Debrief, instruct students to complete the Exit Ticket. A review of their work will help with assessing students' understanding of the concepts that were presented in today's lesson and planning more effectively for future lessons. The questions may be read aloud to the students.

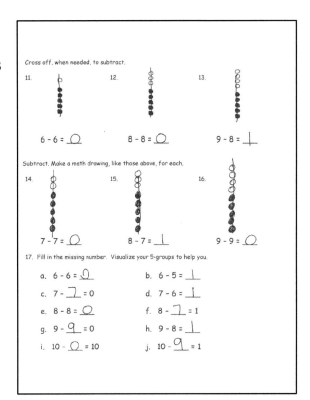

Cross off, when needed, to subtract.

11.   12.   13.

6 - 6 = 0   8 - 8 = 0   9 - 8 = 1

Subtract. Make a math drawing, like those above, for each.

14.   15.   16.

7 - 7 = 0   8 - 7 = 1   9 - 9 = 0

17. Fill in the missing number. Visualize your 5-groups to help you.

a. 6 - 6 = 0   b. 6 - 5 = 1

c. 7 - 7 = 0   d. 7 - 6 = 1

e. 8 - 8 = 0   f. 8 - 7 = 1

g. 9 - 9 = 0   h. 9 - 8 = 1

i. 10 - 0 = 10   j. 10 - 9 = 1

EUREKA MATH™

Lesson 34: Model *n – n* and *n – (n – 1)* pictorially and as subtraction sentences.

413

A

Name _____

Date _____

Number Correct: _____

*Write the missing number from each subtraction sentence. Pay attention to the = sign.

1.	2 – 1 = ☐		16.	☐ = 10 - 0	
2.	1 – 1 = ☐		17.	☐ = 10 - 1	
3.	1 – 0 = ☐		18.	☐ = 9 - 1	
4.	3 – 1 = ☐		19.	☐ = 7 - 1	
5.	3 – 0 = ☐		20.	☐ = 6 - 1	
6.	4 – 0 = ☐		21.	☐ = 6 - 0	
7.	4 – 1 = ☐		22.	☐ = 8 - 0	
8.	5 – 1 = ☐		23.	8 - ☐ = 8	
9.	6 – 1 = ☐		24.	☐ - 0 = 8	
10.	6 – 0 = ☐		25.	7 - ☐ = 6	
11.	8 – 0 = ☐		26.	7 = 7 - ☐	
12.	10 – 0 = ☐		27.	9 = 9 - ☐	
13.	9 – 0 = ☐		28.	☐ - 1 = 7	
14.	9 – 1 = ☐		29.	☐ - 0 = 8	
15.	10 – 1 = ☐		30.	9 = ☐ - 1	

Lesson 34: Model $n - n$ and $n - (n - 1)$ pictorially and as subtraction sentences.

EUREKA MATH

B

Name _____

Date _____

Number Correct:

*Write the missing number from each subtraction sentence. Pay attention to the = sign.

1.	$3 - 1 = \square$		16.	$\square = 10 - 1$	
2.	$2 - 1 = \square$		17.	$\square = 9 - 1$	
3.	$1 - 1 = \square$		18.	$\square = 7 - 1$	
4.	$1 - 0 = \square$		19.	$\square = 7 - 0$	
5.	$2 - 0 = \square$		20.	$\square = 8 - 0$	
6.	$4 - 0 = \square$		21.	$\square = 10 - 0$	
7.	$5 - 1 = \square$		22.	$\square = 9 - 1$	
8.	$7 - 1 = \square$		23.	$9 - \square = 8$	
9.	$8 - 1 = \square$		24.	$\square - 1 = 8$	
10.	$9 - 0 = \square$		25.	$7 - \square = 6$	
11.	$10 - 0 = \square$		26.	$6 = 7 - \square$	
12.	$7 - 0 = \square$		27.	$9 = 9 - \square$	
13.	$8 - 0 = \square$		28.	$\square - 0 = 9$	
14.	$10 - 1 = \square$		29.	$\square - 0 = 10$	
15.	$9 - 1 = \square$		30.	$8 = \square - 1$	

EUREKA MATH™

Lesson 34: Model $n - n$ and $n - (n - 1)$ pictorially and as subtraction sentences.

415

Name _____   Date _____

Cross off to subtract.

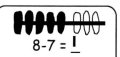

8-7 = _1_

1. ⬛⬛⬛⬛⬛ ⬜   2. ⬛⬛⬛⬛⬛ ⬜

    6 – 6 = ___   6 – 5 = ___

Subtract. Make a math drawing, like those above, for each.

3.   4.

    7 – 7 = ___   7 – 6 = ___

5.   6.

    10 – 10 = ___   10 – 9 = ___

7.   8.

    8 – 8 = ___   8 – 7 = ___

9.   10.

    9 – 9 = ___   9 – 8 = ___

Lesson 34:   Model $n - n$ and $n - (n - 1)$ pictorially and as subtraction sentences.

EUREKA MATH

Cross off, when needed, to subtract.

11.

6 – 6 = ___

12.

8 – 8 = ___

13.

9 – 8 = ___

Subtract.   Make a math drawing, like those above, for each.

14.

7 – 7 = ___

15.

8 – 7 = ___

16.

9 – 9 = ___

17. Fill in the missing number.   Visualize your 5-groups to help you.

  a. 6 – 6 = ___

  b. 6 – 5 = ___

  c. 7 – ___ = 0

  d. 7 – 6 = ___

  e. 8 – 8 = ___

  f. 8 – ___ = 1

  g. 9 – ___ = 0

  h. 9 – 8 = ___

  i. 10 – ___ = 10

  j. 10 – ___ = 1

EUREKA
MATH

Lesson 34:   Model $n - n$ and $n - (n - 1)$ pictorially and as subtraction sentences.

417

©2015 Great Minds. eureka-math.org
G1-M1-TE-BK1-1.3.1-01.2016

Name _____   Date _____

Make 5-group drawings to show the subtraction.

1.

$9 - \underline{\hspace{1cm}} = 1$

2.

$0 = 10 - \underline{\hspace{1cm}}$

3.

$1 = \underline{\hspace{1cm}} - 7$

4.

$0 = \underline{\hspace{1cm}} - 9$

EUREKA
MATH™

Name _____   Date _____

Cross off to subtract.

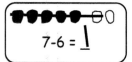

7-6 = 1

1.   ●●●●● ○○○○○   2.   ●●●●● ○○○○

     10 – 10 = _____   9 – 8 = _____

Make a 5-group drawing like those above. Show the subtraction.

3.   4.

     1 = ____ – 7   8 – ____ = 0

5.   6.

     0 = ____ – 7   6 – ____ = 1

Make a 5-group drawing like the model for each problem. Show the subtraction.

7.   8.

     9 – ____ = 1   0 = 8 – ____

                                       9 – 9 = 0

EUREKA MATH

Lesson 34:   Model n – n and n – (n – 1) pictorially and as subtraction sentences.

419

©2015 Great Minds. eureka-math.org
G1-M1-TE-BK1-1.3.1-01.2016

Write the subtraction number sentence to match the 5-group drawing.

9.    10.   11.

___ - ___ = ___   ___ - ___ = ___   ___ - ___ = ___

12.    13.

___ - ___ = ___   ___ - ___ = ___

14. Fill in the missing number. Visualize your 5-groups to help you.

a. 7 – ___ = 0   b. 1 = 7 – ___

c. 8 – ___ = 1   d. 6 – ___ = 0

e. 0 = 9 – ___   f. 1 = 10 – ___

g. 10 - ___ = 0   h. 9 – ___ = 1

Lesson 34:   Model $n - n$ and $n - (n - 1)$ pictorially and as subtraction sentences.

EUREKA
MATH

Lesson 35

Objective: Relate subtraction facts involving fives and doubles to corresponding decompositions.

Suggested Lesson Structure

■ Fluency Practice   (14 minutes)
▨ Application Problem   (5 minutes)
▨ Concept Development   (31 minutes)
■ Student Debrief   (10 minutes)
   Total Time   **(60 minutes)**

Fluency Practice (14 minutes)

▪ Cold Call **1.OA.6**   (2 minutes)
▪ Sprint: $n - n, n - (n - 1)$ **1.OA.6**   (10 minutes)
▪ Speed Writing   (2 minutes)

Cold Call (2 minutes)

Note: This activity addresses the core fluency objective for Grade 1 of adding and subtracting within 10.

Ask questions to practice subtraction situations for $n - n$ or $n - (n - 1)$ problem types. Tell students you will cold call them to say the answer as quickly as possible. Alternate between calling on individual students, the whole class, and groups of students (e.g., only boys or only girls). Use the example dialogue below as a reference.

T: Listen carefully to my question so you will be ready if I call on you. What is $6 - 6$? (Pause to provide thinking time.) Everybody.
S: 0.
T: 1 less than 6 is…? (Pause.) Boys?
S: (Only boys.) 5.
T: We know $6 - 6$ is 0. What is $6 - 5$? (Pause.) Girls.
S: (Only girls.) 1.

Sprint: $n - n, n - (n - 1)$ (10 minutes)

Materials: (S) $n - n, n - (n - 1)$ Sprint

Note: This activity addresses the core fluency objective for Grade 1 of adding and subtracting within 10.

Speed Writing (2 minutes)

Materials: (S) Personal white board

Note: This activity focuses on the counting sequence to 120 while continuing to develop foundational skills for place value. By writing and whispering, students engage multi-modalities for learning.

Tell students to write their numbers from 10 to the highest number they know in 1 minute while whisper-counting the Say Ten way.

Application Problem (5 minutes)

The teacher spilled 18 beads on the floor today. A student picked up 17 of the beads. How many beads are still left on the floor? Write a number bond, number sentence, and a statement to share your solution.

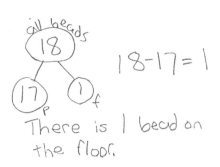

Extension: If the 17 beads had been picked up by two students, how many beads might each student have picked up? Make a number bond to show your solution.

Note: This problem enables students to apply the Lesson 34 objective to a number they cannot visualize easily. During the Student Debrief, students consider how tools such as 5-groups and Rekenreks might help them solve the problem.

Concept Development (31 minutes)

Materials: (S) Number bracelet of 10 beads, 5 red and 5 white (see Lesson 8), personal white board

> NOTES ON
> MULTIPLE MEANS
> OF ENGAGEMENT:
>
> Some students may need to make real life connections to concepts such as doubles and 5-groups. Allow students the opportunity to explore doubles and 5-groups they see in real life (e.g., pairs of shoes, 4-wheelers, legs of a spider, doubles on dominoes, and their fingers).

T: Show me 7 the Math Way. How many fingers did you use on your left hand?

S: (Hold up 5 fingers on their left hands and the thumb and index finger on their right hands.) 5.

T: Show me 7 – 5 by hiding your 5.

S: (Hide their left hands.)

©2015 Great Minds. eureka-math.org
G1-M1-TE-BK1-1.3.1-01.2016

T: What's the answer?

S: 2.

T: Give me the complete number sentence.

S: 7 minus 5 is 2.

T: Show me your 7 again. Subtract 2 by hiding your 2. The answer is…?

S: 5.

T: Give me the complete number sentence.

S: 7 minus 2 is 5.

Quickly repeat the same process, subtracting 5 and its partner from 6 through 10.

T: Please take out your bracelets and start with 8 beads. (Project 8 – 5.) Use your beads in one movement to show me the answer. Write the number sentence and number bond.

S: (Push 5 beads in one movement away from the set and write 8 – 5 = 3.

T: (Circulate. If students move the beads one, two, three, or four at a time, have students repeat the exercise.)

T: How did you solve this so quickly?

S: I moved just my red beads in a 5-group. → I moved a group of 5 without counting out 1, 2, 3, 4, 5.

T: How did you know how many to push at once?

S: The beads are in groups of 5.

T: Push them back together to have 8, and try this one. (Project 8 – 3.)

S: (Push the 3 white beads away from the set and write 8 – 3 = 5.)

T: What did you push away as a group?

S: The 3 white beads.

T: What did you have left?

S: The 5 red beads.

Repeat the process using the following suggested sequence: 9 – 5, 9 – 4, 7 – 5, and 7 – 2.

T: Great job visualizing larger groups to help you subtract quickly. Now, we will use a different way to visualize, or see, groups to help us subtract. Put your bracelets back together so you have 10 beads total. What two equal parts do you see?

S: 5 and 5.

T: That's right. Remember, facts like 5 + 5 are part of a special group of addition facts. What are they called?

S: Doubles.

T: Starting at 1 + 1, let's recite our doubles facts. Point your fingers together as we say them.

MP.7

NOTES ON MULTIPLE MEANS OF REPRESENTATION:

Provide students who are developing fluency with math facts a visual tool, such as the addition chart with the doubles facts, for reference until this skill becomes automatic.

T/S: 1 + 1 = 2, 2 + 2 = 4, 3 + 3 = 6, 4 + 4 = 8, 5 + 5 = 10.

T: Doubles can be easy to see, just like 5-groups. Let's see if we can spot which of these subtraction facts are made from doubles. Visualize your doubles facts as we look for them.

MP.7

T: (Project three subtraction expressions: 7 – 3, 8 – 4, and 9 – 2.)

T: Which subtraction expression is splitting up a double? Turn and talk with your partner to decide. Talk about how you know. Write the number sentence and number bond on your paper. (Circulate and listen.)

S: (Discuss with a partner.)

T: I like how you proved your idea to your partner by showing the doubles on your fingers. Try more.

Repeat the process using the following suggested sequence of three sets of expressions:
(a) 5 – 2, 8 – 3, 4– 2; (b) 7 – 4, 6 – 3, 10 – 4;
(c) 8 – 4, 6 – 3, 10 – 5. The last set purposely has three doubles facts as students begin to visualize their doubles and recognize the facts within the subtraction context more quickly.

Problem Set (10 minutes)

Students should do their personal best to complete the problem set within the allotted 10 minutes. For some classes, it may be appropriate to modify the assignment by specifying which problems they work on first. Some problems do not specify a method for solving. Students solve these problems using the RDW approach used for Application Problems.

On this Problem Set, most all students begin with Problems 1 through Problem 5 and possibly leave Problems 6 through Problem 11 to the end if they still have time.

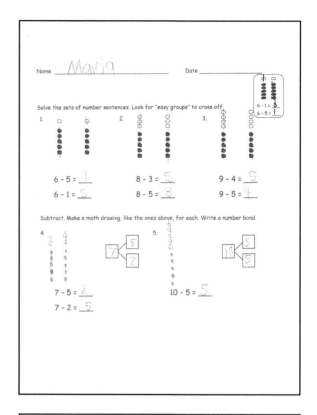

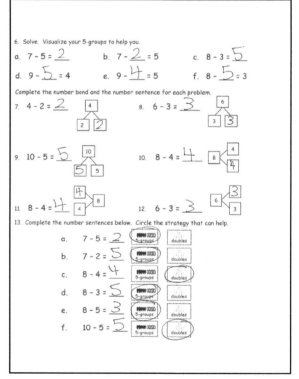

     Lesson 35:   Relate subtraction facts involving fives and doubles to corresponding decompositions.

                                      EUREKA MATH™

Student Debrief (10 minutes)

Lesson Objective: Relate subtraction facts involving fives and doubles to corresponding decompositions.

The Student Debrief is intended to invite reflection and active processing of the total lesson experience.

Invite students to review their solutions for the Problem Set. They should check work by comparing answers with a partner before going over answers as a class. Look for misconceptions or misunderstandings that can be addressed in the Debrief. Guide students in a conversation to debrief the Problem Set and process the lesson.

Any combination of the questions below may be used to lead the discussion.

- Look at Problems 6(a) through 6(f). Talk to your partner about what you visualized to help you solve these problems.
- How can your hands help you solve problems like these? (Fingers are like 5-groups.)
- How are your hands similar to the number bracelet? How are they different?
- Look at Problems 13(a) through 13(f). For which problems did you use 5-groups? For which problems did you use doubles? Could you use both of them on any of the problems?
- Look at how you solved the Application Problem. How can we use the Rekenrek to solve this same problem? How can we use 5-groups to solve this problem?

Exit Ticket (3 minutes)

After the Student Debrief, instruct students to complete the Exit Ticket. A review of their work will help with assessing students' understanding of the concepts that were presented in today's lesson and planning more effectively for future lessons. The questions may be read aloud to the students.

EUREKA
MATH™

Lesson 35:   Relate subtraction facts involving fives and doubles to corresponding   **425**
              decompositions.

©2015 Great Minds. eureka-math.org
G1-M1-TE-BK1-1.3.1-01.2016

A

Name _____

Date _____

Write the missing number for each subtraction sentence. Pay attention to the = sign.

1.	$2 - 2 = \square$		16.	$0 = 10 - \square$	
2.	$1 - 1 = \square$		17.	$0 = 9 - \square$	
3.	$1 - 0 = \square$		18.	$0 = 8 - \square$	
4.	$3 - 3 = \square$		19.	$0 = 6 - \square$	
5.	$3 - 2 = \square$		20.	$1 = 6 - \square$	
6.	$4 - 4 = \square$		21.	$1 = 7 - \square$	
7.	$4 - 3 = \square$		22.	$1 = 10 - \square$	
8.	$6 - 6 = \square$		23.	$10 - \square = 1$	
9.	$7 - 7 = \square$		24.	$\square - 9 = 1$	
10.	$8 - 8 = \square$		25.	$7 - \square = 0$	
11.	$8 - 7 = \square$		26.	$0 = 7 - \square$	
12.	$9 - 9 = \square$		27.	$0 = 9 - \square$	
13.	$9 - 8 = \square$		28.	$\square - 8 = 0$	
14.	$10 - 10 = \square$		29.	$\square - 7 = 1$	
15.	$10 - 9 = \square$		30.	$1 = \square - 5$	

Lesson 35: Relate subtraction facts involving fives and doubles to corresponding decompositions.

©2015 Great Minds. eureka-math.org
G1-M1-TE-BK1-1.3.1-01.2016

EUREKA MATH™

B

Name _____ Date _____

Number Correct:

Write the missing number for each subtraction sentence. Pay attention to the = sign.

1.	3 – 3 = ☐		16.	0 = 6 - ☐	
2.	2 – 2 = ☐		17.	0 = 7 - ☐	
3.	1 – 1 = ☐		18.	0 = 8 - ☐	
4.	1 – 0 = ☐		19.	0 = 10 - ☐	
5.	2 – 1 = ☐		20.	1 = 10 - ☐	
6.	4 – 3 = ☐		21.	1 = 9 - ☐	
7.	5 – 4 = ☐		22.	1 = 7 - ☐	
8.	7 – 7 = ☐		23.	7 - ☐ = 1	
9.	8 – 8 = ☐		24.	☐ - 6 = 1	
10.	9 – 9 = ☐		25.	6 - ☐ = 0	
11.	10 – 10 = ☐		26.	0 = 6 - ☐	
12.	10 – 9 = ☐		27.	0 = 8 - ☐	
13.	8 – 7 = ☐		28.	☐ - 8 = 0	
14.	6 – 5 = ☐		29.	☐ - 6 = 1	
15.	6 – 6 = ☐		30.	1 = ☐ - 6	

EUREKA MATH™

Lesson 35:   Relate subtraction facts involving fives and doubles to corresponding decompositions.

427

Name _____ Date _____

Solve the sets of number sentences. Look for easy groups to cross off.

1.

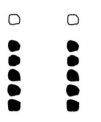

6 – 5 = ___

6 – 1 = ___

2.

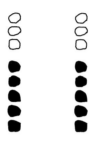

8 – 3 = ___

8 – 5 = ___

3.

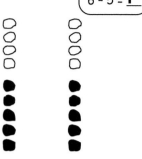

9 – 4 = ___

9 – 5 = ___

Subtract. Make a math drawing for each problem like the ones above. Write a number bond.

4.

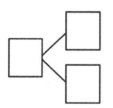

7 – 5 = ___

7 – 2 = ___

5.

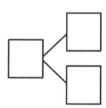

10 – 5 = ___

Relate subtraction facts involving fives and doubles to corresponding decompositions.

EUREKA
MATH™

6. Solve. Visualize your 5-groups to help you.

   a. 7 – 5 = ____   b. 7 – ____ = 5   c. 8 – 3 = ____

   d. 9 – ____ = 4   e. 9 – ____ = 5   f. 8 – ____ = 3

Complete the number bond and number sentence for each problem.

7. 4 – 2 = ____

8. 6 – 3 = ____

9. 10 – 5 = ____

10. 8 – 4 = ____

11. 8 – 4 = ____

12. 6 – 3 = ____

13. Complete the number sentences below. Circle the strategy that can help.

   a. 7 – 5 = ____

   b. 7 – 2 = ____

   c. 8 – 4 = ____

   d. 8 – 3 = ____

   e. 8 – 5 = ____

   f. 10 – 5 = ____

Name _____   Date _____

Solve the number sentences. Make a number bond.
Draw a picture or write a statement about the strategy that helped you.

Doubles helped me solve!

$6 - 3 = 3$

1. ____ $- 5 = 5$ 2. $8 -$ ____ $= 4$ 3. $9 -$ ____ $= 4$

Lesson 35:   Relate subtraction facts involving fives and doubles to corresponding decompositions.   EUREKA MATH

Name _____   Date _____

Solve the sets of number sentences. Look for easy groups to cross off.

6 – 1 = 5
6 – 5 = 1

1.   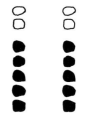   2.      3.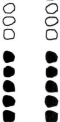

7 – 5 = _____   6 – 5 = _____   9 – _____ = 4

7 – 2 = _____   6 – 1 = _____   9 – _____ = 5

Subtract. Make a math drawing for each problem like the ones above. Write a number bond.

4.   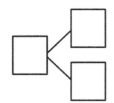   5.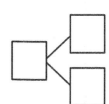

10 – 5 = _____   8 – 5 = _____

                           8 – _____ = 5

6. Solve. Visualize 5-groups to help you.

   a. 9 – _____ = 4   b. _____ – 5 = 5   c. 8 – _____ = 5

   d. _____ – 5 = 2   e. _____ – 5 = 3   f. _____ – 4 = 5

EUREKA
MATH

Lesson 35:   Relate subtraction facts involving fives and doubles to corresponding
              decompositions.

431

©2015 Great Minds. eureka-math.org
G1-M1-TE-BK1-1.3.1-01.2016

Complete the number sentence and number bond for each problem.

7.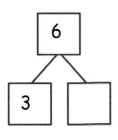

8.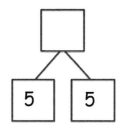

9.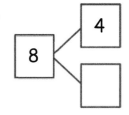

6 – 3 = ___   ___ – 5 = 5   8 – ___ = 4

10. Match the number sentence to the strategy that helps you solve.

a. 7 - ___ = 2
                                            doubles

b. 8 – ___ = 3   ●●●●● ○○○○○
                                            5-groups

c. 10 – ___ = 5   ●●●●● ○○○○○
                                            5-groups

d. ___ – 3 = 3   doubles

e. 8 – ___ = 4   ●●●●● ○○○○○
                                            5-groups

f. 9 – ___ = 5
                                            doubles

Lesson 35:   Relate subtraction facts involving fives and doubles to corresponding
                                            decompositions.

©2015 Great Minds. eureka-math.org
G1-M1-TE-BK1-1.3.1-01.2016

EUREKA
MATH™

Lesson 36

Objective: Relate subtraction from 10 to corresponding decompositions.

Suggested Lesson Structure

■ Fluency Practice	(13 minutes)
■ Application Problem	(5 minutes)
■ Concept Development	(32 minutes)
■ Student Debrief	(10 minutes)
Total Time	**(60 minutes)**

Fluency Practice (13 minutes)

- Counting the Say Ten Way **K.NBT.1**   (2 minutes)
- 5-Group Flash **K.OA.5, 1.OA.6**   (3 minutes)
- Number Bonds of Ten **K.OA.5, 1.OA.6**   (8 minutes)

Counting the Say Ten Way (2 minutes)

Note: Say Ten counting reinforces place value and prepares students to decompose teen numbers.

Count in the teens, alternating between saying numbers the regular way and the Say Ten way: 2 ten, 19, ten 8, 17, ten 6, 15, ten 4, 13, ten 2, 11, etc.

5-Group Flash (3 minutes)

Materials: (T) 5-group cards (Lesson 5 Template 1)

Note: This activity prepares students for Module 2, where they will learn how to make ten to facilitate adding (e.g., 9 + 4 can be thought of as 9 + 1 + 3 or 10 + 3).

Take out the 7 dot 5-group card and ask students to compare and contrast it with the 7 dot ten-frame card.

Flash a 5-group card for two to three seconds, and instruct students to identify the number at a signal (or snap). Flash the cards a second time and ask for the partner to 10. Begin with numbers closest to 10 first, because it is easier to identify the partner to 10.

Number Bonds of 10 (8 minutes)

Materials: (S) Numeral cards 1–10 (single-sided numerals from 5-group cards Lesson 5, Template 1), 10 two-sided beans or counters, a personal board with ten-frame (Fluency Template)

Note: This activity addresses the core fluency objective for Grade 1 of adding and subtracting within 10.

Assign students partners of equal ability. Students put numeral cards face down in front of them. One partner flips a card and adds counters to the ten-frame (e.g., a partner flips 9 and adds 9 red counters to the ten-frame). The other partner fills up the empty cells, using the other side of the counters (e.g., 1 white counter). The partners then work together to fill in a number bond and write two number sentences to match.

NOTES ON MULTIPLE MEANS OF ENGAGEMENT:

Provide challenging extensions for students who are ready by connecting partners to 10 with numbers up to 100. For example, some pairs could have double-digit numbers. Their goal would be to find the partner to make the next ten and complete a number bond (46, 4, 50).

Application Problem (5 minutes)

MP.1

There are 10 beads on the floor. There is the same number of red beads as white beads. A student picks up the white beads. How many beads are still on the floor? Write a number bond, number sentence, and a statement to share your solution. Make a math drawing to show how you know.

Note: This problem enables students to apply their learning from the previous lesson, using doubles facts and 5-groups to solve subtraction. Additionally, the problem bridges to the current lesson, which will focus on decompositions of 10.

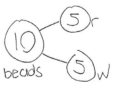

Concept Development (32 minutes)

Materials: (T) Number bracelet of 10 beads (5 red, 5 white) (from Lesson 8), white board or easel
(S) Number bracelet, personal white boards

Before students come to the meeting area, slip 4 white beads off of the demonstration pipe cleaner and place them in a pocket, out of view of the students. Have students bring materials to the meeting area and sit in a semicircle.

NOTES ON MULTIPLE MEANS OF ACTION AND EXPRESSIONS:
Partner share time provides a good opportunity to facilitate student analysis of work, allowing students to evaluate the process and analyze errors. Careful choice of partners is important when students are developing these skills.

©2015 Great Minds. eureka-math.org
G1-M1-TE-BK1-1.3.1-01.2016

T: Oh, no! My bracelet broke and is missing some of its beads. (Show the pipe cleaner to the class, holding it far enough away so that students cannot touch each bead to count.)

T: How many beads are on my bracelet?

S: 6 beads.

T: Wait, how many beads do you have on your bracelet?

S: 10.

T: Use one movement of beads to find out how many fell off my bracelet.

S: (Push 6 away in one movement from the set to find 4.) Four of your beads fell off.

MP.7

T: Write a number sentence and number bond to show what just happened to my bracelet.

S: (Write 10 – 4 = 6, and then write the corresponding number bond.)

T: (Assign partners. Project 10 – 1.) Partner A, use your beads to show Partner B the answer to this problem. Write the number sentence and number bond on your board.

S: (Partner A pushes 1 bead away from the set, writes 10 – 1 = 9, and writes the number bond.)

T: How many beads are left?

S: 9 beads.

T: (Project 10 – 9.) Partner B, use your beads to show Partner A the answer to this problem. Write the number sentence and number bond on your board.

S: (Partner B pushes 9 beads away from the set, writes 10 – 9 = 1, and writes the number bond.)

T: Look at your stretched out bracelets. Talk with your partner: What's the same or different about them? (Circulate and listen.)

S: (Discuss with a partner.) They're the same; mine is just facing the other way. → When I flip my bracelet over, it's exactly the same as my partner's.

T: Look at your number bonds and equations. Talk with your partner: What's the same or different about them? (Circulate and listen.)

S: (Discuss with a partner.) Our number bonds are the same. → Our number sentences use the same numbers and always start with 10 as the whole.

T: (Project 10 – 7.) Partner A, use your beads to show Partner B the answer to this problem. Write the number sentence and number bond on your board.

S: (Partner A pushes 7 beads away from the set, writes 10 – 7 = 3, and writes the number bond.)

T: Partner B, use your bracelet to show Partner A the other subtraction sentence, which matches your number bond. Write the number sentence.

S: (Partner B pushes 3 beads away from the set and writes 10 – 3 = 7.)

Repeat this process using 10 – 6, starting with Partner B so that Partner A has a hand at coming up with the other subtraction equation. If it seems necessary, continue the process two more times, using 10 – 8 and 10 – 3.

T: You've been writing some wonderful number bonds, taking apart 10. Now, I'm going to show you a number bond that's not quite finished. (Show number bond with 10 in the total box, 4 in a part box, and the other part blank.) What part goes with 4 to make 10?

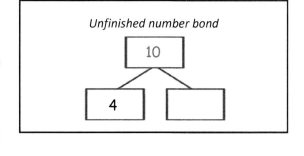

Unfinished number bond

S: 6.

T: Good. Now, write both subtraction sentences all by yourself.

S: (Write 10 − 4 = 6 and 10 − 6 = 4.)

Repeat this process with the following number bonds:

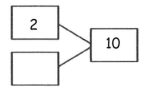   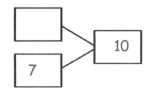

Problem Set (10 minutes)

Students should do their personal best to complete the Problem Set within the allotted 10 minutes. For some classes, it may be appropriate to modify the assignment by specifying which problems they work on first. Some problems do not specify a method for solving. Students solve these problems using the RDW approach used for Application Problems.

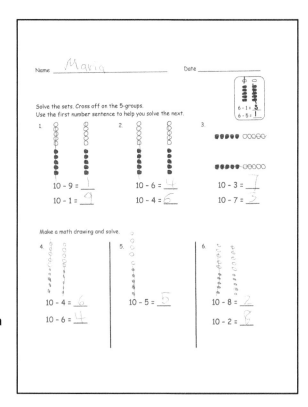

Student Debrief (10 minutes)

Lesson Objective: Relate subtraction from 10 to corresponding decompositions.

The Student Debrief is intended to invite reflection and active processing of the total lesson experience.

Invite students to review their solutions for the Problem Set. They should check work by comparing answers with a partner before going over answers as a class. Look for misconceptions or misunderstandings that can be addressed in the Debrief.

EUREKA
MATH™

Guide students in a conversation to debrief the Problem Set and process the lesson.

Any combination of the questions below may be used to lead the discussion.

- How are 5-groups and our bracelets the same in appearance? What can they help us do? How are they different?

- Which Problem Set problem(s) are similar to the Application Problem? How do you know? How did you solve them similarly or differently?

- Look at Problem 4 and Problem 6. How could Problem 4 help you solve Problem 6? What's different about them?

- Why is there only one number sentence for Problem 5?

- Explain to your partner how you decided to solve Problem 7, Problem 8, Problem 9, and Problem 10. What helped you? How did you solve them differently or similarly?

- Can we visualize rather than holding our bracelets or 5-groups?

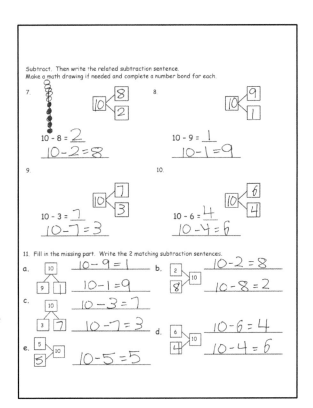

Exit Ticket (3 minutes)

After the Student Debrief, instruct students to complete the Exit Ticket. A review of their work will help with assessing students' understanding of the concepts that were presented in today's lesson and planning more effectively for future lessons. The questions may be read aloud to the students.

Name _____   Date _____

Solve the sets. Cross off on the 5-groups.
Use the first number sentence to help you solve the next.

1.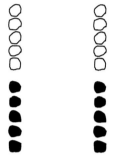

10 – 9 = ____

10 – 1 = ____

2.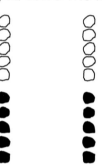

10 – 6 = ____

10 – 4 = ____

3.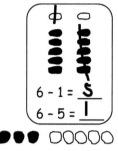

6 – 1 = _S_
6 – 5 = _I_

10 – 3 = ____

10 – 7 = ____

Make a math drawing and solve.

4.

10 – 4 = ____

10 – 6 = ____

5.

10 – 5 = ____

6.

10 – 8 = ____

10 – 2 = ____

Lesson 36:   Relate subtraction from 10 to corresponding decompositions.

EUREKA
MATH

©2015 Great Minds. eureka-math.org
G1-M1-TE-BK1-1.3.1-01.2016

Subtract. Then, write the related subtraction sentence.
Make a math drawing if needed, and complete a number bond for each.

7.

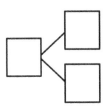

10 – 8 = ___

_____

8.

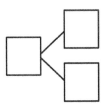

10 – 9 = ___

_____

9.

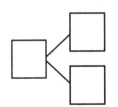

10 – 3 = ___

_____

10.

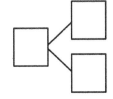

10 – 6 = ___

_____

11. Fill in the missing part. Write the 2 matching subtraction sentences.

a.

_____

_____

b.

_____

_____

c.

_____

_____

d.
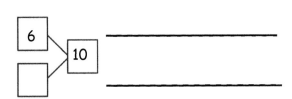

_____

_____

e.
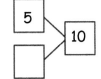

_____

_____

Name _____ Date _____

Fill in the missing part. Draw a math picture if needed. Write the 2 matching subtraction sentences.

1.
```
      ┌────┐
      │ 10 │
      └────┘
      ╱    ╲
  ┌───┐  ┌───┐
  │ 7 │  │   │
  └───┘  └───┘
```

_____

_____

2.
```
      ┌────┐
      │ 10 │
      └────┘
      ╱    ╲
  ┌───┐  ┌───┐
  │ 2 │  │   │
  └───┘  └───┘
```

_____

_____

3.
```
      ┌────┐
      │ 10 │
      └────┘
      ╱    ╲
  ┌───┐  ┌───┐
  │ 4 │  │   │
  └───┘  └───┘
```

_____

_____

Lesson 36:   Relate subtraction from 10 to corresponding decompositions.

EUREKA MATH

©2015 Great Minds. eureka-math.org
G1-M1-TE-BK1-1.3.1-01.2016

Name _____   Date _____

Make a math drawing, and solve. Use the first number sentence to help
you write a related number sentence that matches your picture.

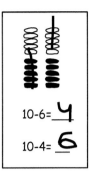

10-6=_4_

10-4= 6

1.   2.   3.

10 – 2 = ____   10 – 1 = ____   10 – 7 = ____

__ - __ = __   __ - __ = __   __ - __ = __

Subtract. Then, write the related subtraction sentence. Make a math drawing if
needed, and complete a number bond for each.

4. 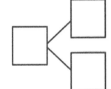   5. 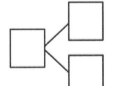   6.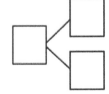

10 – 2 = __   10 – __ = 9   10 - __ = 6

_____   _____   _____

7. 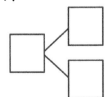   10 – __ = 1   8. 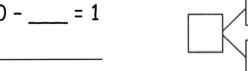 __ = 10 - 5

                     _____   _____

9. Complete the number bond. Match the number bond to the related subtraction sentence. Write the other related subtraction number sentence.

a.

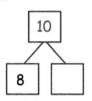

10 – 5 = ____   ____ - ____ = ____

b.

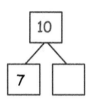

10 – 1 = ____   ____ - ____ = ____

c.

10 - 2 = ____   ____ - ____ = ____

d.

10 – 4 = ____   ____ - ____ = ____

e.

10 - 3 =____   ____ - ____ = ____

Lesson 36:   Relate subtraction from 10 to corresponding decompositions.

EUREKA
MATH™

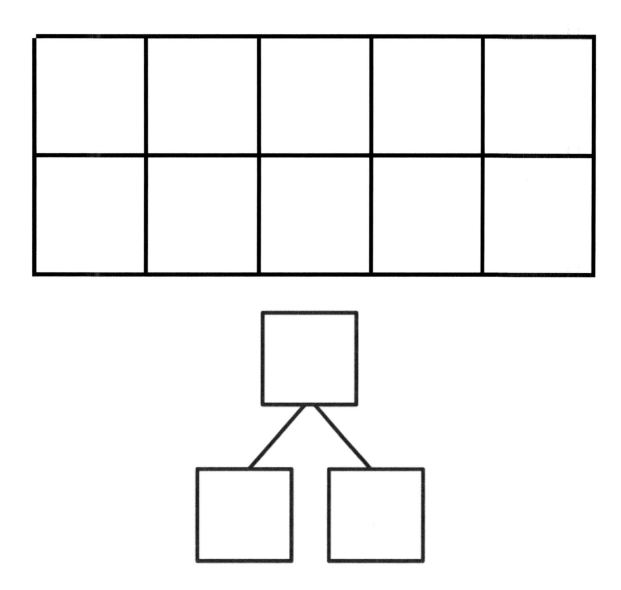

_____

ten-frame

Lesson 36: Relate subtraction from 10 to corresponding decompositions.

443

©2015 Great Minds. eureka-math.org
G1-M1-TE-BK1-1.3.1-01.2016

Lesson 37

Objective: Relate subtraction from 9 to corresponding decompositions.

Suggested Lesson Structure

- ■ Fluency Practice   (14 minutes)
- ■ Application Problem   (6 minutes)
- ▪ Concept Development   (30 minutes)
- ■ Student Debrief   (10 minutes)
- **Total Time**   **(60 minutes)**

Fluency Practice (14 minutes)

- ▪ Choral Counting: The Regular and the Say Ten Way **1.NBT.2**   (2 minutes)
- ▪ 5-Group Flash **K.OA.5, 1.OA.6**   (2 minutes)
- ▪ Sprint: Partners to 10 **K.OA.5, 1.OA.6**   (10 minutes)

Choral Counting: The Regular and the Say Ten Way (2 minutes)

Note: This activity supports students' ability to maintain their fluency with the counting sequence while also building the foundational skills for place value.

Tell students to count along, alternating between the regular and the Say Ten way (e.g., 12, ten 3, 14, ten 5, etc.). Start at different numbers within 40. If students are ready, try counting back, too.

5-Group Flash (2 minutes)

Materials: (T) 5-group cards (Lesson 5 Template 1)

Note: This activity addresses the core fluency objective for Grade 1 of adding and subtracting with 10, using visual models to support stronger foundational development.

Flash a 5-group card for 2–3 seconds and instruct students to identify the number at a signal (or snap). Ask for a number sentence to solve 10 minus the number flashed.

Sprint: Partners to 10 (10 minutes)

Materials: (S) Partners to 10 Sprint

Note: This activity addresses the core fluency objective for Grade 1 of adding and subtracting within 10.

NOTES ON MULTIPLE MEANS OF ACTION AND EXPRESSION:

Some students would benefit from having a set of ten-frame cards to use as a reference and to have available for practice. This practice should include flipping the cards over to encourage visualization of the numbers and their partners.

Application Problem (6 minutes)

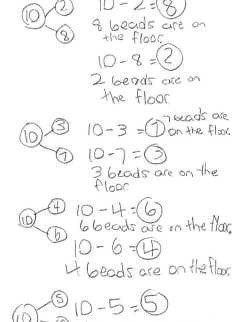

There are 10 beads on the floor. A student picked up some of the beads but left some on the floor. Write a number bond and a number sentence that would match this story.

Extension: What other number bonds and number sentences could match this story? Try to list all of the possibilities. (Encourage all students to attempt this.)

Note: This problem applies the objective from Lesson 36, decompositions of 10 and their related subtraction facts. This also connects to the current lesson's Concept Development, which focuses on all of the decompositions of 9 in a similar way.

Concept Development (30 minutes)

Materials: (T) Number bracelet of 10 beads (5 red, 5 white)
(see Lesson 8) (S) Number bracelet of 10 beads (5 red, 5 white), personal white board

Have students bring materials to meeting area and sit in a semi-circle.

T: (Assign partners. Project $10 - 5$.) Partner A, use your beads to solve, and also show Partner B the number sentence and number bond on your board. Explain as you go.

S: (Complete the task with partner.)

T: (Project $9 - 5$.) Partner B, take off 1 bead and put it behind you to have 9. (Pause.) Use your beads to solve, and also show Partner A a number sentence and number bond on your board. Explain what you did.

S: (Complete the task with partner.)

T: Compare your bracelets, your number sentences, and number bonds. How can Partner A's work help you solve Partner B's work? (Circulate and listen.)

S: (Discuss with partner.) Partner B starts with 1 less as the whole. But, we both took 5 away, and Partner B's answer is 1 less. → Nine is 1 less than 10. So, when we take 5 away, our answer will be 1 less. → It's just like on the addition chart! → We take away a five group, so it's 4 left not 5.

T: Good! Now, Partner A, please remove 1 bead and place it behind you to make sure you have 9. (Pause.) Our 10 is now…

S: 9.

T: (Project $9 - 1$.) Use your beads to solve and also show the number sentence and number bond on your personal board.

S: (Push 1 bead away from the set, finish the number bond, and write $9 - 1 = 8$.)

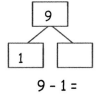

$9 - 1 =$

T: What is the other number sentence you can write to describe this number bond?

S: 9 – 8 = 1.

T: Yes. Now, please write it below your first number sentence.

S: (Write 9 – 8 = 1.)

T: Now, you're going to write all of the other number bonds with 9 as the total or the whole and the subtraction sentences that describe each number bond. You can move around the room to do this. Hmmm, what tools can you use to help you do this?

S: Our bracelets! → Our hands. → Our 5-group cards. → Our math drawings. → Our addition chart. → Visualizing. → Our brains. → The charts in the room!

T: Talk with your partner!

As students work, circulate and support them as appropriate. When most students have finished, have them return to the meeting area.

T: What strategies did you use to be sure that you got every way to make 9?

S: I used my bracelet and showed 1 less each time! → I checked mine over a couple of times and showed it with my bracelet.

T: What strategies did you use to be sure that you showed the subtraction sentences that described the number bonds?

S: I actually took the beads away on my bracelet! → I flipped my bracelet after I made the first subtraction sentence.

Problem Set (10 minutes)

Students should do their personal best to complete the Problem Set within the allotted 10 minutes. For some classes, it may be appropriate to modify the assignment by specifying which problems they work on first. Some problems do not specify a method for solving. Students solve these problems using the RDW approach used for Application Problems.

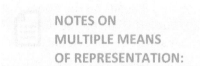

NOTES ON
MULTIPLE MEANS
OF REPRESENTATION:

During this lesson, it is important for students to articulate how using strategies helps to solve problems so that other students can hear how they are thinking. This should help guide them toward a better understanding of the patterns and structures.

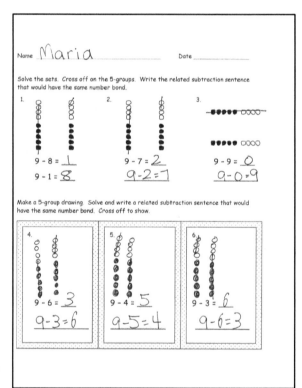

Lesson 37:   Relate subtraction from 9 to corresponding decompositions.

©2015 Great Minds. eureka-math.org
G1-M1-TE-BK1-1.3.1-01.2016

Student Debrief (10 minutes)

Lesson Objective: Relate subtraction from 9 to corresponding decompositions.

The Student Debrief is intended to invite reflection and active processing of the total lesson experience.

Invite students to review their solutions for the Problem Set. They should check work by comparing answers with a partner before going over answers as a class. Look for misconceptions or misunderstandings that can be addressed in the Debrief. Guide students in a conversation to debrief the Problem Set and process the lesson.

Any combination of the questions below may be used to lead the discussion.

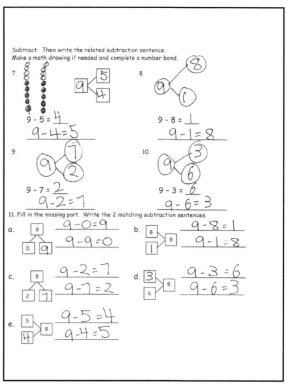

- Look at Problem 2 and Problem 6. What is similar and different about them? How did you use Problem 2 to help you solve Problem 6?

- Look at Problems 7–10. What strategy or strategies did you use to solve these? How was your strategy different from or similar to your partner's?

- Which strategy is the most efficient for solving Problems 7 –10? Why?

- How did the Application Problem connect to today's lesson?

- How can you visualize 9? What do you see in your brain? Does that help you to subtract from 9?

Exit Ticket (3 minutes)

After the Student Debrief, instruct students to complete the Exit Ticket. A review of their work will help with assessing students' understanding of the concepts that were presented in today's lesson and planning more effectively for future lessons. The questions may be read aloud to the students.

A

Name _____   Date _____

Number Correct: ☆

*Write the missing number for each number sentence. Pay attention to the + and – signs.

1.	$9 + 1 = \square$		16.	$10 - 7 = \square$	
2.	$1 + 9 = \square$		17.	$10 = 7 + \square$	
3.	$10 - 1 = \square$		18.	$10 = 3 + \square$	
4.	$10 - 9 = \square$		19.	$10 = 6 + \square$	
5.	$10 + 0 = \square$		20.	$10 = 4 + \square$	
6.	$0 + 10 = \square$		21.	$10 = 5 + \square$	
7.	$10 - 0 = \square$		22.	$10 - \square = 5$	
8.	$10 - 10 = \square$		23.	$5 = 10 - \square$	
9.	$8 + 2 = \square$		24.	$6 = 10 - \square$	
10.	$2 + 8 = \square$		25.	$7 = 10 - \square$	
11.	$10 - 2 = \square$		26.	$7 = \square - 3$	
12.	$10 - 8 = \square$		27.	$4 = 10 - \square$	
13.	$7 + 3 = \square$		28.	$5 = \square - 5$	
14.	$3 + 7 = \square$		29.	$6 = 10 - \square$	
15.	$10 - 3 = \square$		30.	$7 = \square - 3$	

Relate subtraction from 9 to corresponding decompositions.

EUREKA MATH™

B

Number Correct:

Name _____   Date _____

*Write the missing number for each number sentence. Pay attention to the + and – signs.

1.	8 + 2 = ☐		16.	10 – 6 = ☐	
2.	2 + 8 = ☐		17.	10 = 8 + ☐	
3.	10 – 2 = ☐		18.	10 = 7 + ☐	
4.	10 – 8 = ☐		19.	10 = 3 + ☐	
5.	9 + 1 = ☐		20.	10 = 4 + ☐	
6.	1 + 9 = ☐		21.	10 = 5 + ☐	
7.	10 – 1 = ☐		22.	10 – ☐ = 5	
8.	10 – 9 = ☐		23.	6 = 10 – ☐	
9.	10 + 0 = ☐		24.	7 = 10 – ☐	
10.	0 + 10 = ☐		25.	8 = 10 – ☐	
11.	10 – 0 = ☐		26.	7 = ☐ – 3	
12.	10 – 10 = ☐		27.	2 = 10 – ☐	
13.	6 + 4 = ☐		28.	4 = ☐ – 6	
14.	4 + 6 = ☐		29.	3 = 10 – ☐	
15.	10 – 4 = ☐		30.	7 = ☐ – 3	

Name _____   Date _____

Solve the sets. Cross off on the 5-groups. Write the related subtraction sentence that would have the same number bond.

1.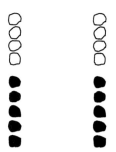

9 – 8 = ___

9 – 1 = ___

2.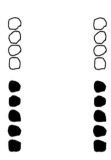

9 – 7 = ___

_____

3.

9 – 9 = ___

_____

Make a 5-group drawing. Solve, and write a related subtraction sentence that would have the same number bond. Cross off to show.

4.

9 – 6 = ___

_____

5.

9 – 4 = ___

_____

6.

9 – 3 = ___

_____

Lesson 37:   Relate subtraction from 9 to corresponding decompositions.

©2015 Great Minds. eureka-math.org
G1-M1-TE-BK1-1.3.1-01.2016

EUREKA MATH™

Subtract. Then, write the related subtraction sentence.
Make a math drawing if needed, and complete a number bond.

7.

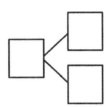

9 – 5 = ___

_____

8.

9 – 8 = ___

_____

9.

9 – 7 = ___

_____

10.

9 – 3 = ___

_____

11. Fill in the missing part. Write the 2 matching subtraction sentences.

a.
9
0 ☐
_____
_____

b.
8
9
☐
_____
_____

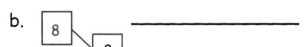

c.
9
2 ☐
_____
_____

d.
☐
9
6
_____
_____

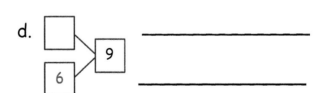

e.
5
9
☐
_____
_____

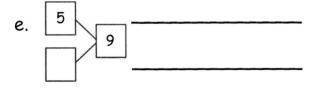

Name _____   Date _____

Fill in the missing part. Draw a math picture if needed. Write the 2 matching subtraction sentences.

1.

_____

_____

2.

_____

_____

3.

_____

_____

Lesson 37:   Relate subtraction from 9 to corresponding decompositions.

EUREKA
MATH™

Name _____ Date _____

Make 5-group drawings and solve. Use the first number sentence to help you write a related number sentence that matches your picture.

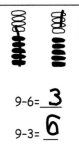

9-6= **3**

9-3= **6**

1.   2.   3.

9 – 2 = ____   9 – 8 = ___   9 – 4 = ___

__ - __ = __   __ - __ = __   __ - __ = __

Subtract. Then, write the related subtraction sentence. Make a math drawing if needed, and complete a number bond for each.

4. 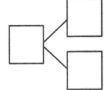   5. 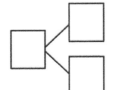   6.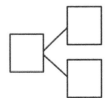

9 – 7 = ___   9 – __ = 9   9 – __ = 6

_____   _____   _____

7. 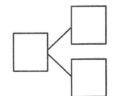 9 – ___ = 1

_____

8. 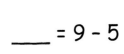___ = 9 – 5

_____

9. Use 5-group drawings to help you complete the number bond. Match the number bond to the related subtraction sentence. Write the other related subtraction number sentence.

a.

9 – 5 = _____   ____ - ____ = ____

b.

9 – 1 = _____   ____ - ____ = ____

c.

9 – 2 = _____   ____ - ____ = ____

d.

9 – 6= _____   ____ - ____ = ____

e.

9 – ____ = 0   ____ - ____ = ____

Lesson 37:   Relate subtraction from 9 to corresponding decompositions.

EUREKA
MATH

©2015 Great Minds. eureka-math.org
G1-M1-TE-BK1-1.3.1-01.2016

Topic J

Development of Subtraction Fluency Within 10

1.OA.6

Focus Standard:	1.OA.6	Add and subtract within 20, demonstrating fluency for addition and subtraction within 10. Use strategies such as counting on; making ten (e.g., 8 + 6 = 8 + 2 + 4 = 10 + 4 = 14); decomposing a number leading to a ten (e.g., 13 − 4 = 13 − 3 − 1 = 10 − 1 = 9); using the relationship between addition and subtraction (e.g., knowing that 8 + 4 = 12, one knows 12 − 8 = 4); and creating equivalent but easier or known sums (e.g., adding 6 + 7 by creating the known equivalent 6 + 6 + 1 = 12 + 1 = 13.)
Instructional Days:	2	
Coherence -Links from:	GK–M4	Number Pairs, Addition and Subtraction to 10
-Links to:	G2–M4	Addition and Subtraction Within 200 with Word Problems to 100

Grade 1's Module 1 closes with Topic J, where students spend Lesson 38 exploring the addition chart (similar to Topic F) and looking for patterns within the context of subtraction (**MP.7, MP.8, 1.OA.6**).

When presented with a subtraction equation such as 7 − 3, students then use their knowledge of the decompositions of 7 to help them solve, and discuss to find related addition equations on the addition chart such as 3 + 4 or 4 + 3.

The final lesson, Lesson 39, allows students to further analyze the addition chart to create their own sets of related addition and subtraction facts for them to practice throughout the year as they work toward mastery of these foundational facts.

1 + 0	1 + 1	1 + 2	1 + 3	1 + 4	1 + 5	1 + 6	1 + 7	1 + 8	1 + 9
2 + 0	2 + 1	2 + 2	2 + 3	2 + 4	2 + 5	2 + 6	2 + 7	2 + 8	
3 + 0	3 + 1	3 + 2	3 + 3	3 + 4	3 + 5	3 + 6	3 + 7		
4 + 0	4 + 1	4 + 2	4 + 3	4 + 4	4 + 5	4 + 6			
5 + 0	5 + 1	5 + 2	5 + 3	5 + 4	5 + 5				
6 + 0	6 + 1	6 + 2	6 + 3	6 + 4					
7 + 0	7 + 1	7 + 2	7 + 3						
8 + 0	8 + 1	8 + 2							
9 + 0	9 + 1								
10 + 0									

A Teaching Sequence Toward Mastery of Development of Subtraction Fluency Within 10

Objective 1: Look for and make use of repeated reasoning and structure using the addition chart to solve subtraction problems.
(Lesson 38)

Objective 2: Analyze the addition chart to create sets of related addition and subtraction facts.
(Lesson 39)

©2015 Great Minds. eureka-math.org
G1-M1-TE-BK1-1.3.1-01.2016

Lesson 38

Objective: Look for and make use of repeated reasoning and structure using the addition chart to solve subtraction problems.

Suggested Lesson Structure

- ■ Fluency Practice   (10 minutes)
- ▨ Application Problem   (7 minutes)
- ▢ Concept Development   (33 minutes)
- ▨ Student Debrief   (10 minutes)

   Total Time   **(60 minutes)**

Fluency Practice (10 minutes)

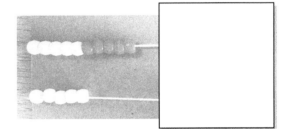

- ▪ Rekenrek: Teen Numbers **K.NBT.1**   (2 minutes)
- ▪ Hide Zero Cards **K.NBT.1**   (3 minutes)
- ▪ Subtraction with Cards **1.OA.6**   (5 minutes)

Rekenrek (2 minutes)

Materials: (T) Rekenrek (cover the unused beads)

Note: Reviewing **K.NBT.1** prepares students for the Make Ten strategy of Module 2.

   T: (Move the top 4 beads on the Rekenrek into view). How many beads do you see?
   S: 4.
   T: How many more do we need to make 10?
   S: 6.
   T: (Move 6 more beads into view.) 4 + 6 = ?
   S: 10.
   T: (Move 3 beads from the bottom row into view.) How many beads are on the bottom row?
   S: 3.
   T: Let's say it the Say Ten way.
   S: Ten 3.
   T: Now, say it the regular way.
   S: Thirteen.

Continue with other examples: 7 and 3 leading to 10 and 4, 8 and 2 leading to 10 and 5, etc.

Lesson 38:   Look for and make use of repeated reasoning and structure using the
                addition chart to solve subtraction problems.

457

Hide Zero Cards: Bonding Teen Numbers (3 minutes)

Hide Zero Cards

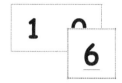

Materials: (T) Hide Zero cards (Fluency Template) (S) Personal white board

Note: This activity continues to maintain students' understanding and use of teen numbers as *10 and some more*. Hide Zero cards are made so that the single digit cards can be laid on top of the 10 card to create teen numbers. The digit in the ones place can be lifted to show the zero from the 10 hiding behind the single digit card.

Use the Hide Zero cards to show teen numbers. For example, show 14 by covering the ones place of 10 with 4. Students write number bonds with 10 as a part. The teacher breaks apart the Hide Zero cards to show the two parts (10 and 4).

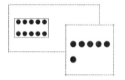

Subtraction with Cards (5 minutes)

Materials: (S) 1 deck of numeral cards (single-sided numerals from 5-group cards Lesson 5, Template 1) with 2 extra tens per pair, counters (if needed)

Note: This activity addresses the fluency objective for Grade 1 of adding and subtracting within 10.

Students place the deck of cards face down between them. Each partner flips over two cards and subtracts the smaller number from the larger number. The partner with the smallest difference keeps the cards played by both players that round. The player with the most cards at the end of the game wins.

NOTES ON MULTIPLE MEANS OF ENGAGEMENT:

Some students need concrete representations to solve word problems. Provide concrete models as needed. Allow students to take on leadership roles as appropriate by developing their own stories for the class to solve.

Application Problem (7 minutes)

Jessie and Carl were comparing the beads they picked up. Jessie picked up 9 beads. 5 of them were red, and the rest were white. Carl picked up 5 red beads and 4 white beads. Carl said they had the same number of white beads. Is Carl correct? Draw and label your work to show your thinking.

Note: This problem incorporates the Lesson 37 objective. It also asks students to solve and compare two types of word problems: *take apart* and *put together*. While students can solve this problem without knowing Carl's total, they must focus on what is being asked in the question in order to determine this. The problem also incorporates an opportunity to relate addition and subtraction, which will be the focus of today's lesson.

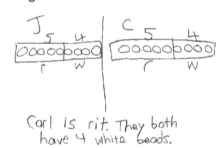

Lesson 38:   Look for and make use of repeated reasoning and structure using the addition chart to solve subtraction problems.

©2015 Great Minds. eureka-math.org
G1-M1-TE-BK1-1.3.1-01.2016

EUREKA MATH™

Concept Development (33 minutes)

Materials: (T) Addition chart (Lesson 21 Template), subtraction
expression cards (Template) (S) Addition chart (Lesson
21 Template), subtraction expression cards (Template)
per group, yellow crayon, personal white board

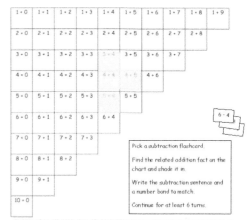

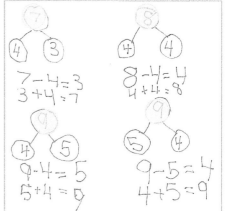

T: (Project addition chart.) How did this addition chart help
us with our addition facts?

S: (Responses will vary.) All the +1 addends are in the same
column. → The rows start with the same part. → The
totals made a staircase. → The ones near each other are
related, like 4 + 3 is 7, and underneath we see 5 + 3; that's
one more—it's 8.

T: (Hold up subtraction expression card 7 − 4.) Write a
number bond and leave the missing part empty for now.

S: (Write number bond.)

T: What is the whole?

S: 7.

T: The known part?

S: 4.

MP.7 & MP.8

T: Which of the addition problems on your chart have a part
that is 4? Talk to your partner.

S: The ones here, going across. → It's the row that starts
with 4 + 0. → There is one here, too, going down.
→ It starts with 1 + 4.

T: The chart tells the parts but not the totals. Which of
those problems have the same total as 7 − 4?
Don't call out the answer.

S: (Wait for the signal.) 4 + 3. → 3 + 4.

T: Let's color in 4 + 3 and 3 + 4 on our chart with yellow
and fill in our number bond with the missing part.

T: Let's also color our totals yellow.

S: (Color in the chart and complete the number bond.)

T: Write the subtraction number sentence from the card
we started with. Write the addition number sentence
that helped us solve it.

S: (Write 7 − 4 = 3 and 4 + 3 = 7.)

**NOTES ON
MULTIPLE MEANS
OF ACTION AND
EXPRESSION:**

Using personal white boards with an
addition chart template allows all
learners to participate. Some students
might not feel comfortable
participating orally, while others may
not be able to respond orally. They can
show what they know on their boards.

Repeat the process with the following suggested sequence: 8 − 4, 9 − 4, and 9 − 5. Record the number
sentences on the board to be used during the Student Debrief.

Lesson 38:   Look for and make use of repeated reasoning and structure using the
addition chart to solve subtraction problems.

459

©2015 Great Minds. eureka-math.org
G1-M1-TE-BK1-1.3.1-01.2016

Problem Set (10 minutes)

Students should do their personal best to complete the Problem Set within the allotted 10 minutes. For some classes, it may be appropriate to modify the assignment by specifying which problems they work on first. Some problems do not specify a method for solving. Students solve these problems using the RDW approach used for Application Problems.

Student Debrief (10 minutes)

Lesson Objective: Look for and make use of repeated reasoning and structure using the addition chart to solve subtraction problems.

The Student Debrief is intended to invite reflection and active processing of the total lesson experience.

Invite students to review their solutions for the Problem Set. They should check work by comparing answers with a partner before going over answers as a class. Look for misconceptions or misunderstandings that can be addressed in the Debrief. Guide students in a conversation to debrief the Problem Set and process the lesson.

Any combination of the questions below may be used to lead the discussion.

- Look at the subtraction problems we solved during the lesson. (Point to sequence of 7 – 4, 8 – 4, 9 – 4, and 9 – 5.) What do you notice about these problems? Where are the helpful addition facts for these subtraction sentences located on your chart? How can solving the first one help you solve the next?
- Look at your work from the class. What pattern do you notice on your chart? How are these subtraction facts related?
- What is another set of subtraction facts that would make a cross on your chart?
- When you worked through the Problem Set, was it tricky to put the totals in the right place? Why?

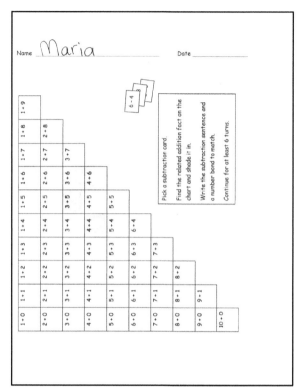

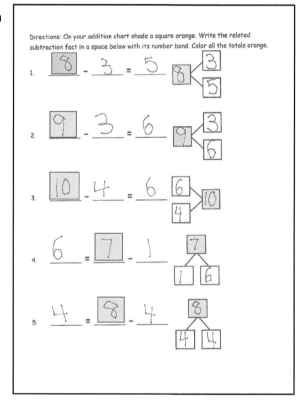

Lesson 38: Look for and make use of repeated reasoning and structure using the addition chart to solve subtraction problems.

EUREKA MATH

©2015 Great Minds. eureka-math.org
G1-M1-TE-BK1-1.3.1-01.2016

- What tool did we use in a new way to solve subtraction problems today? Explain how the tool helped you.
- How did the Application Problem connect to today's lesson?

Exit Ticket (3 minutes)

After the Student Debrief, instruct students to complete the Exit Ticket. A review of their work will help with assessing students' understanding of the concepts that were presented in today's lesson and planning more effectively for future lessons. The questions may be read aloud to the students.

     Lesson 38:   Look for and make use of repeated reasoning and structure using the   **461**
                                addition chart to solve subtraction problems.

©2015 Great Minds. eureka-math.org
G1-M1-TE-BK1-1.3.1-01.2016

Name _____   Date _____

1 + 9									
1 + 8	2 + 8								
1 + 7	2 + 7	3 + 7							
1 + 6	2 + 6	3 + 6	4 + 6						
1 + 5	2 + 5	3 + 5	4 + 5	5 + 5					
1 + 4	2 + 4	3 + 4	4 + 4	5 + 4	6 + 4				
1 + 3	2 + 3	3 + 3	4 + 3	5 + 3	6 + 3	7 + 3			
1 + 2	2 + 2	3 + 2	4 + 2	5 + 2	6 + 2	7 + 2	8 + 2		
1 + 1	2 + 1	3 + 1	4 + 1	5 + 1	6 + 1	7 + 1	8 + 1	9 + 1	
1 + 0	2 + 0	3 + 0	4 + 0	5 + 0	6 + 0	7 + 0	8 + 0	9 + 0	10 + 0

6 – 4

Pick a subtraction card.

Find the related addition fact on the chart and shade it in.

Write the subtraction sentence and a number bond to match.

Continue for at least 6 turns.

Lesson 38:   Look for and make use of repeated reasoning and structure using the addition chart to solve subtraction problems.

EUREKA MATH

On your addition chart, shade a square orange. Write the related subtraction fact in a space below with its number bond. Color all the totals orange.

1. _____ - _____ = _____

2. _____ - _____ = _____

3. _____ - _____ = _____

4. _____ = _____ - _____

5. _____ = _____ - _____

EUREKA
MATH™

Lesson 38:   Look for and make use of repeated reasoning and structure using the
addition chart to solve subtraction problems.

463

©2015 Great Minds. eureka-math.org
G1-M1-TE-BK1-1.3.1-01.2016

Name _____   Date _____

Write the related number sentences for the number bonds.

1.

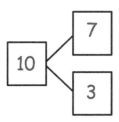

2.

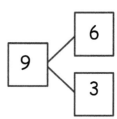

_____ - _____ = _____   _____ - _____ = _____

_____ + _____ = _____   _____ + _____ = _____

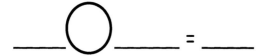

_____ ◯ _____ = _____   _____ ◯ _____ = _____

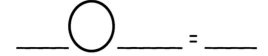   

_____ ◯ _____ = _____   _____ ◯ _____ = _____

Lesson 38:   Look for and make use of repeated reasoning and structure using the
addition chart to solve subtraction problems.

©2015 Great Minds. eureka-math.org
G1-M1-TE-BK1-1.3.1-01.2016

EUREKA
MATH

Name _____   Date _____

Find and solve the 7 unshaded addition problems that are doubles and 5-groups.

Make subtraction flashcards for the related subtraction facts. (Remember, doubles will only make 1 related subtraction fact instead of 2 related facts.)

Make a number bond card and use your cards to play Memory.

1 + 0	1 + 1	1 + 2	1 + 3	1 + 4	1 + 5	1 + 6	1 + 7	1 + 8	1 + 9
2 + 0	2 + 1	2 + 2	2 + 3	2 + 4	2 + 5	2 + 6	2 + 7	2 + 8	
3 + 0	3 + 1	3 + 2	3 + 3	3 + 4	3 + 5	3 + 6	3 + 7		
4 + 0	4 + 1	4 + 2	4 + 3	4 + 4	4 + 5	4 + 6			
5 + 0	5 + 1	5 + 2	5 + 3	5 + 4	5 + 5				
6 + 0	6 + 1	6 + 2	6 + 3	6 + 4					
7 + 0	7 + 1	7 + 2	7 + 3						
8 + 0	8 + 1	8 + 2							
9 + 0	9 + 1								
10 + 0									

Lesson 38:   Look for and make use of repeated reasoning and structure using the
             addition chart to solve subtraction problems.

465

©2015 Great Minds. eureka-math.org
G1-M1-TE-BK1-1.3.1-01.2016

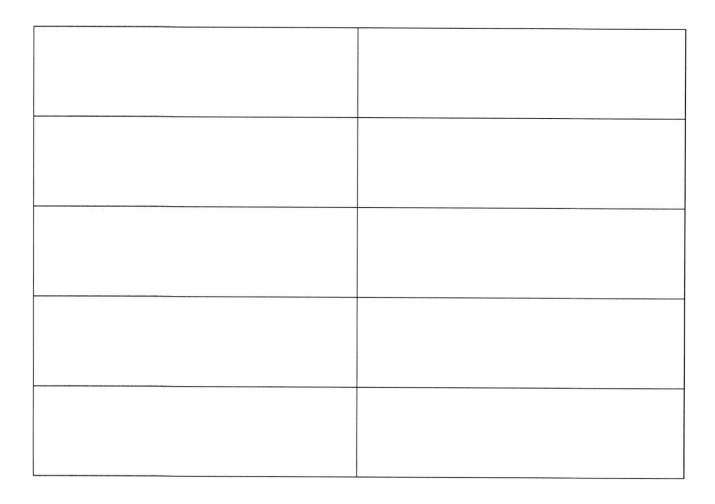

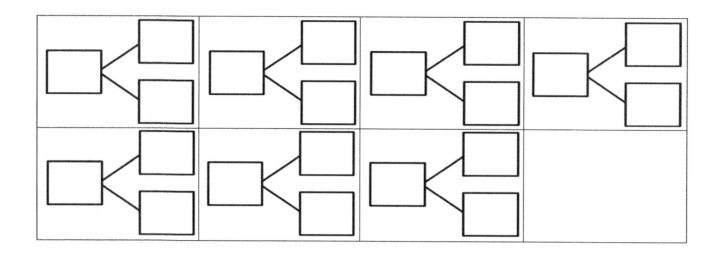

Lesson 38: Look for and make use of repeated reasoning and structure using the addition chart to solve subtraction problems.

©2015 Great Minds. eureka-math.org
G1-M1-TE-BK1-1.3.1-01.2016

1	0	2	0
0	1	2	3
4	5	6	7
8	9		

hide zero cards, numeral side (Copy double-sided with next page.)

Lesson 38:   Look for and make use of repeated reasoning and structure using the
             addition chart to solve subtraction problems.

©2015 Great Minds. eureka-math.org
G1-M1-TE-BK1-1.3.1-01.2016

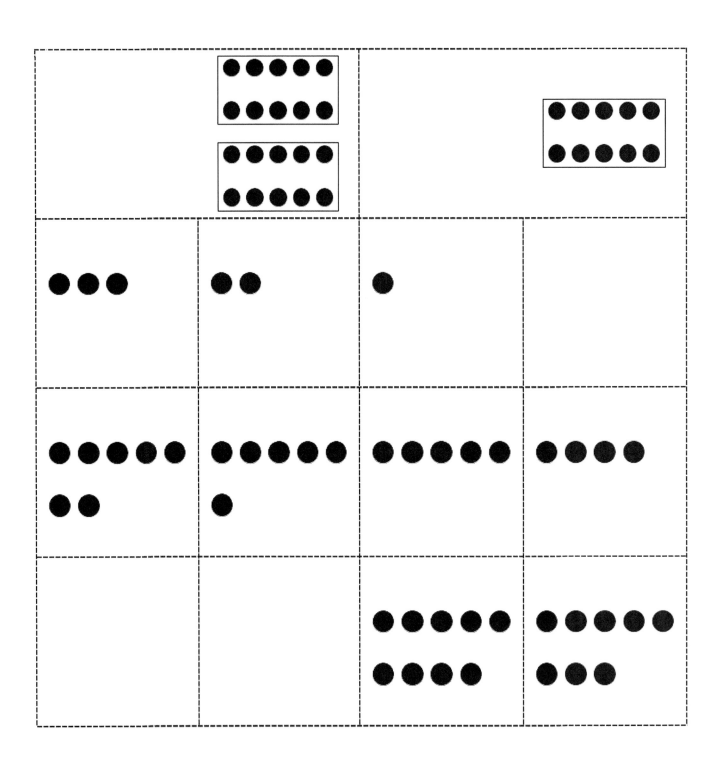

hide zero cards, 5-group side (Copy double-sided with previous page.)

Lesson 38: Look for and make use of repeated reasoning and structure using the addition chart to solve subtraction problems.

©2015 Great Minds. eureka-math.org
G1-M1-TE-BK1-1.3.1-01.2016

EUREKA
MATH™

6 – 4	9 – 1
5 – 2	10 – 4
9 – 7	4 – 3
8 – 3	7 – 1
3 – 2	9 – 8

subtraction expression cards

Lesson 38: Look for and make use of repeated reasoning and structure using the addition chart to solve subtraction problems.

469

©2015 Great Minds. eureka-math.org
G1-M1-TE-BK1-1.3.1-01.2016

4 - 1	8 - 7
10 - 2	7 - 3
9 - 5	5 - 0
10 - 7	7 - 2
9 - 3	5 - 4

subtraction expression cards

Lesson 38:   Look for and make use of repeated reasoning and structure using the addition chart to solve subtraction problems.

EUREKA
MATH

6 - 5	8 - 0
3 - 1	6 - 2
10 - 10	9 - 2
8 - 6	4 - 4
1 - 1	4 - 2

subtraction expression cards

EUREKA MATH™

Lesson 38: Look for and make use of repeated reasoning and structure using the addition chart to solve subtraction problems.

471

©2015 Great Minds. eureka-math.org
G1-M1-TE-BK1-1.3.1-01.2016

7 − 0	7 − 6
7 − 4	9 − 9
4 − 0	5 − 1
2 − 1	5 − 3
0 − 0	10 − 0

subtraction expression cards

Lesson 38:   Look for and make use of repeated reasoning and structure using the addition chart to solve subtraction problems.

EUREKA
MATH™

8 - 1	3 - 3
6 - 3	10 - 1
8 - 2	10 - 8
6 - 1	7 - 7
1 - 0	5 - 5

subtraction expression cards

Lesson 38:   Look for and make use of repeated reasoning and structure using the
addition chart to solve subtraction problems.

473

©2015 Great Minds. eureka-math.org
G1-M1-TE-BK1-1.3.1-01.2016

6 - 0	10 - 9
8 - 4	10 - 3
6 - 6	10 - 6
9 - 6	10 - 5
3 - 0	2 - 2

subtraction expression cards

Lesson 38:   Look for and make use of repeated reasoning and structure using the
addition chart to solve subtraction problems.

©2015 Great Minds. eureka-math.org
G1-M1-TE-BK1-1.3.1-01.2016

EUREKA MATH™

2 – 0	7 – 5
8 – 5	8 – 8
9 – 0	9 – 4

subtraction expression cards

Lesson 38:   Look for and make use of repeated reasoning and structure using the
             addition chart to solve subtraction problems.

©2015 Great Minds. eureka-math.org
G1-M1-TE-BK1-1.3.1-01.2016

Lesson 39

Objective: Analyze the addition chart to create sets of related addition and subtraction facts.

Suggested Lesson Structure

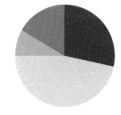

■ Fluency Practice   (17 minutes)

▨ Application Problem   (5 minutes)

▨ Concept Development   (28 minutes)

■ Student Debrief   (10 minutes)

   Total Time   **(60 minutes)**

Fluency Practice (17 minutes)

- Decompose Teen Numbers **K.NBT.1**   (2 minutes)
- Sprint: Decomposing Teen Numbers **K.NBT.1**   (10 minutes)
- Number Bond Roll **1.OA.6**   (5 minutes)

Decompose Teen Numbers (2 minutes)

Note: Reviewing the Kindergarten standard **K.NBT.1** will prepare students for problem-solving strategies presented in Module 2.

Ask questions to decompose teen numbers. Instruct students to answer at a signal.

Use the following suggested questions: What is 14 the Say Ten way? 12 is 10 and…? 17 is 7 and…?

Sprint: Decomposing Teen Numbers (10 minutes)

Materials: (S) Decomposing Teen Numbers Sprint

Note: This activity addresses the core fluency objective for Grade 1 of adding and subtracting within 10.

Number Bond Roll (5 minutes)

Materials: (S) Die (with 6 replaced by 0), personal white board

Note: Reviewing number bonds allows students to build and maintain fluency with addition and subtraction facts within 10.

Assign partners of equal ability. Each student rolls 1 die. Students use the numbers on their own die and their partner's die as the parts of a number bond. Instruct each student to write a number bond, two addition sentences, and two subtraction sentences on their boards. Once completed, the students check each other's work.

Application Problem (5 minutes)

John has 10 pencils. Mark has 9 pencils. Anna has 8 pencils. They each lost two of their pencils. How many do they each have now? Write a number bond and number sentence for each student.

Note: This problem continues to apply subtraction objectives in solving word problems. During the Student Debrief, the relationship between the three embedded problems will be discussed.

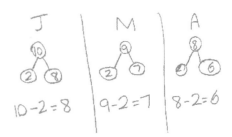

Concept Development (28 minutes)

Materials: (T) Addition chart (Lesson 21 Template) (S) Addition chart (Lesson 21 Template), subtraction expression cards (Lesson 38 Template) per group, personal white board

T: Look at 5 + 2 on the addition chart. (Point to 5 + 2 on the chart.) Who can share a subtraction sentence and an addition sentence that have the same parts and total?

S: 7 – 5 = 2 and 5 + 2 = 7.

T: Let's all write that set on our board. Write the number bond, too.

T/S: (Write 7 – 5 = 2, 5 + 2 = 7, and matching number bond.)

T: There are more addition facts that we can make from this same number bond. What is one of them?

S: 2 + 5 = 7.

T: Let's write that number sentence as well.

S: (Write 2 + 5 = 7.)

T: We can also write a number sentence matching two addition expressions without totals. Turn and talk with your partner to discuss what this number sentence might be. Write it on your board. (Circulate and listen.)

MP.7

S: (Discuss and write 5 + 2 = 2 + 5.)

T: I saw many of you write 5 + 2 = 2 + 5. 5 + 2 is equal to, or the same as, 2 + 5.

T: There are other number sentences that have the same parts and total. Talk with your partner to decide what they could be, and write them on your board. (Circulate and listen.)

S: (Discuss and write 7 – 2 = 5.)

T: See if you can write your number bond in different ways, too. Circle your totals!

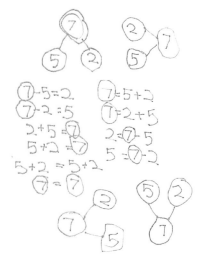

Lesson 39:   Analyze the addition chart to create sets of related addition and
                subtraction facts.

©2015 Great Minds. eureka-math.org
G1-M1-TE-BK1-1.3.1-01.2016

477

T: Look how many facts you can share using your knowledge of *one* fact.

Assign pairs of students different number bonds from which to make as many varied number sentences as they can. Have them make a poster and prepare to share their ideas with peers.

Problem Set (10 minutes)

Students should do their personal best to complete the Problem Set within the allotted 10 minutes. For some classes, it may be appropriate to modify the assignment by specifying which problems they work on first. Some problems do not specify a method for solving. Students solve these problems using the RDW approach used for Application Problems.

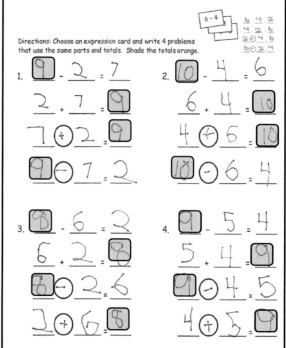

Student Debrief (10 minutes)

Lesson Objective: Analyze the addition chart to create sets of related addition and subtraction facts.

The Student Debrief is intended to invite reflection and active processing of the total lesson experience.

Invite students to review their solutions for the Problem Set. They should check work by comparing answers with a partner before going over answers as a class. Look for misconceptions or misunderstandings that can be addressed in the Debrief. Guide students in a conversation to debrief the Problem Set and process the lesson.

Any combination of the questions below may be used to lead the discussion.

- Hold up a subtraction expression. What number sentences we can make? What number sentence can we make that uses *both* of the addition expressions?

- Look at Problem 1. Write the number sentence that uses both addition expressions below your work.

- How does knowledge of one addition or subtraction fact help you know other facts? Use an example from your Problem Set to explain your thinking.

- Look at your Application Problem. Where are the related addition facts on the addition chart? How are the three number bonds similar? How are they different?

- Have different groups present their work from the Concept Development. Let the others ask them questions about their work.

NOTES ON MULTIPLE MEANS OF ENGAGEMENT:

Adjust Problem Set directions as needed to suit specific learning needs. Some students may need to write a number bond before writing the number sentences.

EUREKA
MATH

Exit Ticket (3 minutes)

After the Student Debrief, instruct students to complete the Exit Ticket. A review of their work will help with assessing students' understanding of the concepts that were presented in today's lesson and planning more effectively for future lessons. The questions may be read aloud to the students.

Lesson 39: Analyze the addition chart to create sets of related addition and subtraction facts.

©2015 Great Minds. eureka-math.org
G1-M1-TE-BK1-1.3.1-01.2016

479

A

Name _____ ._____   Date _____

*Write the missing number for each sentence.

1.	8 and 2 make ☐		16.	11 is 10 and ☐	
2.	9 and 1 make ☐		17.	11 is 1 and ☐	
3.	7 and 3 make ☐		18.	12 is 2 and ☐	
4.	6 and ☐ make 10		19.	11 is ☐ and 1	
5.	4 and ☐ make 10		20.	14 is 10 and ☐	
6.	5 and ☐ make 10		21.	15 is 5 and ☐	
7.	☐ and 5 make 10		22.	18 is 8 and ☐	
8.	13 is 10 and ☐		23.	20 is 10 and ☐	
9.	14 is 10 and ☐		24.	2 more than 10 is ☐	
10.	16 is 10 and ☐		25.	10 more than 2 is ☐	
11.	17 is 10 and ☐		26.	10 is ☐ less than 12	
12.	19 is 10 and ☐		27.	10 is ☐ less than 12	
13.	18 is 10 and ☐		28.	8 less than 18 is ☐	
14.	12 is 10 and ☐		29.	6 less than 16 is ☐	
15.	13 is 10 and ☐		30.	10 less than 20 is ☐	

Lesson 39:   Analyze the addition chart to create sets of related addition and subtraction facts.

EUREKA
MATH™

B

Number Correct:

Name _____   Date _____

*Write the missing number for each sentence.

1.	9 and 1 make ☐		16.	13 is 10 and ☐	
2.	8 and 2 make ☐		17.	13 is 3 and ☐	
3.	6 and 4 make ☐		18.	11 is 1 and ☐	
4.	7 and ☐ make 10		19.	11 is ☐ and 1	
5.	3 and ☐ make 10		20.	15 is ☐ and 10	
6.	4 and ☐ make 10		21.	14 is 4 and ☐	
7.	☐ and 5 make 10		22.	19 is 9 and ☐	
8.	14 is 10 and ☐		23.	20 is 10 and ☐	
9.	13 is 10 and ☐		24.	1 more than 10 is ☐	
10.	17 is 10 and ☐		25.	10 more than 1 is ☐	
11.	16 is 10 and ☐		26.	10 is ☐ less than 11	
12.	15 is 10 and ☐		27.	10 is ☐ less than 14	
13.	19 is 10 and ☐		28.	7 less than 18 is ☐	
14.	11 is 10 and ☐		29.	7 less than 16 is ☐	
15.	12 is 10 and ☐		30.	10 less than 20 is ☐	

Lesson 39:   Analyze the addition chart to create sets of related addition and subtraction facts.

481

Name _____   Date _____

Study the addition chart to solve and write related problems.

1 + 9									
1 + 8	2 + 8								
1 + 7	2 + 7	3 + 7							
1 + 6	2 + 6	3 + 6	4 + 6						
1 + 5	2 + 5	3 + 5	4 + 5	5 + 5					
1 + 4	2 + 4	3 + 4	4 + 4	5 + 4	6 + 4				
1 + 3	2 + 3	3 + 3	4 + 3	5 + 3	6 + 3	7 + 3			
1 + 2	2 + 2	3 + 2	4 + 2	5 + 2	6 + 2	7 + 2	8 + 2		
1 + 1	2 + 1	3 + 1	4 + 1	5 + 1	6 + 1	7 + 1	8 + 1	9 + 1	
1 + 0	2 + 0	3 + 0	4 + 0	5 + 0	6 + 0	7 + 0	8 + 0	9 + 0	10 + 0

Pick a subtraction card.

Find the related addition fact on the chart and shade it in.

Write the subtraction sentence and the shaded addition sentence.

Write the other two related facts.

Continue for at least 4 turns.

Lesson 39:   Analyze the addition chart to create sets of related addition and
               subtraction facts.

©2015 Great Minds. eureka-math.org
G1-M1-TE-BK1-1.3.1-01.2016

Choose an expression card, and write 4 problems that use the same parts and totals. Shade the totals orange.

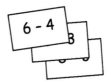

6 . 4 . 2
4 . 2 . 6
2 ⊕ 4 . 6
6 ⊖ 2 . 4

1. _____ - _____ = _____

   _____ + _____ = _____

   _____ ◯ _____ = _____

   _____ ◯ _____ = _____

2. _____ - _____ = _____

   _____ + _____ = _____

   _____ ◯ _____ = _____

   _____ ◯ _____ = _____

3. _____ - _____ = _____

   _____ + _____ = _____

   _____ ◯ _____ = _____

   _____ ◯ _____ = _____

4. _____ - _____ = _____

   _____ + _____ = _____

   _____ ◯ _____ = _____

   _____ ◯ _____ = _____

EUREKA MATH

Lesson 39: Analyze the addition chart to create sets of related addition and subtraction facts.

483

Name _____   Date _____

Write the related number sentences for the number bonds.

1.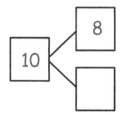

2.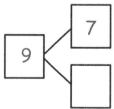

_____ - _____ = _____   _____ - _____ = _____

_____ + _____ = _____   _____ + _____ = _____

_____ ◯ _____ = _____   _____ ◯ _____ = _____

_____ ◯ _____ = _____   _____ ◯ _____ = _____

Lesson 39:   Analyze the addition chart to create sets of related addition and subtraction facts.

EUREKA
MATH™

Name _____   Date _____

Solve the unshaded addition problems below.

1 + 0	1 + 1	1 + 2	1 + 3	1 + 4	1 + 5	1 + 6	1 + 7	1 + 8	1 + 9
2 + 0	2 + 1	2 + 2	2 + 3	2 + 4	2 + 5	2 + 6	2 + 7	2 + 8	
3 + 0	3 + 1	3 + 2	3 + 3	3 + 4	3 + 5	3 + 6	3 + 7		
4 + 0	4 + 1	4 + 2	4 + 3	4 + 4	4 + 5	4 + 6			
5 + 0	5 + 1	5 + 2	5 + 3	5 + 4	5 + 5				
6 + 0	6 + 1	6 + 2	6 + 3	6 + 4					
7 + 0	7 + 1	7 + 2	7 + 3						
8 + 0	8 + 1	8 + 2							
9 + 0	9 + 1								
10 + 0									

4 + 2

Pick an addition fact from the chart. Use the grid to write the two subtraction facts that would have the same number bond. Repeat in order to make a set of subtraction flash cards. To help you practice your addition and subtraction facts even more, make your own number bond flash cards with the templates on the last page.

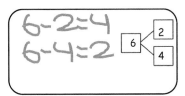

EUREKA
MATH™

Lesson 39:   Analyze the addition chart to create sets of related addition and
                subtraction facts.

485

©2015 Great Minds. eureka-math.org
G1-M1-TE-BK1-1.3.1-01.2016

Lesson 39: Analyze the addition chart to create sets of related addition and subtraction facts.

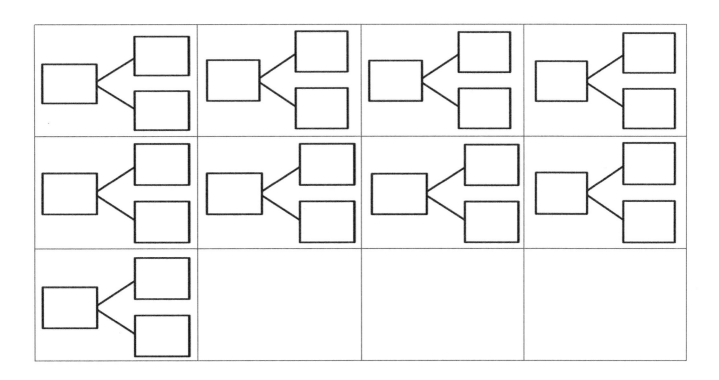

Lesson 39: Analyze the addition chart to create sets of related addition and subtraction facts.

487

©2015 Great Minds. eureka-math.org
G1-M1-TE-BK1-1.3.1-01.2016

Name _____   Date _____

1. There are 9 ducks swimming along in a line. There are 2 grown-up ducks, and the rest are babies. How many of the ducks are babies?

    a. Explain your thinking using pictures, numbers, or words.

    b. Write a number sentence that shows how you solved the problem.

    _____

2. Jennifer says you can use addition to solve subtraction.
    She says to solve $9 - 6 = \boxed{}$, just add $9 + 6$.
    Explain how Jennifer is right **and** wrong using words, pictures, and numbers.

EUREKA
MATH

3. Jeremy is confused about this problem: ☐ = 10 – 8. Be his teacher. Write two addition number sentences that might help him understand and solve it. Explain to Jeremy using words, pictures, or numbers, too.

4. At the park, there are 6 friends playing baseball. Some more friends come. Now, there are 10 friends playing.

   a. How many friends come to play with the first 6 friends? Explain your thinking using a math drawing, numbers, and words.

   b. Write an addition sentence and a subtraction sentence to match the story.

   _____   _____

   c. Write the addition sentence you found when solving the problem, and use the same 3 numbers to write 3 more number sentences:

   _____   _____

   _____   _____

End-of-Module Assessment Task	Topics A–J
Standards Addressed	

Represent and solve problems involving addition and subtraction.

1.OA.1   Use addition and subtraction within 20 to solve word problems involving situations of adding to, taking from, putting together, taking apart, and comparing, with unknowns in all positions, e.g., by using objects, drawings, and equations with a symbol for the unknown number to represent the problem. (See Glossary, Table 1.)

Understand and apply properties of operations and the relationship between addition and subtraction.

1.OA.3   Apply properties of operations as strategies to add and subtract. (Students need not use formal terms for these properties.) *Example: If 8 + 3 = 11 is known, then 3 + 8 = 11 is also known. (Commutative property of addition.) To add 2 + 6 + 4, the second two numbers can be added to make a ten, so 2 + 6 + 4 = 2 + 10 = 12. (Associative property of addition.)*

1.OA.4   Understand subtraction as an unknown-addend problem. *For example, subtract 10 – 8 by finding the number that makes 10 when added to 8.*

Add and subtract within 20.

1.OA.5   Relate counting to addition and subtraction (e.g., by counting on 2 to add 2).

1.OA.6   Add and subtract within 20, demonstrating fluency for addition and subtraction within 10. Use strategies such as counting on; making ten (e.g., 8 + 6 = 8 + 2 + 4 = 10 + 4 = 14); decomposing a number leading to a ten (e.g., 13 – 4 = 13 – 3 – 1 = 10 – 1 = 9); using the relationship between addition and subtraction (e.g., knowing that 8 + 4 = 12, one knows 12 – 8 = 4); and creating equivalent but easier or known sums (e.g., adding 6 + 7 by creating the known equivalent 6 + 6 + 1 = 12 + 1 = 13).

Work with addition and subtraction equations.

1.OA.7   Understand the meaning of the equal sign, and determine if equations involving addition and subtraction are true or false. *For example, which of the following equations are true and which are false? 6 = 6, 7 = 8 – 1, 5 + 2 = 2 + 5, 4 + 1 = 5 + 2.*

1.OA.8   Determine the unknown whole number in an addition or subtraction equation relating three whole numbers. *For example, determine the unknown number that makes the equation true in each of the equations 8 + ? = 11, 5 = ☐ – 3, 6 + 6 = ☐.*

Evaluating Student Learning Outcomes

A Progression Toward Mastery is provided to describe steps that illuminate the gradually increasing understandings that students develop *on their way to proficiency.* In this chart, this progress is presented from left (Step 1) to right (Step 4). The learning goal for students is to achieve Step 4 mastery. These steps are meant to help teachers and students identify and celebrate what the students CAN do now and what they need to work on next.

©2015 Great Minds. eureka-math.org
G1-M1-TE-BK1-1.3.1-01.2016

A Progression Toward Mastery				
Assessment Task Item	STEP 1 Little evidence of reasoning without a correct answer. (1 Point)	STEP 2 Evidence of some reasoning without a correct answer. (2 Points)	STEP 3 Evidence of some reasoning with a correct answer or evidence of solid reasoning with an incorrect answer. (3 Points)	STEP 4 Evidence of solid reasoning with a correct answer. (4 Points)
1 **1.OA.1** **1.OA.4** **1.OA.6** **1.OA.8**	The student demonstrates a limited ability to both explain his thinking and answer accurately.	The student demonstrates a beginning concept of how to solve an *addend unknown* relationship problem using pictures, words, or numbers by attempting to show her thinking but provides an inaccurate answer.	The student correctly solves the *addend unknown* relationship problem and writes a corresponding equation but cannot explain his thinking in pictures, words, or numbers. Or, the student explains her thinking using pictures, words, or numbers, but is unable to write an accurate equation.	The student correctly ■ Solves the *addend unknown* relationship problem and determines that 7 ducks are babies. ■ Explains thinking by drawing a picture, writing numbers or equations, or words. ■ Writes an equation that corresponds with her solution process (addition or subtraction).
2 **1.OA.4** **1.OA.5** **1.OA.7** **1.OA.8**	The student shows little evidence of understanding how addition and subtraction differ or is unable to complete the task.	The student shows evidence of beginning to understand how addition and subtraction differ through his explanation but demonstrates incomplete reasoning or an incorrect answer.	The student identifies that Jennifer is incorrect but cannot fully support the claim or explain his thinking clearly.	The student correctly identifies that Jennifer is correct, that addition can be used to solve a subtraction problem, and that she is incorrect in adding 9 and 6 to solve 9 − 6. The student shows her thinking using words, pictures, or numbers.

©2015 Great Minds. eureka-math.org
G1-M1-TE-BK1-1.3.1-01.2016

A Progression Toward Mastery

3 1.OA.5 1.OA.4 1.OA.7 1.OA.8	The student demonstrates little to no understanding of the concept of the connection between addition and subtraction and is unable to explain her thinking.	The student demonstrates a beginning understanding of the connection between addition and subtraction but does not answer accurately.	The student correctly writes two accurate equations using 8, 2, and 10 but is unable to explain her thinking. Or, the student is able to explain her thinking, somehow citing the connection between addition and subtraction, but is unable to write two accurate equations.	The student correctly ■ Writes two accurate addition equations using 8, 2, and 10. ■ Explains her thinking using pictures, numbers, or words, and cites the connection between addition and subtraction in her explanation.
4 1.OA.1 1.OA.3 1.OA.4 1.OA.6 1.OA.7 1.OA.8 1.OA.5	The student shows very little understanding of how to solve the *add to with change unknown* problem and cannot write corresponding equations.	The student shows a beginning understanding of how to solve the *add to with change unknown* problem, but lacks reasoning or equation writing skills.	The student correctly answers the *add to with change unknown* problem (4 friends came to play), writes accurate addition and subtraction equations, including those that demonstrate an understanding of the commutative property, but is unable to explain his thinking. Or, the student writes addition and subtraction equations correctly and clearly explains his thinking, but does not answer accurately (something other than 4 friends came to play). Or, the student solves the problem (4 friends came to play) and explains thinking clearly, but does not write all addition and subtraction sentences accurately.	The student clearly ■ Solves the *add to with change unknown* problem, determines that 4 friends came to play, and explains his thinking. ■ Writes addition and subtraction equations which correspond to the problem. ■ Applies the commutative property and knowledge of the equal sign to write three additional equations ($10 = 6 + 4$; $4 + 6 = 10$; $10 - 4 = 6$; etc.).

Name __Maria__   Date _____

1. There are 9 ducks swimming along in a line. There are 2 grown-up ducks, and the rest are babies. How many of the ducks are babies?

   a. Explain your thinking using pictures, numbers or words.

   Grown ups   Babies $2 + \boxed{7} = 9$

   b. Write a number sentence that shows how you solved the problem.

   $2 + \boxed{7} = 9$ $2 + \square = 9$
         B

2. Jennifer says you can use addition to solve subtraction.

   She says to solve $9 - 6 = \boxed{}$, just add $9 + 6$.

   Explain how Jennifer is right **and** wrong using words, pictures, and numbers.

   $6 + \underline{} = 9$
   $9 - 6 = 3$
   rite

   $9 + 6$ is not 3
   rong
   $6 + \underline{} = 9$

3. Jeremy is confused about this problem: ___ = 10 – 8. Be his teacher. Write two addition number sentences that might help him understand and solve it. Explain to Jeremy using words, pictures, or numbers, too.

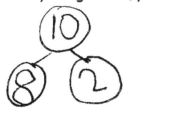

10 – 8 = ___ is the same.

8 + [2] = 10

[2] + 8 = 10

4. At the park, there are 6 friends playing baseball. Some more friends come. Now, there are 10 friends playing.

   a. How many friends come to play with the first 6 friends? Explain your thinking using a math drawing, numbers, and words.

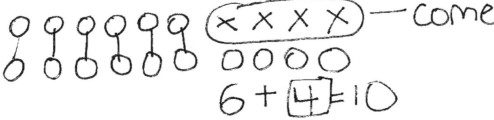

— come

6 + [4] = 10

   b. Write an addition sentence and a subtraction sentence to match the story.

   6 + [4] = 10   10 – 6 = [4]

   c. Write the addition sentence you found when solving the problem, and use the same 3 numbers to write 3 more number sentences:

   6 + 4 = 10   10 = 6 + 4

   4 + 6 = 10   10 = 4 – 6

EUREKA MATH

Answer Key

Eureka Math
Grade 1
Module 1

Special thanks go to the Gordon A. Cain Center and to the Department of Mathematics at Louisiana State University for their support in the development of *Eureka Math*.

For a free *Eureka Math* Teacher
Resource Pack, Parent Tip
Sheets, and more please
visit www.Eureka.tools

Published by the non-profit Great Minds

Copyright © 2015 Great Minds. No part of this work may be reproduced, sold, or commercialized, in whole or in part, without written permission from Great Minds. Non-commercial use is licensed pursuant to a Creative Commons Attribution-NonCommercial-ShareAlike 4.0 license; for more information, go to http://greatminds.net/maps/math/copyright. "Great Minds" and "Eureka Math" are registered trademarks of Great Minds.

Printed in the U.S.A.
This book may be purchased from the publisher at eureka-math.org
10 9 8 7 6 5 4 3 2
ISBN 978-1-63255-348-5

Answer Key

GRADE 1 • MODULE 1

Sums and Differences to 10

©2015 Great Minds. eureka-math.org
G1-M1-TE-BK1-1.3.1-01.2016

Lesson 1

Sprint

Side A

1.	2	11.	5	21.	9
2.	3	12.	4	22.	10
3.	4	13.	6	23.	9
4.	3	14.	8	24.	8
5.	1	15.	7	25.	10
6.	4	16.	9	26.	7
7.	5	17.	8	27.	10
8.	4	18.	10	28.	9
9.	6	19.	7	29.	8
10.	7	20.	6	30.	10

Side B

1.	1	11.	8	21.	9
2.	2	12.	6	22.	10
3.	1	13.	5	23.	10
4.	4	14.	7	24.	10
5.	3	15.	6	25.	7
6.	5	16.	8	26.	8
7.	4	17.	9	27.	10
8.	5	18.	7	28.	9
9.	7	19.	8	29.	9
10.	6	20.	10	30.	9

EUREKA
MATH™

Problem Set

1. Group of 5 circled
    8, 3
2. Group of 5 circled
    6, 1
3. Group of 5 circled
    7, 2
4. Group of 5 circled
    9, 4

5. 5, 3
6. 5, 1
7. 5, 1, 6
8. 5, 2, 7
9. 5, 5, 10
10. 5, 3, 8
11. 5, 4, 9
12. 5, 0, 5

Exit Ticket

1. 9, 5, 4
2. 7, 5, 2

Homework

1. Group of 5 circled
    9, 4
2. Group of 5 circled
    7, 2
3. Group of 5 circled
    10, 5
4. Group of 5 circled
    5, 5, 0
5. 5, 3, 8
6. 5, 1, 6
7. 5, 2, 7
8. 5, 5, 10

9. 5, 3, 8
10. 1, 5, 6
11. 5, 2, 7
12. 5, 5, 10
13. Group of 5 circled
    8, 5, 3
14. Group of 5 circled
    6, 5, 1
15. Group of 5 circled
    9, 5, 4
16. Group of 5 circled
    7, 5, 2

Module 1:   Sums and Differences to 10

499

©2015 Great Minds. eureka-math.org
G1-M1-TE-BK1-1.3.1-01.2016

Lesson 2

Number Bond Dash

1. 1
2. 0
3. 1
4. 2
5. 1
6. 2
7. 3
8. 1
9. 4
10. 3
11. 5

12. 4
13. 3
14. 2
15. 1
16. 0
17. 1
18. 2
19. 3
20. 4
21. 0
22. 5

23. 4
24. 2
25. 3

Problem Set

1. 6, parts will vary.
2. 6, parts will vary.
3. 7, parts will vary.
4. 7, parts will vary.
5. 8, parts will vary.

6. 8, parts will vary.
7. 9, parts will vary.
8. 9, parts will vary.
9. 9, parts will vary; 9, parts will vary.

Exit Ticket

1. 6, parts will vary.
2. 7, parts will vary.
3. 7, parts will vary.
4. 10, parts will vary.

©2015 Great Minds. eureka-math.org
G1-M1-TE-BK1-1.3.1-01.2016

EUREKA MATH

Homework

1. 6, parts will vary.

2. 7, parts will vary.

3. 9, parts will vary.

4. 8, parts will vary.

5. 7, parts will vary.

6. 6, parts will vary.

7. 8, parts will vary.

8. 8, parts will vary.

9. 6, parts will vary; 6, parts will vary.

10. 7, parts will vary; 7, parts will vary.

Lesson 3

Number Bond Dash

1. 1
2. 0
3. 1
4. 2
5. 1
6. 2
7. 3
8. 1
9. 4
10. 3
11. 5

12. 4
13. 3
14. 2
15. 1
16. 0
17. 1
18. 2
19. 3
20. 4
21. 0
22. 5

23. 4
24. 2
25. 3

Problem Set

1. 1 more drawn; 8; 8
2. 1 more drawn; 10; 10
3. 1 more drawn; 7; 7;
   7, 6, 1
4. 1 more drawn; 6; 6;
   5, 1, 6

5. 1 more drawn; 9; 9
6. 1 more drawn; 8; 8
7. 1 more drawn; 7; 7
8. 1 more drawn; 6; 6
9. 8, 7, 1; 8; 7, 8

Exit Ticket

1. 1 more drawn; 10; 10; 10, 9, 1
2. 1 more drawn; 7; 6, 7; 7, 6, 1

Module 1: Sums and Differences to 10

EUREKA
MATH™

Homework

1. 1 more drawn; 10; 10;
   10, 9, 1

2. 1 more drawn; 8; 8;
   8, 7, 1

3. 1 more drawn; 6; 6;
   6, 5, 1

4. 1 more drawn; 9; 8, 9;
   9, 8, 1

5. 6; 6; 6, 5, 1

6. 9; 8, 9; 8, 1, 9

Lesson 4

Sprint

Side A

1.	4	11.	7	21.	8
2.	3	12.	8	22.	9
3.	4	13.	8	23.	10
4.	5	14.	9	24.	11
5.	6	15.	9	25.	11
6.	7	16.	10	26.	9
7.	6	17.	10	27.	9
8.	6	18.	8	28.	10
9.	8	19.	8	29.	10
10.	7	20.	9	30.	13

Side B

1.	3	11.	6	21.	11
2.	2	12.	8	22.	9
3.	3	13.	8	23.	10
4.	4	14.	7	24.	11
5.	5	15.	7	25.	10
6.	6	16.	9	26.	10
7.	5	17.	9	27.	9
8.	5	18.	10	28.	9
9.	6	19.	10	29.	10
10.	6	20.	11	30.	14

EUREKA MATH™

Problem Set

Answers will vary.

Exit Ticket

Answers will vary.

Homework

Answers will vary.

Lesson 5

Number Bond Dash

1.	0	12.	2	23.	2
2.	1	13.	4	24.	4
3.	2	14.	3	25.	3
4.	1	15.	4		
5.	0	16.	1		
6.	1	17.	5		
7.	2	18.	6		
8.	1	19.	5		
9.	2	20.	6		
10.	3	21.	5		
11.	3	22.	1		

Problem Set

Answers will vary.

Exit Ticket

Answers will vary.

Homework

1. a. Answer provided
   b. 2 matched to 5;
      2, 5, 7
   c. 3 matched to 4;
      7, 4, 3

2. Answers will vary.
3. 7; 7, 0; 0, 7
4. First, third, fifth, and sixth dominoes colored
5. 7, 7; 7, 1;
   7, 3; 7, 2

EUREKA
MATH™

Lesson 6

Number Bond Dash

1. 1
2. 0
3. 1
4. 2
5. 1
6. 0
7. 1
8. 2
9. 3
10. 4
11. 3

12. 4
13. 5
14. 2
15. 5
16. 1
17. 6
18. 7
19. 5
20. 2
21. 6
22. 2

23. 4
24. 7
25. 1

Problem Set

1. Group of 6 circled;
    2; 6, 2; 2, 6
2. Group of 5 circled;
    5, 3; 5, 3; 3, 5
3. Group of 4 circled; 8, 4, 4; 4, 4; 4, 4

4. a. Answer provided
    b. 1
    c. 2
    d. 5
    e. 4, 4
5. 8, 3, 5; group of 3 and group of 5 objects drawn
6. 8, 8, 0; group of 8 objects drawn

Exit Ticket

1. 3, 8; 5, 3, 8; 3, 5, 8
2. 6, 2, 8; 8, 6, 2; 8, 2, 6

Module 1:   Sums and Differences to 10

507

©2015 Great Minds. eureka-math.org
G1-M1-TE-BK1-1.3.1-01.2016

Homework

1. a. Answer provided

    b. 2 matched to 6;

        2, 6, 8

    c. 1 matched to 7;

        8, 1, 7

2. 5; answers will vary.

3. 0; 0, 8, 8; 8, 8, 0

4. a. Answer provided

    b. 7

    c. 2

    d. 5

    e. 4, 4

5. 8, 2, 6; group of 2 and group of 6 objects drawn

6. 8, 0, 8; group of 8 objects drawn

EUREKA
MATH™

Lesson 7

Number Bond Dash

1.	0	12.	3	23.	6
2.	1	13.	5	24.	8
3.	2	14.	4	25.	7
4.	1	15.	5		
5.	2	16.	2		
6.	3	17.	6		
7.	2	18.	2		
8.	3	19.	3		
9.	4	20.	5		
10.	5	21.	4		
11.	4	22.	7		

Problem Set

1. Group of 7 circled;

   2; 7, 2; 2, 7

2. Group of 4 circled;

   9, 4, 5; 4, 5; 5, 4

3. Group of 3 circled;

   9, 3, 6; 3, 6; 6, 3

4. a. Answer provided

   b. 3

   c. 8

   d. 0

   e. 5

5. a. 7

   b. 9, 6, 3

   c. 9, 1, 8

   d. 9, 9, 0

   e. 9, 4, 5; $4 + 5 = 9$; $5 + 4 = 9$

Exit Ticket

1. Pairs circled: 6 and 3; 8 and 1; 7 and 2; 5 and 4

2. a. 9, 5; 4, 5

    b. Answers will vary.

Homework

Answers will vary.

©2015 Great Minds. eureka-math.org
G1-M1-TE-BK1-1.3.1-01.2016

EUREKA MATH

Lesson 8

Number Bond Dash

1. 1
2. 2
3. 1
4. 2
5. 0
6. 3
7. 2
8. 3
9. 4
10. 5
11. 1

12. 8
13. 2
14. 7
15. 3
16. 4
17. 3
18. 2
19. 7
20. 6
21. 4
22. 8

23. 7
24. 9
25. 7

Problem Set

1. Answers will vary.
2. a. Answer provided
    b. 9 matched to 1; 9, 1, 10
    c. 8 matched to 2; 10, 2, 8
    d. 7 matched to 3; 7, 3, 10
    e. 6 matched to 4; 10, 6, 4
    f. 5 matched to 5; 5, 5, 10
3. Number bond showing 5 and 5 is 10 colored; 5, 5, 10; 10, 5, 5

Exit Ticket

Partners colored: 7 and 3; 4 and 6; 8 and 2; 1 and 9

©2015 Great Minds. eureka-math.org
G1-M1-TE-BK1-1.3.1-01.2016

Homework

1. a. 5

    b. 4

    c. 3

    d. 2

    e. 1

2. 3, 7, 10; 7, 3, 10; 10, 3, 7; 10, 7, 3

EUREKA
MATH™

Lesson 9

Number Bond Dash

1. 0
2. 1
3. 2
4. 1
5. 0
6. 1
7. 2
8. 3
9. 2
10. 3
11. 4

12. 3
13. 4
14. 5
15. 6
16. 4
17. 6
18. 7
19. 6
20. 7
21. 10
22. 9

23. 8
24. 6
25. 8

Problem Set

1. 5, 2, 7; 5, 2, 7; 5, 2, 7
2. 6, 1, 7; 6, 1, 7; 6, 1, 7

3. 4, 3, 7; 4, 3, 7; 4, 3, 7
4. 5, 4, 9; 5, 4, 9; 5, 4, 9

Exit Ticket

Group of 3 and group of 5 objects drawn; 3, 5, 8; 8

Homework

1. Answers will vary; 8
2. Answers will vary; 7
3. Group of 4 and group of 3 objects drawn; 4, 3, 7; 7
4. Group of 3 and group of 6 objects drawn; 9, 3, 6; 9

EUREKA
MATH™

Module 1:   Sums and Differences to 10

513

©2015 Great Minds. eureka-math.org
G1-M1-TE-BK1-1.3.1-01.2016

Lesson 10

Fluency Activity

Answers will vary.

Problem Set

1. 4, 3, 7; 7, 4, 3
2. 5, 5, 10; 10, 5, 5
3. 5, 2, 7; 7, 5, 2
4. a. Matched to 5 and 3

   b. Matched to 4 and 3

   c. Matched to 5 and 2

   d. Matched to 2 and 2

Exit Ticket

1. Group of 3 and group of 4 objects drawn; 3, 4, 7; 7
2. Second set of numeral tiles (3 and 4) circled

Homework

1. 3, 5, 8; 3 dots drawn
2. 8, 4, 4; 4 dots drawn
3. Group of 4 and group of 5 objects drawn; 9; 4, 5, 9; 5, 4, 9
4. Group of 3 and group of 5 objects drawn; 8; 3, 5, 8; 3, 5, 8

EUREKA
MATH™

Lesson 11

Problem Set

1. Group of 2 flowers drawn; 2; 5, 3, 2; 5, 2, 3

2. Group of 6 square cookies drawn; 6; 8, 2, 6

3. Line separating 2 trucks and 3 trucks drawn; 3; 3; 5, 2, 3

4. Line separating 7 fish and 2 fish drawn; 2; 7, 2, 9; 7, 2, 9

Exit Ticket

Group of 3 objects drawn; 3; 5, 3, 8

Homework

1. a. 5; 5 dots drawn on second card

    b. 3; 3 dots drawn on second card

    c. 2; 2 dots drawn on second card

    d. 0; no dots drawn on first card

2. a. 5; matched to $3 + ? = 8$

    b. 3; matched to $6 + ? = 9$

©2015 Great Minds. eureka-math.org
G1-M1-TE-BK1-1.3.1-01.2016

Lesson 12

Problem Set

1. 2

2. 4

3. 6

4. 6, 2, 4; 4

5. 3, 7, 10; 7

Exit Ticket

Group of 5 and group of 2 objects drawn; 5, 2, 7; 2

Homework

1. 2; 2 dots card shown

2. 6; 6 dots card shown

3. 3; 3 dots card shown

4. Numeral 4 and 3 dots cards shown; 4, 3, 7; 3

5. Numeral 1 and 6 dots cards shown; 1, 6, 7; 6

6. Numeral 6 and 3 dots cards shown; 6, 3, 9; 3

EUREKA
MATH™

Lesson 13

Problem Set

1. 8; answers will vary; 8, 6, 2

2. 10; answers will vary; 10, 5, 5

3. 2; answers will vary; 7, 5, 2

4. 4; answers will vary; 10, 6, 4

Exit Ticket

1. Answers will vary.

2. 5; answers will vary.

Homework

1. Answers will vary; 5, 2, 7

2. Answers will vary; 9, 6, 3

3. 2; Answers will vary; 7, 2, 9

©2015 Great Minds. eureka-math.org
G1-M1-TE-BK1-1.3.1-01.2016

Lesson 14

Problem Set

1. 6, 1, 7; 7
2. 7, 5, 2; 7
3. 8, 5, 3; 8
4. a. 7
   b. 9
   c. 9
   d. 8

5. a. 10
   b. 5
   c. 7
   d. 9

Exit Ticket

1. 8; 8
2. a. 10
   b. 10

Homework

a. 6
b. 7; 5, 6, 7
c. 9; 7, 8, 9
d. 9; 6, 7, 8, 9
e. Answers will vary.

EUREKA MATH

©2015 Great Minds. eureka-math.org
G1-M1-TE-BK1-1.3.1-01.2016

Lesson 15

Sprint

Side A

1.	2	11.	7	21.	8
2.	3	12.	10	22.	7
3.	4	13.	9	23.	7
4.	5	14.	8	24.	8
5.	3	15.	10	25.	9
6.	4	16.	7	26.	10
7.	5	17.	8	27.	10
8.	3	18.	10	28.	8
9.	4	19.	9	29.	9
10.	5	20.	10	30.	9

Side B

1.	2	11.	3	21.	9
2.	4	12.	3	22.	8
3.	5	13.	4	23.	8
4.	4	14.	6	24.	7
5.	3	15.	8	25.	9
6.	4	16.	6	26.	8
7.	5	17.	5	27.	8
8.	5	18.	7	28.	9
9.	4	19.	9	29.	10
10.	6	20.	10	30.	11

Module 1:   Sums and Differences to 10

519

©2015 Great Minds. eureka-math.org
G1-M1-TE-BK1-1.3.1-01.2016

Problem Set

1. a. 5, 1, 6; 6

   b. 5, 2, 7; 7

   c. 7, 4, 3; 7

2. a. 5

   b. 7

   c. 8

   d. 8

   e. 8

   f. 9

   g. 10

   h. 7

   i. 9

   j. 10

   k. 6

   l. 7

   m. 8

   n. 10

Exit Ticket

Answers will vary; 6, 3, 9; 9

Homework

1. 8

2. 8; answers will vary.

3. 10

4. 10

5. 9

6. 9; answers will vary.

EUREKA
MATH™

©2015 Great Minds. eureka-math.org
G1-M1-TE-BK1-1.3.1-01.2016

Lesson 16

Problem Set

1. 2 objects drawn; 2; 2

2. 2

3. 2

4. 2

5. a. 1; answers will vary.

    b. 3; answers will vary.

    c. 3; answers will vary.

    d. 2; answers will vary.

    e. 1; answers will vary.

    f. 2; answers will vary.

    g. 2; answers will vary.

    h. 3; answers will vary.

Exit Ticket

    a. 2; answers will vary.

    b. 3; answers will vary.

Homework

1. Group of 2 objects drawn; 2

2. Group of 2 objects drawn; 2

3. 8, 9, 10; 3

Lesson 17

Problem Set

1. 3, 4, equal sign, 2, 5

2. 4, 4, equal sign, 6, 2

3. 5, 4, equal sign, 6, 3

4. 5, 3, equal sign, 6, 2

5. a. $4 + 3$

   b. $0 + 9$

   c. $5 + 5$

   d. $4 + 4$

   e. $6 + 4$

   f. $3 + 3$

   g. $5 + 5 = 6 + 4$

6. a. $10 + 0$

   b. $5 + 2$

   c. $3 + 6$

   d. $6 + 2$

   e. $1 + 7$

   f. $1 + 0$

   g. $6 + 2 = 1 + 7$

Exit Ticket

1. 5 objects separated into 2 groups drawn in the empty basket; answers will vary.

2. Second and third domino shaded; $4 + 4 = 2 + 6$

Homework

1. a. Matched to 0 and 9; $6 + 3 = 0 + 9$

   b. Matched to 5 and 3; $4 + 4 = 5 + 3$

   c. Matched to 5 and 5; $6 + 4 = 5 + 5$

2. a. $5 + 2 = 4 + 3$

   b. $8 + 2 = 7 + 3$

EUREKA
MATH

Lesson 18

Problem Set

1. a. 5 + 1 and 3 + 3 colored; 5 + 1 = 3 + 3

    b. 5 + 3 and 4 + 4 colored; 5 + 3 = 4 + 4

2. a. ✓

    b. X; answers will vary.

    c. ✓

    d. ✓

    e. X; answers will vary.

    f. ✓

    g. ✓

    h. X; answers will vary.

3. a. Answers will vary.

    b. Answers will vary.

    c. Answers will vary.

    d. Answers will vary.

Exit Ticket

a. Answer provided; answers will vary.

b. Answers will vary.

Homework

1. Group of 3 objects drawn in the second box;

    5 + 4 = 6 + 3

2. a. Circled

    b. Answers will vary.

    c. Circled

    d. Circled

    e. Answers will vary.

    f. Circled

    g. Answers will vary.

    h. Circled

    i. Circled

3. a. 4

    b. 0

    c. 3

    d. 1

    e. 1

    f. 6

Lesson 19

Sprint

Side A

1.	2	11.	7	21.	6
2.	3	12.	8	22.	7
3.	4	13.	7	23.	7
4.	5	14.	8	24.	8
5.	4	15.	9	25.	9
6.	5	16.	7	26.	9
7.	4	17.	6	27.	9
8.	3	18.	7	28.	10
9.	4	19.	7	29.	10
10.	5	20.	6	30.	9

Side B

1.	3	11.	8	21.	4
2.	2	12.	7	22.	7
3.	3	13.	8	23.	7
4.	4	14.	9	24.	8
5.	5	15.	8	25.	8
6.	4	16.	7	26.	9
7.	5	17.	6	27.	10
8.	4	18.	5	28.	9
9.	6	19.	4	29.	8
10.	7	20.	3	30.	9

EUREKA
MATH™

Problem Set

1. a. 5, 3, 2

   Answers will vary.

   b. 8, 5, 3

   Answers will vary.

   c. 10, 2, 8

   Answers will vary.

2. 3, 2, =, 2, 3

3. 3, 4, = , 4, 3

4. Group of 1 and group of 6 objects drawn on second plate; 6, 1, =

5. Answers will vary.

Exit Ticket

Sequence of number sentences may vary: $5 + 4 = 9$; $9 = 5 + 4$; $4 + 5 = 9$; $9 = 4 + 5$

Homework

1. 7, 5, 2; 5, 2, 7; 2, 5, 7

2. a. 5, 3, 8; 3, 5, 8

   b. 8, 6, 2; 8, 2, 6

   c. 10; 8, 2, 10; 2, 8, 10

   d. 2; 2, 5, 7; 5, 2, 7

   e. 7; 10, 7, 3; 10, 3, 7

   f. 6; 6, 3, 9; 3, 6, 9

©2015 Great Minds. eureka-math.org
G1-M1-TE-BK1-1.3.1-01.2016

Lesson 20

Problem Set

1. Group of 7 skateboards circled; 7, 2, 9
2. 5 colored; 7; 5, 2, 7
3. 4 colored; 7; 4, 3, 7
4. 6 colored: 10; 6, 4, 10
5. 7 colored; 9; 7, 9; 7, 2, 9

6. 6 colored; 9; 6, 9; 6, 3, 9
7. 5 circled; 6
8. 6 circled; 8
9. 4 circled; 7
10. 6 circled; 9

Exit Ticket

a. 5 circled; 8; 5, 3, 8
b. 7 circled; 9; 7, 2, 9

Homework

1. Group of 3 pencils colored; 5, 3; 3, 2, 5
2. 7, 2, 9; bag of 7 food items colored; 9, 2
3. 6 colored; 7; 6, 1, 7
4. 4 colored; 6; 4, 2, 6
5. 5 colored; 8; 5, 3, 8
6. 4 colored; 8; 4, 4, 8
7. 5 colored; 9; 5, 4, 9

Module 1:   Sums and Differences to 10

EUREKA
MATH

©2015 Great Minds. eureka-math.org
G1-M1-TE-BK1-1.3.1-01.2016

Lesson 21

Problem Set

1. 3 + 3 = 6; colored red
2. 4 + 4 = 8; colored red
3. 3 + 4 = 7; colored blue
4. 5 + 4 = 9; colored blue
5. 9; 2 groups of 4 circled; 4 + 4 = 8
6. 7; 2 groups of 3 circled; 3 + 3 = 6
7. a. 0; 1
    b. 4; 5
    c. 6; 7
    d. 8; 9
    e. 3; 4
    f. 5; 5

8. 11; 5 + 5 = 10
9. Acceptable answers: 4 + 4 = 8; 8 = 4 + 4 ;
    4 + 5 = 9; 5 + 4 = 9; 9 = 4 + 5; 9 = 5 + 4

Exit Ticket

3 + 3 = 6; 3 + 4 = 7

4 + 4 = 8; 4 + 5 = 9

5 + 5 = 10; 5 + 6 = 11

Homework

1. a. 4; 4 + 4 = 8

   b. 3; 3 + 3 = 6

   c. 5; 5 + 5 = 10

2. a. 1 + 1 = 2

   b. 2, 2 + 2 = 4

   c. 3, 3; 3 + 3 = 6

   d. 4; 4 + 4 = 8

   e. 5, 5; 5 + 5 = 10

3. a. 6

   b. 5

   c. 1

   d. 2

   e. 4

4. a. 1 matched to 2

   b. 4 matched to 5

   c. 3 matched to 4

   d. 2 matched to 3

5. a. 5; 2 + 2 = 4

   b. 4; 3 + 3 = 6

   c. 5; 4 + 4 = 8

Module 1:   Sums and Differences to 10

EUREKA
MATH™

Lesson 22

Problem Set

1. First column: red; 1, 2, 3, 4, 5, 6, 7, 8, 9, 10

2. Second column: orange; 2, 3, 4, 5, 6, 7, 8, 9, 10

    First row: orange; 1, 2, 3, 4, 5, 6, 7, 8, 9, 10

3. Third column: yellow; 3, 4, 5, 6, 7, 8, 9, 10

    Second row: yellow; 2, 3, 4, 5, 6, 7, 8, 9, 10

4. Fourth column: green; 4, 5, 6, 7, 8, 9, 10

    Third row: green; 3, 4, 5, 6, 7, 8, 9, 10

5. Remaining columns and rows: blue; 8, 9, 10; 9, 10; 10

Exit Ticket

1. First column: 0

2. Second column: 1

3. Fourth column: 3

4. Fifth column: 4

5. Sixth column: 4

6. Seventh column: 4

Homework

1. a. 8; blue
    b. 1; blue
    c. 4; blue
    d. 8; yellow
    e. 2; green
    f. 3; yellow
    g. 9; yellow
    h. 2; green
    i. 3; blue
    j. 1; blue
    k. 3; blue
    l. 8; green

    m. 3; yellow
    n. 1; blue
    o. 5; green
    p. 6; blue
    q. 4; green
    r. 2; green
    s. 5; blue
    t. 9; green
    u. 1; blue
    v. 10; blue
    w. 10; yellow
    x. 2; blue

©2015 Great Minds. eureka-math.org
G1-M1-TE-BK1-1.3.1-01.2016

Lesson 23

Problem Set

Totals of 10	Totals of 9	Totals of 8	Totals of 7
0 + 10 = 10	0 + 9 = 9	0 + 8 = 8	0 + 7 = 7
1 + 9 = 10	1 + 8 = 9	1 + 7 = 8	1 + 6 = 7
2 + 8 = 10	2 + 7 = 9	2 + 6 = 8	2 + 5 = 7
3 + 7 = 10	3 + 6 = 9	3 + 5 = 8	3 + 4 = 7
4 + 6 = 10	4 + 5 = 9	4 + 4 = 8	
5 + 5 = 10			
Answers will vary; order may be reversed	Answers will vary; order may be reversed	Answers will vary; order may be reversed	Answers will vary; order may be reversed

Exit Ticket

1. Boxes circled:

   10 + 0; 9 + 1; 8 + 2; 7 + 3; 6 + 4; 5 + 5; 4 + 6; 3 + 7; 2 + 8; 1 + 9

2. Boxes "x"ed:

   8 + 0; 7 + 1; 6 + 2; 5 + 3; 4 + 4; 3 + 5; 2 + 6; 1 + 7

Homework

1. 3; 4; 5; 4; 2 + 3, 5; 6
2. 7; 8; 8 + 1, 9; 10; 8; 7 + 2, 9; 10
3. 8; 9; 10; 9; 5 + 5, 10; 4 + 6, 10
4. 6; 3 + 4, 7; 2 + 5, 7; 8; 8; 3 + 6, 9

EUREKA MATH™

Lesson 24

Problem Set

1. Answers will vary.
2. Answers will vary.
3. Answers will vary.
4. Answers will vary.
5. Answers will vary.
6. Answers will vary.

Exit Ticket

a. 7 ; green

b. 9; green

c. 5; brown or green

d. 6; red

e. 6; blue

f. 1; red or blue

g. 8; red

h. 10; green

i. 7; brown

j. 9; brown

k. 9; blue

l. 5; red

Challenge: $2 + 3 = 5$; $1 + 1 = 2$

EUREKA
MATH™

©2015 Great Minds. eureka-math.org
G1-M1-TE-BK1-1.3.1-01.2016

Homework

1. 6; placed in +1 column
2. 6; placed in doubles column
3. 8; placed in doubles column
4. 9; placed in doubles +1 column and mentally Visualized 5-groups column
5. 8; placed in +2 column
6. 8; placed in +1 column

7. 10; placed in +2 column
8. 9; placed in 1+ column
9. 5; placed in doubles +1 column and +2 column
10. 4; placed in doubles column and +2 column
11. 7; placed in doubles +1 column
12. 7; placed in mentally visualized 5-groups column and +2 column

Answers will vary.

1	2	3	4	5	6	7	8	9	10
2	3	4	5	6	7	8	9	10	
3	4	5	6	7	8	9	10		
4	5	6	7	8	9	10			
5	6	7	8	9	10				
6	7	8	9	10					
7	8	9	10						
8	9	10							
9	10								
10									

EUREKA
MATH™

Lesson 25

Problem Set

1. 5, 2, 3; 3; 3; 3

2. 9, 7, 2; 7, 2; 7, 2; 2

3. 6, 2, 4; 2, 4; 2, 4; 4

4. 7, 3, 4; 3, 4; 3, 4; 4

Exit Ticket

6, 3, 9; 6, 3, 9; 9, 6, 3; numeral 3 colored; 3

Homework

1. Line separating 6 and 2 drawn; 8, 6, 2; 6, 2, 8; 8, 6, 2; 2

2. Line separating 4 and 5 drawn; 9, 4, 5; 4, 5, 9; 9, 4, 5; 5

3. Groups of 2 objects and 4 objects drawn; 6, 2, 4; 2, 4, 6; 6, 2, 4; 4

4. Groups of 3 objects and 6 objects drawn; 9, 3, 6; 3, 6, 9; 9, 3, 6; 6

5. Groups of 2 objects and 8 objects drawn; 10, 2, 8; 2, 8, 10; 10, 2, 8; 8

©2015 Great Minds. eureka-math.org
G1-M1-TE-BK1-1.3.1-01.2016

Lesson 26

Problem Set

1. 2; 2
2. 3; 3
3. 3; 3
4. 6; 6
5. 1; 1

6. 4; 4
7. 2; 2
8. 4; 4
9. 6; 6

Exit Ticket

   a. 2; 5 + 2 = 7

   b. 7; 2 + 7 = 9

   c. 7; 3 + 7 = 10

Homework

1. 2; 2
2.   a. 2; 2

    b. 3; 3

    c. 6; 2 + 6 = 8

    d. 3; 6 + 3 = 9

3.   a. 2; 6 = 4 + 2

    b. 4; 4 + 5 = 9

    c. 4; 6 + 4 = 10

    d. 3; 10 = 7 + 3

4.   a. 5; 8 − 3 = 5; 3 + 5 = 8

      Number sentences may vary.

    b. 6; 9 - 6 = 3; 3 + 6 = 9

      Number sentences may vary.

EUREKA MATH

©2015 Great Minds. eureka-math.org
G1-M1-TE-BK1-1.3.1-01.2016

Lesson 27

Problem Set

1. 1; 3, 1, 4; rectangle drawn around 1
2. 4; 2, 4, 6; rectangle drawn around 4
3. 4; 3, 4, 7; rectangle drawn around 4
4. 3; 6 + 3 = 9; rectangle drawn around 3
5. 8; 2 + 8 = 10; rectangle drawn around 8
6. 4; 4
7. 4; 4
8. 9
9. 7

10. a. 1; count on
    b. 8; count back
    c. 3; count on
    d. 2; count on
    e. 3; count on
    f. 3; answers will vary.

Exit Ticket

1; count on; drawings will vary.

Homework

1. a. 7; 7 + 3 = 10; 10 − 7 = 3
      (Number sentences may vary.)
   b. 4; 4 + 6 = 10; 10 − 6 = 4
      (Number sentences may vary.)

2. a. 2; count on
   b. 6; count back
   c. 2; count on

3. a. 2; count on; curved lines from 5 to 6 and 6 to 7 drawn; on
   b. 8; count back; curved line from 9 to 8 drawn; back
   c. 2; count on; answers will vary.

©2015 Great Minds. eureka-math.org
G1-M1-TE-BK1-1.3.1-01.2016

Lesson 28

Sprint

Side A

1.	4	11.	6	21.	0
2.	3	12.	8	22.	10
3.	2	13.	7	23.	20
4.	4	14.	8	24.	3
5.	2	15.	9	25.	13
6.	0	16.	9	26.	23
7.	3	17.	7	27.	9
8.	4	18.	10	28.	19
9.	6	19.	9	29.	20
10.	5	20.	8	30.	30

Side B

1.	2	11.	9	21.	10
2.	1	12.	8	22.	0
3.	0	13.	7	23.	10
4.	5	14.	5	24.	20
5.	3	15.	16	25.	4
6.	1	16.	9	26.	14
7.	0	17.	8	27.	24
8.	2	18.	10	28.	19
9.	4	19.	8	29.	9
10.	6	20.	12	30.	20

EUREKA
MATH

©2015 Great Minds. eureka-math.org
G1-M1-TE-BK1-1.3.1-01.2016

Problem Set

1. 4; 4; 4

2. Group of 3 eggs crossed out; 3, 3; 3; 3, 3

3. 8 objects drawn; group of 3 objects crossed out; 8, 3, 5; 5; 8, 3, 5

4. 7 objects drawn; group of 2 objects crossed out; 7, 2, 5; 5; 7, 2, 5

Exit Ticket

9 objects drawn; group of 3 objects crossed out; 9, 3, 6; 9, 3, 6; 6

Homework

1. 6 objects drawn; group of 2 objects crossed out; 2, 4; 2, 4; 4

2. 8 objects drawn; group of 3 objects crossed out; 8, 3, 5; 8, 3, 5; 5

3. 7 objects drawn; group of 3 objects crossed out; 7, 3, 4; 7, 3, 4; 4

4. 9 objects drawn; group of 6 objects crossed out; 9, 6, 3; 9, 6, 3; 3

5. 10 objects drawn; group of 7 objects crossed out; 10, 7, 3; 10, 7, 3; 3

6. 10 objects drawn; group of 4 objects crossed out; 10, 4, 6; 10, 4, 6; 6

Lesson 29

Problem Set

1. 6; 3; 3, 3; labels will vary; 3, 3; 3
2. 9; 5; 9, 5, 4; labels will vary; 5, 4; 4
3. 8 objects drawn; group of 2 objects circled; 8, 2, 6; labels will vary; 8, 2, 6; 6
4. Answers will vary.

Exit Ticket

9 objects drawn; group of 7 objects circled; 9, 7, 2; labels will vary; 9, 7, 2; 2

Homework

1. 7 objects drawn; group of 5 objects circled; 7, 5, 2; labels will vary; 7, 5, 2; 2
2. 8 objects drawn; group of 2 objects circled; 8, 2, 6; labels will vary; 8, 2, 6; 6
3. 9 objects drawn; group of 4 objects circled; 9, 4, 5; labels will vary; 9, 4, 5; 5
4. 10 objects drawn; group of 6 objects circled; 10, 6, 4; labels will vary; 10, 6, 4; 4
5. 7 objects drawn; group of 2 objects circled; 2, 5, 7; labels will vary; 7, 2, 5; 5
6. 10 objects drawn; group of 2 objects circled; 2, 8, 10; labels will vary; 10, 2, 8; 8 fingers are not hurt.

©2015 Great Minds. eureka-math.org
G1-M1-TE-BK1-1.3.1-01.2016

Lesson 30

Problem Set

1. 2 objects drawn; 5, 3, 2; labels will vary; 2; 2; numeral 2 in both number sentences shaded

2. 5, 3, and 8 objects drawn; 5, 3, 8; labels will vary; 3; 3; numeral 3 in both number sentences shaded

3. 2, 4, and 6 objects drawn; 6, 2, 4; labels will vary; 2, 4; 2, 4; numeral 4 in both number sentences circled; 4

4. 5, 4, and 9 objects drawn; 5, 4, 9; labels will vary; 5, 4; 5, 4; numeral 4 in both number sentences circled; 4

Exit Ticket

6, 3, and 9 objects drawn; 9, 6, 3; labels will vary; 6, 3, 9; 9, 6, 3; 3

Homework

1. 7, 2, and 5 objects drawn; 7, 2, 5; labels will vary; 2, 5; 2, 5; numeral 5 in both number sentences circled; 5

2. 8, 3, and 5 objects drawn; 8, 3, 5; labels will vary; 3, 5; 3, 5; numeral 5 in both number sentences circled; 5

3. 9, 5, and 4 objects drawn; 9, 5, 4; labels will vary; 5, 4; 9, 5, 4; numeral 4 in both number sentences circled; 4

4. 10, 7, and 3 objects drawn; 10, 7, 3; labels will vary; 7, 3, 10; 10, 7, 3; numeral 3 in both number sentences circled; 3

©2015 Great Minds. eureka-math.org
G1-M1-TE-BK1-1.3.1-01.2016

Lesson 31

Problem Set

1. Group of 5 objects circled; group of 2 objects crossed out; 7, 5, 2; 5, 2; 2

2. 8 objects drawn; group of 4 objects circled, group of 4 objects crossed out;
    8, 4, 4; 8, 4, 4; 4

3. 6 objects drawn; group of 2 objects circled, group of 4 objects crossed out;
    6, 2, 4; 6, 2, 4; 4

4. 9 objects drawn; group of 5 objects circled, group of 4 objects crossed out;
    9, 5, 4; 9, 5, 4; 4

Exit Ticket

9 objects drawn; group of 3 objects circled, group of 6 objects crossed out;

9, 3, 6; 9, 3, 6; 6

Homework

1. 6 objects drawn; group of 4 objects circled, group of 2 objects crossed out;
    4, 2; 4, 2; 2

2. 8 objects drawn; group of 6 objects circled, group of 2 objects crossed out;
    8, 6, 2; 8, 6, 2; 2

3. 7 objects drawn; group of 5 objects circled, group of 2 objects crossed out;
    7, 5, 2; 7, 5, 2; 2

4. 8 objects drawn; group of 5 objects circled, group of 3 objects crossed out;
    8, 5, 3; 8, 5, 3; 3

5. 10 objects drawn; group of 7 objects circled, group of 3 objects crossed out;
    10, 7, 3; 10, 7, 3; 3

6. 10 objects drawn; group of 3 objects circled, group of 7 objects crossed out;
    10, 3, 7; 10, 3, 7; 7

©2015 Great Minds. eureka-math.org
G1-M1-TE-BK1-1.3.1-01.2016

Lesson 32

Problem Set

1.   5 objects drawn; group of 4 objects circled; 4, 1; labels will vary; 4, 1; 4, 1; 1

2.   8 objects drawn; group of 5 objects circled; 5, 3; labels will vary; 5, 3; 5, 3; 3

3.   2; math stories will vary; 8 objects drawn; group of 6 objects circled; 6, 2; 6, 2

4.   6; math stories will vary; 9 objects drawn; group of 3 objects circled; 3, 6, 9; 9, 3, 6

Exit Ticket

9 objects drawn; group of 5 objects circled; 4; 9, 5, 4; 9, 5, 4; 5, 4, 9

Homework

1.   a.   10 objects drawn; group of 6 objects circled; matched to 6 + 4 = 10; 10 − 6 = 4

     b.   9 objects drawn; group of 6 objects circled; matched to 6 + 3 = 9; 9 − 6 = 3

     c.   10 objects drawn; group of 3 objects circled; matched to 3 + 7 = 10; 10 − 3 = 7

2.   3; group of 3 objects and group of 4 objects drawn; 3 + 4 = 7;

     group of 7 objects drawn with a group of 4 circled or crossed out; 7 − 4 = 3; drawings and number sentences may vary.

3.   3; group of 3 objects and group of 5 objects drawn; 3 + 5 = 8;

     group of 8 objects drawn with a group of 5 circled or crossed out; 8 − 5 = 3; drawings and number sentences may vary.

Lesson 33

Sprint

Side A

1.	4	12.	4	23.	3	34.	9
2.	5	13.	5	24.	9	35.	10
3.	6	14.	6	25.	9	36.	10
4.	10	15.	10	26.	5	37.	7
5.	7	16.	7	27.	5	38.	8
6.	9	17.	8	28.	6	39.	8
7.	3	18.	9	29.	4	40.	9
8.	8	19.	9	30.	6	41.	10
9.	8	20.	10	31.	6	42.	10
10.	10	21.	7	32.	7	43.	9
11.	7	22.	8	33.	8	44.	10

Side B

1.	3	12.	4	23.	9	34.	10
2.	4	13.	5	24.	10	35.	9
3.	5	14.	6	25.	6	36.	9
4.	9	15.	9	26.	6	37.	8
5.	6	16.	7	27.	5	38.	7
6.	8	17.	10	28.	5	39.	8
7.	10	18.	8	29.	4	40.	9
8.	7	19.	8	30.	3	41.	10
9.	7	20.	10	31.	6	42.	10
10.	10	21.	7	32.	7	43.	9
11.	8	22.	9	33.	8	44.	10

Module 1:   Sums and Differences to 10

EUREKA MATH™

©2015 Great Minds. eureka-math.org
G1-M1-TE-BK1-1.3.1-01.2016

Problem Set

1. 1 circle crossed off; 5

2. No circles crossed off; 6

3. 6; 5-group drawing: 7 circles with 1 circle crossed off

4. 7; 5-group drawing: 7 circles

5. 9; 5-group drawing: 10 circles with 1 circle crossed off

6. 10; 5-group drawing: 10 circles

7. 7; 5-group drawing: 8 circles with 1 circle crossed off

8. 8; 5-group drawing: 8 circles

9. 8; 5-group drawing: 9 circles with 1 circle crossed off

10. 9; 5-group drawing: 9 circles

11. 1 circle crossed off; 5

12. 1 circle crossed off; 7

13. No circles crossed off; 9

14. 6

15. 8

16. 8

17. a. 6
     b. 5
     c. 0
     d. 6
     e. 8
     f. 1
     g. 0
     h. 8
     i. 0
     j. 1

Exit Ticket

1. 8; 5-group drawing: 9 circles with 1 circle crossed off

2. 8; 5-group drawing: 8 circles

3. 9; 5-group drawing: 9 circles with 1 circle crossed off

4. 0; 5-group drawing: 10 circles

Module 1:   Sums and Differences to 10

543

©2015 Great Minds. eureka-math.org
G1-M1-TE-BK1-1.3.1-01.2016

Homework

1. 8; 5-group drawing: 9 circles with 1 circle crossed off

2. 9; 5-group drawing: 9 circles

3. 0; 5-group drawing: 6 circles

4. 1; 5-group drawing: 7 circles with 1 circle crossed off

5. 0; vertical 5-group drawing: 9 circles

6. 0; vertical 5-group drawing: 8 circles

7. 1; vertical 5-group drawing: 10 circles with 1 circle crossed off

8. 0; vertical 5-group drawing: 7 circles

9. 6, 1, 5

10. 7, 0, 7

11. 9, 1, 8

12. 9, 0, 9

13. 8, 1, 7

14. a. 1

    b. 7

    c. 1

    d. 1

    e. 1

    f. 1

    g. 0

    h. 1

EUREKA
MATH™

Lesson 34

Sprint

Side A

1.	1	11.	8	21.	6
2.	0	12.	10	22.	8
3.	1	13.	9	23.	0
4.	2	14.	8	24.	8
5.	3	15.	9	25.	1
6.	4	16.	10	26.	0
7.	3	17.	9	27.	0
8.	4	18.	8	28.	8
9.	5	19.	6	29.	8
10.	6	20.	5	30.	10

Side B

1.	2	11.	10	21.	10
2.	1	12.	7	22.	8
3.	0	13.	8	23.	1
4.	1	14.	9	24.	9
5.	2	15.	8	25.	1
6.	4	16.	9	26.	1
7.	4	17.	8	27.	0
8.	6	18.	6	28.	9
9.	7	19.	7	29.	10
10.	9	20.	8	30.	9

©2015 Great Minds. eureka-math.org
G1-M1-TE-BK1-1.3.1-01.2016

Problem Set

1. 6 circles crossed off; 0
2. 5 circles crossed off; 1
3. 5-group drawing of 7; 7 circles crossed off; 0
4. 5-group drawing of 7; 6 circles crossed off; 1
5. 5-group drawing of 10; 10 circles crossed off; 0
6. 5-group drawing of 10; 9 circles crossed off; 1
7. 5-group drawing of 8; 8 circles crossed off; 0
8. 5-group drawing of 8; 7 circles crossed off; 1
9. 5-group drawing of 9; 9 circles crossed off; 0
10. 5-group drawing of 9; 8 circles crossed off; 1
11. 6 circles crossed off; 0
12. 8 circles crossed off; 0
13. 8 circles crossed off; 1
14. Vertical 5-group drawing of 7; 7 circles crossed off; 0
15. Vertical 5-group drawing of 8; 7 circles crossed off; 1
16. Vertical 5-group drawing of 9; 9 circles crossed off; 0

17. a. 0
     b. 1
     c. 7
     d. 1
     e. 0
     f. 7
     g. 9
     h. 1
     i. 0
     j. 9

Exit Ticket

1. 5-group drawing of 9; 8 circles crossed off; 8
2. 5-group drawing of 10; 10 circles crossed off; 10
3. 5-group drawing of 8; 7 circles crossed off; 8
4. 5-group drawing of 9; 9 circles crossed off; 9

EUREKA
MATH

Homework

1. 10 circles crossed off; 0

2. 8 circles crossed off; 1

3. 5-group drawing of 8; 7 circles crossed off; 8

4. 5-group drawing of 8; 8 circles crossed off; 8

5. 5-group drawing of 7; 7 circles crossed off; 7

6. 5-group drawing of 6; 5 circles crossed off; 5

7. Vertical 5-group drawing of 9; 8 circles crossed off; 8

8. Vertical 5-group drawing of 8; 8 circles crossed off; 8

9. 7, 7, 0

10. 10, 9, 1

11. 9, 9, 0

12. 9, 8, 1

13. 8, 8, 0

14. a. 7

    b. 6

    c. 7

    d. 6

    e. 9

    f. 9

    g. 10

    h. 8

Module 1:   Sums and Differences to 10

547

©2015 Great Minds. eureka-math.org
G1-M1-TE-BK1-1.3.1-01.2016

Lesson 35

Sprint

Side A

1.	0	11.	1	21.	6
2.	0	12.	0	22.	9
3.	1	13.	1	23.	9
4.	0	14.	0	24.	10
5.	1	15.	1	25.	7
6.	0	16.	10	26.	7
7.	1	17.	9	27.	9
8.	0	18.	8	28.	8
9.	0	19.	6	29.	8
10.	0	20.	5	30.	6

Side B

1.	0	11.	0	21.	8
2.	0	12.	1	22.	6
3.	0	13.	1	23.	6
4.	1	14.	1	24.	7
5.	1	15.	0	25.	6
6.	1	16.	6	26.	6
7.	1	17.	7	27.	8
8.	0	18.	8	28.	8
9.	0	19.	10	29.	7
10.	0	20.	9	30.	7

Module 1: Sums and Differences to 10

EUREKA MATH

Problem Set

1. 5 black circles crossed off; 1

   1 white circle crossed off; 5

2. 3 white circles crossed off; 5

   5 black circles crossed off; 3

3. 4 white circles crossed off; 5

   5 black circles crossed off; 4

4. 5-group drawing of 7; group of 5 circles

   crossed off; 2

   5-group drawing of 7; group of 2 circles

   crossed off; 5

   7, 2, 5

5. 5-group drawing of 10; group of 5

   circles crossed off; 5

   10, 5, 5

6. a. 2

   b. 2

   c. 5

   d. 5

   e. 4

   f. 5

7. 2; 2

8. 3; 3

9. 5; 5

10. 4; 4

11. 4; 4

12. 3; 3

13 a. 2; 5-groups

   b. 5; 5-groups

   c. 4; doubles

   d. 5; 5-groups

   e. 3; 5-groups

   f. 5; doubles

Exit Ticket

1. 10, 5, 5; 10; doubles or 5-group

2. 8, 4, 4; 4; doubles

3. 9, 5, 4; 5; 5-group or doubles plus one

Homework

1. 5 black circles crossed off; 2

    2 white circles crossed off; 5

2. 5 black circles crossed off; 1

    1 white circle crossed off; 5

3. 5 black circles crossed off; 5

    4 white circles crossed off; 4

4. 5-group drawing of 10; group of 5 circles

    crossed off; 5

    10, 5, 5

5. 5-group drawing of 8; group of 5 circles

    crossed off; 3

    5-group drawing of 8; group of 3

    circles crossed off; 3

    8, 5, 3

6. a. 5

    b. 10

    c. 3

    d. 7

    e. 8

    f. 9

7. 3; 3

8. 10; 10

9. 4; 4

10. a. 5; 5-group

    b. 5; 5-group

    c. 5; doubles or 5-group

    d. 6; doubles

    e. 4; doubles

    f. 4; 5-group

EUREKA
MATH™

Lesson 36

Problem Set

1. 9 circles crossed off; 1

   1 circle crossed off; 9

2. 6 circles crossed off; 4

   4 circles crossed off; 6

3. 3 circles crossed off; 7

   7 circle crossed off; 3

4. 5-group drawing of 10; 4 circles crossed off; 6

   5-group drawing of 10; 6 circles crossed off; 4

5. 5-group drawing of 10; 5 circles crossed off; 5

6. 5-group drawing of 10; 8 circles crossed off; 2

   5-group drawing of 10; 2 circles crossed off; 8

7. 2; 10 − 2 = 8; 10, 8, 2

8. 1; 10 − 1 = 9; 10, 1, 9

9. 7; 10 − 7 = 3; 10, 3, 7

10. 4; 10 − 4 = 6; 10, 6, 4

11. a. 1; 10 − 9 = 1; 10 − 1 = 9

    b. 8; 10 − 2 = 8; 10 − 8 = 2

    c. 7; 10 − 3 = 7; 10 − 7 = 3

    d. 4; 10 − 6 = 4; 10 − 4 = 6

    e. 5; 10 − 5 = 5

Exit Ticket

1. 3; 10 − 7 = 3; 10 − 3 = 7

2. 8; 10 − 2 = 8; 10 − 8 = 2

3. 6; 10 − 4 = 6; 10 − 6 = 4

Homework

1. 5-group drawing of 10; 2 circles crossed off; 8
    5-group drawing of 10; 8 circles crossed off; 10, 8, 2

2. 5-group drawing of 10; 1 circle crossed off; 9
    5-group drawing of 10; 9 circles crossed off; 10, 9, 1

3. 5-group drawing of 10; 7 circles crossed off; 3
    5-group drawing of 10; 3 circles crossed off; 10, 3, 7

4. 8; $10 - 8 = 2$; 10, 2, 8

5. 1; $10 - 9 = 1$; 10, 1, 9

6. 4; $10 - 6 = 4$; 10, 4, 6

7. 9, $10 - 1 = 9$; 10, 9, 1

8. 5; 10, 5, 5

9. a. 2; matched to $10 - 2 = 8$; $10 - 8 = 2$
    b. 3; matched to $10 - 3 = 7$; $10 - 7 = 3$
    c. 4; matched to $10 - 4 = 6$; $10 - 6 = 4$
    d. 5; matched to $10 - 5 = 5$; $10 - 5 = 5$
    e. 1; matched to $10 - 1 = 9$; $10 - 9 = 1$

EUREKA MATH

Lesson 37

Sprint

Side A

1.	10	11.	8	21.	5
2.	10	12.	2	22.	5
3.	9	13.	10	23.	5
4.	1	14.	10	24.	4
5.	10	15.	7	25.	3
6.	10	16.	3	26.	10
7.	10	17.	3	27.	6
8.	0	18.	7	28.	10
9.	10	19.	4	29.	4
10.	10	20.	6	30.	10

Side B

1.	10	11.	10	21.	5
2.	10	12.	0	22.	5
3.	8	13.	10	23.	4
4.	2	14.	10	24.	3
5.	10	15.	6	25.	2
6.	10	16.	4	26.	10
7.	9	17.	2	27.	8
8.	1	18.	3	28.	10
9.	10	19.	7	29.	7
10.	10	20.	6	30.	10

Problem Set

1. 8 circles crossed off; 1

    1 circle crossed off; 8

2. 7 circles crossed off; 2

    2 circles crossed off; $9 - 7 = 2$

3. 9 circles crossed off; 0

    0 circles crossed off; $9 - 0 = 9$

4. 5-group drawing of 9; 6 circles crossed

    off; 3

    5-group drawing of 9; 3 circles crossed

    off; $9 - 3 = 6$

5. 5-group drawing of 9; 4 circles crossed

    off; 5

    5-group drawing of 9; 5 circles crossed

    off; $9 - 5 = 4$

6. 5-group drawing of 9; 3 circles crossed

    off; 6

    5-group drawing of 9; 6 circles crossed

    off; $9 - 6 = 3$

7. 4; $9 - 4 = 5$;

    9, 4, 5

8. 1; $9 - 1 = 8$; number bond showing that 8 and 1

    is 9

9. 2; $9 - 2 = 7$; number bond showing that 7 and 2

    is 9

10. 6; $9 - 6 = 3$; number bond showing that 6 and 3

    is 9

11. a.   9; $9 - 0 = 9$; $9 - 9 = 0$

    b.   1; $9 - 8 = 1$; $9 - 1 = 8$

    c.   7; $9 - 2 = 7$; $9 - 7 = 2$

    d.   3; $9 - 6 = 3$; $9 - 3 = 6$

    e.   4; $9 - 5 = 4$; $9 - 4 = 5$

Exit Ticket

1. 2; $9 - 7 = 2$; $9 - 2 = 7$

2. 6; $9 - 3 = 6$; $9 - 6 = 3$

3. 5; $9 - 4 = 5$; $9 - 5 = 4$

EUREKA
MATH

©2015 Great Minds. eureka-math.org
G1-M1-TE-BK1-1.3.1-01.2016

Homework

1. 5-group drawing of 9; 2 circles crossed off; 7

    5-group drawing of 9; 7 circles crossed

    off; 9 – 7 = 2

2. 5-group drawing of 9; 8 circles crossed off; 1

    5-group drawing of 9; 1 circle crossed

    off; 9 – 1 = 8

3. 5-group drawing of 9; 4 circles crossed off; 5

    5-group drawing of 9; 5 circles crossed

    off; 9 – 5 = 4

4. 2; 9 – 2 = 7;

    9, 7, 2

5. 0; 9 – 9 = 0;

    9, 9, 0

6. 3; 9 – 6 = 3;

    9, 3, 6

7. 8; 9 – 1 = 8; 9, 8, 1

8. 4; 9 – 4 = 5; 9, 4, 5

9. a. 1; matched to 9 – 1 = 8; 9 – 8 = 1

    b. 2; matched to 9 – 2 = 7; 9 – 7 = 2

    c. 6; matched to 9 – 6 = 3; 9 – 3 = 6

    d. 4; matched to 9 – 5 = 4; 9 – 4 = 5

    e. 0; matched to 9 – 9 = 0; 9 – 0 = 9

Lesson 38

Problem Set

1. Answers will vary.

2. Answers will vary.

3. Answers will vary.

4. Answers will vary.

5. Answers will vary.

Exit Ticket

1. Sequence of number sentences may vary; $10 - 7 = 3$; $3 + 7 = 10$; $10 - 3 = 7$; $7 + 3 = 10$

2. Sequence of number sentences may vary; $9 - 6 = 3$; $6 + 3 = 9$; $9 - 3 = 6$; $3 + 6 = 9$

Homework

$2 + 2$; $3 + 3$; $4 + 4$; $5 + 5$ doubles shaded

$2 + 5$; $3 + 5$; $4 + 5$ 5-groups shaded

Module 1:   Sums and Differences to 10

EUREKA
MATH™

Lesson 39

Sprint

Side A

1.	10	11.	7	21.	10
2.	10	12.	9	22.	10
3.	10	13.	8	23.	10
4.	4	14.	2	24.	12
5.	6	15.	3	25.	12
6.	5	16.	1	26.	2
7.	5	17.	10	27.	2
8.	3	18.	10	28.	10
9.	4	19.	10	29.	10
10.	6	20.	4	30.	10

Side B

1.	10	11.	6	21.	10
2.	10	12.	5	22.	10
3.	10	13.	9	23.	10
4.	3	14.	1	24.	11
5.	7	15.	2	25.	11
6.	6	16.	3	26.	1
7.	5	17.	10	27.	4
8.	4	18.	10	28.	11
9.	3	19.	10	29.	9
10.	7	20.	5	30.	10

Problem Set

1. Answers will vary.
2. Answers will vary.
3. Answers will vary.
4. Answers will vary.

Exit Ticket

1. $2; 10 - 8 = 2; 8 + 2 = 10; 10 - 2 = 8; 2 + 8 = 10$
2. $2; 9 - 7 = 2; 7 + 2 = 9; 9 - 2 = 7; 2 + 7 = 9$

Homework

1. $2 + 3 = 5$
2. $2 + 4 = 6$
3. $2 + 6 = 8$
4. $2 + 7 = 9$
5. $2 + 8 = 10$
6. $3 + 4 = 7$
7. $3 + 6 = 9$
8. $3 + 7 = 10$
9. $4 + 6 = 10$
10. Answers will vary; see homework example.

EUREKA MATH